Electronics Pocket Book

Electronics Pocket Book

5th edition

Edited by
E. A. Parr
BSc., CEng., MIEE

Heinemann Professional Publishing

Heinemann Professional Publishing Ltd
Halley Court, Jordan Hill, Oxford OX2 8EJ

OXFORD   LONDON   MELBOURNE   AUCKLAND

First published by Newnes Books 1963
Fifth edition published by William Heinemann Ltd 1986
Reprinted 1988

ISBN 0 434 91519 X

Typeset by Vision Typesetting, Manchester
Printed by Butler & Tanner Ltd, Frome

Contents

Preface

The *Electronics Pocket Book* has been in existence for some twenty years and as such has uniquely covered the development of electronics. The book has consequently evolved from valve to semiconductor technology and from transistors to LSI integrated circuits and the microprocessor. To keep up to date with the rapidly changing world of electronics, continuous revision has been necessary.

This Fifth Edition has been revised to take account of recent changes and developments, along with the inclusion of suggestions made by readers of previous editions. New material on op-amp applications and the design of digital circuits has been added, along with a totally new chapter on Computing, plus other material of relevance. It is, perhaps, significant that this edition was revised on a wordprocessor, so technology even catches up with authors! It is also interesting to note that the majority of the book now deals with Communications, Computing and Digital Circuits, reflecting the increasing importance of the blanket topic of Information Technology.

Despite the increasing emphasis on microcomputers, the aims of the book are unchanged; namely, the presentation of all aspects of electronics in a readable and largely non-mathematical form for both the hobbyist and the professional engineer.

I would like to thank my family for their support during the work, the previous editors, J.P. Hawker, J.A. Reddihough and P.J. McGoldrick, for establishing the *Pocket Book*, plus the readers whose suggestions have, hopefully, been incorporated in this revision.

Andrew Parr
Isle of Sheppey

1
Electron physics

Molecules and atoms 1.1

All matter consists of molecules, which are defined as the smallest portion of a substance capable of independent existence and having the properties of the substance. Studies by Dalton and others in the early part of the nineteenth century showed that molecules consist of groupings of various types of atoms. These atoms relate to the basic elements of which all matter is constructed. There are over 100 elements, from hydrogen (the lightest) to uranium (one of the heaviest).

A molecule of table salt, for example, consists of one atom of sodium and one atom of chlorine. A molecule of copper sulphate consists of one atom of copper, one atom of sulphur and four atoms of oxygen.

Atoms are far too small to be observed directly by a microscope, but their existence and properties can be inferred by experiments.

Atomic structure 1.2

Experimental work on gas discharge effects suggested that an atom is not a single entity but is itself composed of smaller particles. These were termed elementary particles. The atom appeared as a small solar system with a heavy nucleus composed of positive particles and neutral particles. These were named protons and neutrons. Around this nucleus, clouds of negatively charged particles, called electrons, circle.

Since an atom is electrically neutral, the negative charge carried by the electrons must be equal in magnitude (but opposite in sign) to the positive charge carried by the protons. Experiments with electrostatic charges have shown that unlike charges attract, so it can be considered that electrostatic forces hold an atom together.

The difference between various atoms is therefore determined by their composition. A hydrogen atom consists of one proton and one electron; a helium atom of two protons, two neutrons and two electrons. These are shown diagrammatically in *Figure 1.1*.

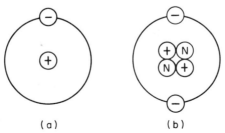

(a)   (b)

Fig. 1.1 Atomic structure: (a) hydrogen atom; (b) helium atom

Work by Bohr and others in the early part of the present century demonstrated that the electron orbits are arranged in shells, and that each shell has a defined maximum number of electrons it can contain. The first shell can contain two electrons, the second eight electrons. The number in each shell is given by $2n^2$, where $n = 1, 2, 3$, etc.

Chemical reaction and electrical effects are all concerned with the behaviour of electrons in the outer shell of any particular atom. If a shell is full, for example, the atom is unable to react with any other atom and is, in fact, one of the inert gases such as helium.

1.3 Electrons and electric currents

If there are few electrons in the outermost shell, the forces binding them to the nucleus are weak. Thermal effects easily detach these electrons, leaving a positively charged atom. These detached electrons drift around inside the substance until they meet another positively charged atom, at which they become captured again. The process of free electron production and recapture is going on continuously, and the substance can be considered as being permeated with a negatively charged gas.

If an electrical potential is now applied across the substance, the free electrons will start to accelerate towards the positive connection. As they move they will collide with atoms in the substance, loosing energy which we observe as heat. The net effect is a drift of electrons at a roughly constant speed towards the positive connection. The motion of electrons is an electric current.

As electrons are removed by the electrical potential source at the positive connection, electrons are being injected at the negative connection. The potential can be considered as a form of electron 'pump'.

This model explains many observed effects. If the magnitude of the electrical potential is increased, the electrons will accelerate faster and their mean velocity will be higher, i.e. the current is increased. The collisions between electrons and atoms transfer energy to the atoms which manifests itself as heat. This effect is known as Joule heating.

Materials such as these are termed ohmic conductors, since they obey the well-known Ohm's law;

$$\frac{V}{I} = \text{constant } (R)$$

The constant is the resistance of the material. If V is in volts, and I is in amps, the constant R is in ohms.

Not all electrical conduction is ohmic; heating and other effects cause some materials to have complex V/I relationships.

If the electrons in the outer orbit are tightly bound, negligible amounts of free electrons will be formed. If an electric potential is applied, very few electrons will move and the current will be small. Substances with these characteristics are called insulators.

Motion of electron in an electric field   1.4

If an electric potential is applied between two plates in a vacuum, and an electron is introduced, the electron will experience an attractive force to the positive plate (*Figure 1.2*).

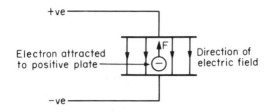

Fig. 1.2 Electric field between parallel plates

This force will cause the electron to accelerate towards the positive plate in a straight line. It suffers no collisions because the area between the plates is *in vacuo*. This effect is used in thermionic valves.

If the electron is given some motion, and the electron field is applied perpendicular to the motion, interesting effects occur. In the system drawn in *Figure 1.3*, a beam of electrons is emitted from a device called an electron gun. These electrons are moving in the x direction. As they emerge they pass between two plates which have a potential applied across them in the y direction.

As the electrons pass between the plates they are accelerated in the y direction, as explained before, but their velocity in the x direction is unaltered. The electron beam is thus deflected as shown. By varying the potential applied to the plates, the angle of deflection can be controlled. This effect is the basis of the cathode ray oscilloscope.

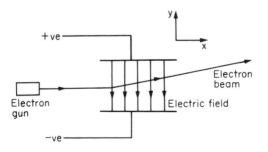

Fig.1.3 Electrostatic deflection of electron beam

1.5 Motion of an electron in a magnetic field

A moving electron is effectively an electric current. Experiments with
electric motors demonstrate that magnetic fields exert a force on
wires carrying current, and similar effects may be expected to occur
with moving electrons.

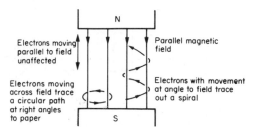

Fig. 1.4 Motion of electrons in a magnetic field

The direction of the force can be predicted from Fleming's left-
hand rule. An electron will experience a force when moving
perpendicular to a magnetic field (*Figure 1.4*). This force will be at
right angles to both the field and the direction of the electron's
motion. It follows that electrons moving parallel to a magnetic field
are unaffected.

There is one important difference between the motion of an
electron in a magnetic field and its motion in an electric field. In an
electric field the force is a fixed direction, whereas in a magnetic field
the force is always at right angles to the electron's motion.

It follows that an electron injected into a suitable magnetic field
can be made to spiral along the field axis. This effect is used in
magnetic focusing coils in a television tube.

1.6 Structure of matter

Matter can exist in three states; solid, liquid and gaseous. In the liquid
and gaseous states molecules can move around freely. In the solid
state the molecules are fixed, and can only vibrate about their mean
position. These vibrations we interpret as heat.

There are several substances which are observed to form crystals:
table salt and copper sulphate are two common examples. Crystals
form because the atoms arrange themselves into a geometrical
pattern, and this pattern continues even though the crystal may be as
large as we are.

At the atomic level, however, the atoms in most substances are
arranged in a crystalline pattern. *Figure 1.5* shows a representation of
he crystalline structure of germanium, and the regular pattern is
)bvious.

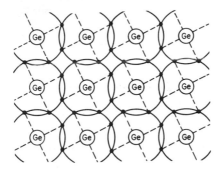

Fig. 1.5 Representation of germanium crystal

The vast majority of electronic devices depend on conduction in solids. The ability of a substance to conduct electricity depends on its ability to produce free electrons, as we saw earlier in Section 1.3.

The elements silicon and germanium both have four electrons in their outer orbit. This results in a tight-knit diamond-type crystal. Because of the tight bond, pure crystals of germanium and silicon are fairly good insulators.

Impurity semiconductors 1.7

Although pure crystals of silicon and germanium are fairly good insulators, their conductivity can be dramatically changed by the addition of small amounts of impurities.

Figure 1.6 is a version of *Figure 1.5*, with one atom of germanium replaced by one atom of arsenic. This is called doping. Arsenic has five electrons in its outer shell, and although it will 'sit' in the crystal it has one electron free from bonding.

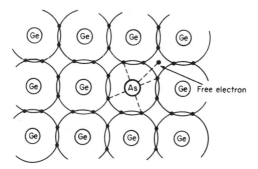

Fig. 1.6 Representation of n-type semiconductor

The surplus electrons are very mobile, and can easily become current carriers when a voltage is applied across the substance. The amount of doping can be controlled easily to control the amount of free electrons available. The impurities are known as donor atoms, and the substance as an impurity semiconductor.

Conduction in the substance is by free electrons, and the substance is called an n-type semiconductor (with n standing for negative).

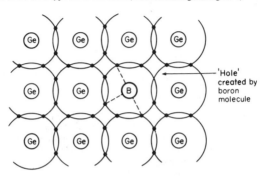

Fig. 1.7 Representation of p-type semiconductor

If an atom with three electrons in its outer shell (e.g. boron, indium) is introduced, a similar effect occurs. The arrangement is shown in *Figure 1.7*. The deficiency of electrons forms a 'hole' in the structure, and the corresponding unbonded electron is free to become a current carrier. If a voltage is applied to the substance, the electrons will move towards the positive connection, and the holes will apparently move in the opposite direction. It is usual to consider the moving hole as the current carrier. This type of material is known as a p-type semiconductor (with p standing for positive), and the impurities are known as acceptor atoms.

As well as the current carriers formed in the semiconductor by the impurities, there will also be current carriers formed by normal thermal action releasing free electrons. These latter current carriers obviously exist as complementary electrons/holes, and are known as minority carriers. The current carriers introduced by the impurities are known as majority carriers.

1.8 The p-n junction

Figure 1.8 shows a crystal, one half of which has been doped to form n-type material, and the other half to form p-type material. At the junction, holes will pass into the n-type and electrons into the p-type material, until a voltage is built up across the junction. This is called a depletion layer, and with no current carriers in the region it forms an insulator.

The build-up of charge at the depletion layer is a localised effect, and no voltage will be detected across the ends of the p–n junction. If, however, a positive voltage is applied from p to n, as shown in *Figure 1.9(a)*, positive holes will flow across the junction from p to n, and electrons from n to p. Current is flowing and the device is conducting.

If a negative voltage is applied from p to n, as shown in *Figure 1.9(b)*, a few electrons and holes will be removed, but the effect is to increase the depletion layer. After a very short current flow (equivalent to charging a small capacitor) the device becomes an insulator. There will, in fact, be a small leakage current caused by the minority carriers described in Section 1.7. This will normally be negligible.

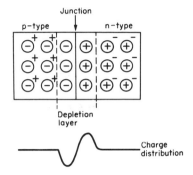

Fig. 1.8 The p–n junction

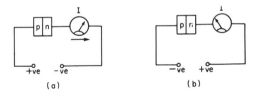

Fig. 1.9 The p–n junction as a rectifier: (a) forward bias; (b) reverse bias

The p–n junction thus has the asymmetrical I/V relationship drawn in *Figure 1.10*. It will be seen that a small forward voltage is needed to start conduction. This corresponds to the charge on the depletion layer, and is about 0·2 V for germanium and 0·7 V for silicon.

In itself the p–n junction is an excellent rectifier, but it is also the basis of more complex semiconductor devices to be described in later chapters.

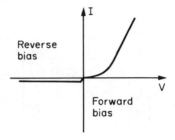

Fig. 1.10 Characteristics of p–n junction

2
Electronic components

Resistors 2.1

Resistors are probably the widest used component in electronic circuits. They are used according to Ohm's law, mentioned in Chapter 1, namely

$$\text{Resistance (in ohms)} = \frac{\text{Volts}}{\text{Amps}}$$

Resistors are available in values from fractions of ohms to tens of megohms. As resistors pass current, energy is absorbed in the form of heat equal to I^2R watts. The temperature of the resistor will rise until the heat radiated equals the heat absorbed. This temperature rise determines the maximum wattage a resistor can dissipate.

The simplest (and cheapest) resistor is the carbon type. This consists of a small rod of carbon, moulded to give the required value. The carbon rod is usually mounted in a protective moulding, with connections brought out on axial leads. Carbon resistors are available from $\frac{1}{8}$ W to 2 W ratings, and having values from a few ohms to around 1 MΩ.

The value of a resistor changes with temperature. The resistance at temperature $t(°C)$ is given by

$$R_t = R_{20}(1 + \alpha t)$$

where R_{20} is the resistance at 20°C, and α is defined as the temperature coefficient (typically 0·01 % per degree Centigrade).

Carbon resistors have a large negative temperature coefficient. The effect of thermal heating can thus become cumulative, and carbon resistors are not suitable for applications where great precision is required.

Greater stability can be obtained from an alternative method of using the resistance of carbon. A thin film of carbon is deposited on to an insulating former, often glass. The resistance value is determined by spiral grooves cut along the body of the resistor. These resistors are called thin-film resistors, and accurate control over their construction makes them suitable for precision applications. Similar construction techniques are used with other resistive materials, such as metals and metallic oxides.

Where high wattage is required, it is necessary to use wire-wound resistors. The required length of thin wire is wound on to a former, then covered with a protective vitreous enamel. Care must be taken in mounting high wattage resistors to allow free air flow and to ensure that the inherently high temperatures do not affect adjacent components. The construction inevitably gives the resistor a large inductance. This can be reduced by use of non-inductive bifilar windings (i.e., a double spiral), but can never be completely eliminated.

Resistors are inherently 'noisy' devices; the random motion of electrons through them produces small voltage changes which are heard as a high frequency 'hiss' in audio circuits, or appears as a

17

dither on video signals. The amplitude of the noise is related to the temperature, voltage and current, and also the type of construction of the resistor. Metallic film resistors are best suited to low noise applications. Typical noise voltages are $0 \cdot 5 \ \mu V/V$ applied, for a 10 KΩ resistor.

Resistors are identified by a colour code showing value and tolerance, or marked according to BS1852, both of which are given in Section 17.1.

Variable resistors are manufactured in a similar manner. Low wattage variable resistors use a carbon track over which a slider is moved. High wattage variable resistors are usually wire wound. Both types have inherent problems; carbon variable resistors tend to produce dirt on the track and are prone to track breakage, whereas wire-wound versions need many turns to give adequate resolution. Tracks based on a fused metal/glass material (called cermet, for CERamic/METal) have superior characteristics to both carbon and wire-wound types, and are increasingly used in industry.

Variable resistors are available in linear or logarithmic forms. The former has a simple linear relationship between slider position and the resistance value. Logarithmic variable resistors follow a log curve, and are used for volume controls to compensate for the peculiar response of the human ear.

2.2 Capacitors

The construction of capacitors is governed by the equation

$$C = \frac{\epsilon A}{d}$$

where A is the area of the plates of the capacitor, ϵ is the permitivity of material between the plates,.and d is the separation of the plates (*Figure 2.1(a)*).

In general, the capacitance of parallel plates is inadequate for practical circuits. For example, two plates of 100 cm^2, separated by 1 mm, would have a capacitance of around 80 pF. The design of high value capacitors is achieved by increasing A and ϵ or by decreasing d. Unfortunately, capacitors need to work at quite high voltages and this presents the component manufacturers with conflicting requirements.

Practical capacitors are often constructed by means of interleaved metal foil and high permittivity dielectrics such as mica or ceramic materials, as shown in *Figure 2.1(b)*. An alternative method is to evaporate metallic films direct on to the dielectric. This method of construction gives a stable capacitor (known as a silver mica capacitor) with good characteristics. Capacitors can be constructed with values from a few pF to around 5000 pF.

Larger values of capacitance can be produced by using foil and paper in alternate layers. There are many variations on the design of foil capacitors, using different materials for the dielectric. Polyester and polycarbonate dielectrics are used in capacitors of the same name.

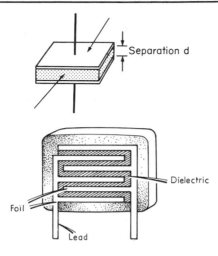

Fig. 2.1 (a) Parallel plate capacitor; (b) Ceramic capacitor

To obtain large values of capacitance it is necessary to reduce the separation of the plates further. This can be achieved by immersing a metal plate in an electrolyte. A thin oxide film forms which behaves as a dielectric between the 'plates' of the metal and the electrolyte. The plate/oxide/electrolyte thus exhibits the properties of a capacitor, and the exceptionally thin oxide layer (typically 10^{-4} mm) ensures that the value is high.

A further increase in capacitance can be obtained by etching the metal plate. This roughens the surface, thereby increasing the surface area. There are many variations on the basic ideas of electrolytic capacitors, the latest of which is the use of tantalum. Tantalum oxide has very high permittivity, and tantalum electrolytics are small, stable and have very low leakage current. Compared with other electrolytics, however, their working voltage range is very limited, typically 10–20 volts.

Electrolytic capacitors always operate with a standing d.c. voltage across them. If the voltage is reversed in polarity, the dielectric oxide film breaks down. Gas can then be formed in the electrolyte, building up an internal pressure which can rupture the casing of the capacitor. It is therefore very important to ensure that electrolytics are always used with the correct polarity across them.

In general, electrolytics are bad capacitors. Compared with conventional capacitors their power factor is poor, they exhibit high leakage and are quite expensive. They have a short life and tend to dry out in high ambient temperatures. Electrolytic capacitors are tolerated where other types of capacitor cannot be used.

All types of capacitor have a maximum working voltage specified. This can range from a few volts for a tantalum electrolytic to several kilovolts for specialised paper capacitors. The circuit must be analysed to find the peak voltage (not r.m.s.) likely to occur (including transients) and the capacitor specified accordingly.

Variable capacitors are required for tuned LC oscillators. The capacitance can be varied by adjusting A, d or ε in the earlier equation. Variable area types use air dielectric and two vane sets whose relative angular position can be adjusted. Trimmer capacitors often vary the separation d of sprung plates. Variable dielectrics are not widely used, but are sometimes found in instrumentation transducers, where a displacement is converted to a capacitance change by the insertion of a dielectric material between two fixed plates. The change in capacitance in all devices is small (typically a few hundred pF). Increasingly, variable capacitance is obtained with varicap diodes, described later in Subsection 2.6.3.

2.3 Inductors

Inductors are generally used as part of a tuned LC circuit in oscillators or RF circuits. It is therefore important to have stable inductors of a reasonable size.

For relatively low value inductors a single layer of wire around a former will suffice. To get higher values, however, it is necessary to use multilayer coils, although these do tend to have a high value of stray capacitance.

Where several inductors are used in a circuit, magnetic coupling will exist between the coils. This can produce undesirable effects such as amplifier instability. If a coil is enclosed in a can, eddy currents will be induced in the can material. These eddy currents will themselves produce a magnetic field in opposition to the field from the coil. This reduces the field in the coil slightly, but reduces the field outside the can to zero.

Ferrite cores are often used to produce inductors of larger values; this allows fewer turns of wire to be used for a given inductance. Adjustable inductors are also implemented by using a movable iron core (*Figure 2.2*). As the iron slug is moved, the permeability of the magnetic circuit, and hence the inductance, is altered. The variation in inductance that can be achieved is only a few per cent, which is adequate for trimming a tuned circuit. Where coarse changes are required (e.g. changing channels in a television), it is usual to switch inductors.

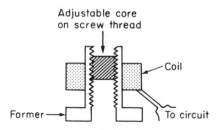

Fig.2.2 Adjustable inductor

Inductors of value greater than 1 H are sometimes used for smoothing-in power supplies, although these are less common nowadays. These inductors are known as chokes, and are constructed around laminations in a similar manner to that employed for transformers.

Transformers 2.4

A transformer is used to change the amplitude of an a.c. signal. Unlike an amplifier a transformer is entirely passive, and there is no power gain. Transformers can be loosely categorised into two classes: power and signal. Power transformers are used to convert a.c. voltages inside power supplies (see Subsection 15.2.1). Signal transformers are used for interstage coupling in amplifiers.

A simple transformer is shown in *Figure 2.3(a)*, with N_1 turns on the primary and N_2 turns on the secondary. With no load on the secondary an a.c. primary voltage e_{in} is applied, which produces an alternating flux ϕ which is dependent on e_{in} and N_1. If this flux in primary and secondary windings is the same we can say:

$$\frac{e_{out}}{e_{in}} = \frac{N_2}{N_1}$$

In the unloaded state, the flux ϕ will induce a voltage in the primary winding which, in a perfect transformer, will be equal to e_{in} and no primary current will flow.

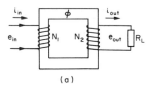

(a)	(b)

Fig. 2.3 The transformer: (a) transformer circuit; (b) transformer laminations

If we now connect a load across the secondary winding, current will flow. This current will oppose the flux from the primary, reducing the total flux in the core. At the primary, the induced voltage no longer equals e_{in} and primary current will flow, increasing the flux until the equation above is met again.

Since there is no power gain, input power and output power must be equal, and for a perfect transformer

$$e_{in} \cdot i_{in} = e_{out} \cdot i_{out}$$

The transformer is sometimes used as an impedance transformer. If we connect a load R_L to the secondary, the impedance seen at the primary is given by

$$R_{in} = \left(\frac{N_1}{N_2}\right)^2 R_L$$

The transformer can thus be used to match impedances for maximum power transference.

Transformers can also be used as current measuring devices in a.c. power applications. In *Figure 2.4* a large a.c. current is passed through the primary of a transformer. This induces a flux which is cancelled by the induced secondary current. If the secondary is effectively short-circuited,

$$\frac{Is}{Ip} = \frac{Np}{Ns}$$

i.e. the secondary current is proportional to the primary current.

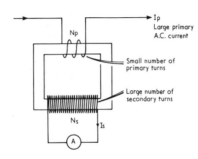

Fig. 2.4 Current transformer

Such a device is called a current transformer, and will typically have a 200:1 ratio (i.e. 200 primary amps will cause 1 amp to flow in the secondary). Often a single primary turn is used.

Current transformers must *always* have a secondary load connected, or dangerously high voltages will be developed across the secondary coil (there being no secondary current with an open-circuit secondary, to oppose the primary induced flux).

In the analysis above, we have assumed a perfect transformer with no losses. Practical transformers lose energy between primary and secondary. The first cause is due to I^2R losses in the transformer windings. This is sometimes referred to as the copper loss.

The second cause is the hysteresis curve of the iron core. Each cycle around the curve loses energy equal to the area of the curve, and this energy again appears as heat. This is sometimes referred to as the iron loss.

If the core was a solid iron block, there would also be considerable loss due to core eddy currents. These are reduced to negligible levels by the use of insulated laminations, as shown in *Figure 2.3(b)*. At frequencies above about 25 kHz, eddy currents in laminations again become significant, and ferrite dust cores are used instead.

Thermionic devices 2.5

2.5.1 Thermionic diode

In Chapter 1, conduction of electricity was discussed, and it was
demonstrated that an electric current is a flow of electrons. If a metal
plate (called a cathode) is enclosed in an evacuated container and
heated, electrons will be liberated from the surface of the metal. The
free electrons will form a negatively charged cloud around the
cathode, and an equilibrium state will be reached where the charge of
the cloud repels any further electrons.

If, however, a second plate (called an anode) is added, as shown in
Figure 2.5, and a supply connected, the positive potential on the
anode will attract electrons from the cloud around the cathode. This
allows further electrons to leave the cathode, causing a steady flow of
electrons from cathode to anode. By definition, an electric current is
flowing.

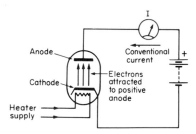

Fig. 2.5 Thermionic diode: electrons flow from cathode to anode;
conventional current flows in the opposite direction

If the anode is at a negative potential, the electron cloud will be
further repelled and no current will flow. The thermionic diode thus
passes current in one direction and behaves as a rectifier.

Thermionic diodes were once used widely in power supplies, but
improved techniques in semiconductor technology have largely
rendered them obsolete. The only common application nowadays is
in television EHT supplies, where semiconductor diodes of the
required PIV rating are expensive.

2.5.2 Thermionic triode and other multi-electrode valves

The thermionic triode is constructed by inserting a wire mesh (called
the control grid) between anode and cathode. The triode is biased
with the anode positive, so that with no connection to the grid,
current will flow.

If the grid is taken to a negative potential, it will retard the electron
flow. If the grid is taken sufficiently negative, current flow will cease
altogether (*Figure 2.6*). The voltage on the grid thus determines the
anode current.

A practical circuit is shown in *Figure 2.7(a)*. The triode operates
with the grid negative to the cathode. This is obtained by the cathode

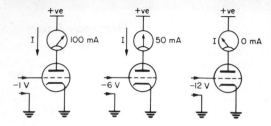

Fig. 2.6 Thermionic triode

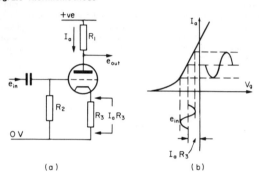

Fig. 2.7 Practical triode amplifier: (a) triode circuit; (b) I_a/V_g curve

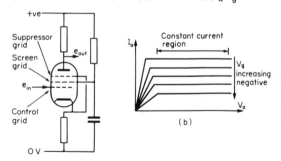

Fig. 2.8 Pentode amplifier: (a) pentode circuit; (b) I_a/V_a curve

resistor R_3. The grid is connected to 0 V by R_2, so the grid potential with respect to the cathode is given by $I_a \times R_3$. This is chosen to be in the centre of the linear region of *Figure 2.7(b)*.

As the input signal varies, the anode current will vary, causing corresponding voltage changes across R_1. The output voltage will be larger than the input voltage, so the circuit is an amplifier.

The performance of a triode can be improved by the addition of further electrodes. The commonest arrangement is the pentode shown in *Figure 2.8(a)*. The two additional grids are known as the suppressor grid and the screen grid. The anode current of a pentode does not vary with anode voltage, *Figure 2.8(b)*, the current being solely determined by the grid voltage. The gain of a pentode amplifier is given by

$$G = g_m R_L$$

where g_m is called the mutual conductance of the valve.

Semiconductor devices 2.6

The basic theory of semiconductor devices and the simple p-n junction were described in Chapter 1. These are the basis for many of the semiconductor devices described below.

2.6.1 Semiconductor diodes

A semiconductor diode is simply a p-n junction, as described in Section 1.8. The basic characteristics of a diode and the circuit symbol are shown in *Figure 2.9*.

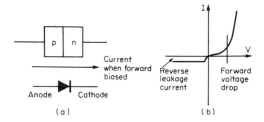

Fig. 2.9 Semiconductor diode: (a) construction and symbol; (b) V/I curve

Diodes broadly fall into two classes: rectifier and signal diodes. Rectifier diodes are used in power supplies to convert a.c. to d.c. Rectifier diodes carry large currents, have to withstand high peak inverse voltages, but generally work at low frequencies (usually 50 or 60 Hz).

Signal diodes are used as logic elements or as demodulators in RF circuits. The currents and voltages are small, but these devices are required to operate at very high speed.

These differences are reflected in the construction. A rectifier diode has to dissipate a considerable amount of heat, the energy absorbed being given by the mean forward current and the forward voltage drop. Rectifier diodes are usually bulky and often have stud mountings for heat sinks to assist cooling.

The speed of a diode depends on factors such as stray capacitance, and signal diodes tend to be very small devices.

Rectifier and signal diodes can be made from germanium or silicon. Germanium diodes have a low forward drop (about 0·2 V), but a junction temperature limit of 75°C. Silicon diodes have a forward voltage drop of about 1 V, but will operate up to nearly 200°C. The reverse leakage current is considerably lower for a silicon diode. In general, silicon diodes are preferred for rectifier diodes and logic applications, and germanium diodes for RF circuits.

2.6.2 Zener diode

If a p–n junction is reverse biased, leakage current will flow. Normally this current is negligible, but if the reverse voltage is increased a breakdown voltage is reached where large current flows, *Figure 2.10(b)*. The breakdown is caused by two distinct mechanisms, both involving somewhat complex semiconductor physics:

(1) *The avalanche effect*. High velocity minority carriers travel through the depletion layer and dislodge valence electrons. The effect is cumulative, causing a sudden increase in current.

(2) *The zener effect*. The diode is manufactured with a deliberate narrow depletion layer. The applied voltage can thus produce a large electric field across the layer which is sufficient to break down the covalent pairs.

These effects occur in normal diodes at voltages well in excess of the PIV. Devices are manufactured, however, to exhibit these breakdowns at predictable low voltages. Regardless of the mechanism of breakdown, the devices are known as zener diodes.

When breakdown occurs it is essential that the current flow is limited. Usually this is done by the series resistor shown in *Figure 2.10(a)*. The slope of the V/I curve at breakdown is very steep, and the circuit of *Figure 2.10(a)* will have an output impedance of a few ohms.

The current flowing through the zener will produce heat, the dissipation being given by

$$W = I_Z \cdot V_Z \text{ watts}$$

Zener diodes are available for dissipations up to 5 W.

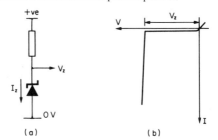

Fig. 2.10 Zener diode: (a) symbol and circuit; (b) V/I curve

The characteristics of a zener diode make them a useful voltage reference for power supplies and other circuits. It should be noted, however, that the mechanisms of breakdown produce a 'noisy' voltage and care should be taken in the application of zener diodes inside amplifiers.

2.6.3 Varicap diodes (varactor diode)

It was mentioned in Section 1.8 that the depletion layer in a reversed biased junction behaves as a capacitor. As the reverse voltage is

increased, carriers are drawn away from the junction. This increases
the depletion layer width and reduces the junction capacitance.

The varicap diode is specially designed to utilise this effect. A
typical diode will exhibit a change in capacitance from 20 pF to 40 pF
for a 5 V change in reverse bias.

Varicap diodes are widely used as tuning devices in LC circuits.
Most TV tuners now utilise varicap tuning.

2.6.4 Tunnel diode

The tunnel diode (sometimes called the Esaki diode, after its
inventor) is a p–n junction in which the doping is very heavy. This
results in a narrow depletion layer, and breakdown occurs without
any external bias at all.

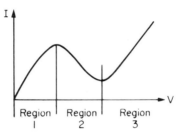

Fig. 2.11 Tunnel diode: V/I curve

The forward characteristics of the diode are shown in *Figure 2.11*.
It will be noted that there are three distinct regions. In region 1,
breakdown is occurring and the forward current is increasing. In
region 2, the device comes out of breakdown and exhibits negative
resistance (falling *I* for increasing *V*). In region 3, the device is
completely out of breakdown and behaves like a normal diode.

The useful portion of the characteristic is region 2, the negative
resistance making the device useful as an oscillator or storage device.

2.6.5 The transistor

The junction transistor is a three-layer device consisting basically of
two p–n junctions back to back. It may be pnp or npn in
construction, as shown in *Figure 2.12*. The three regions are called the
base, collector and emitter.

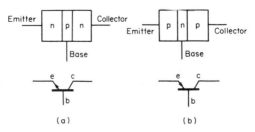

Fig. 2.12 Transistor construction: (a) npn transistor; (b) pnp transistor

For a transistor to operate, the base region must be made very thin and the doping of the emitter must be much heavier than that of the base region. *Figure 2.13* shows a pnp transistor biased correctly for operation (an npn transistor could be substituted if the voltages were reversed in polarity).

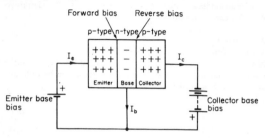

Fig. 2.13 PNP transistor, d.c. conditions

The emitter base junction is forward biased, and holes diffuse into the base region. These holes would normally exit via the base, but because of the narrowness of the base region they also come under the influence of the negatively charged collector. The holes pass into the collector assisted by the collector base potential, and collector current I_c flows.

A few holes do recombine with electrons in the base region to form a small base current I_b. The ratio I_c/I_e is approximately constant, at about 0·98, and is sometimes referred to as α. Since Kirchoff's laws apply we can say that

$$I_e = I_c + I_b$$

and it follows that the base current is about $0·02 I_e$. Correctly, α is referred to as h_{FB}.

Figure 2.14 shows a practical circuit with a signal source V_{in} and a load R_L. Resistor R_1 sets I_e and I_b to suitable levels. This arrangement is known as the common base connection and is, in fact, the least used amplifier circuit.

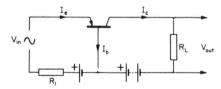

Fig. 2.14 Transistor amplifier

The input impedance is low (around 30 Ω) due to the forward biased base emitter junction. If R_L is high (say 3 kΩ) the voltage gain will be

$$G = \frac{I_c R_L}{I_e R_{in}} = \alpha \frac{R_L}{R_{in}}$$

The power gain will be $\alpha^2 (R_L/R_{in})$.

In all practical transistors the reverse biased collector base junction will have a leakage current independent of any emitter current. This is denoted by I_{co}, so the total collector current is represented by

$$I_c = \alpha I_e + I_{co}$$

In the common base circuit of *Figure 2.14* the emitter is used as the input. A commoner arrangement (known as the common emitter amplifier) using the base as the input, is shown in *Figure 2.15*. It has been shown above that if I_e changes by 1 mA (say), I_b will change by 20 μA for an α of 0·98. It follows that if I_b is changed by 20 μA, the emitter current will change by 1 mA, since the basic relationship between the three currents, I_b, I_c, I_e, holds regardless of the controlling element.

The current gain of *Figure 2.15* is given by I_c/I_b. This is often denoted by β. By simple analysis it can be seen that

$$\beta = \frac{\alpha}{1 - \alpha}$$

If α = 0·98, as above, β̂ will be 49. Correctly, β is referred to as h_{FE}.

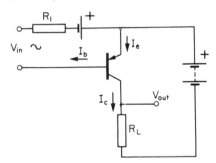

Fig. 2.15 Common emitter amplifier

The characteristics of a typical common emitter amplifier are shown in *Figure 2.16*. The output impedance is around 50 kΩ, the input impedance around 1 kΩ. Again we have voltage and power gain.

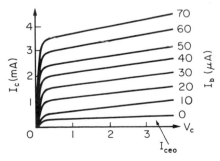

Fig. 2.16 Characteristics of common emitter amplifier

Leakage current presents a problem with common emitter amplifiers. The leakage current in the common emitter amplifier is denoted by I_{ceo}, and has a typical value of 150 μA. Effectively this is the collector base leakage current being treated as a base current, i.e.

$$I_{ceo} = \beta I_{co}$$

hence

$$I_c = \alpha I_e + \beta I_{co}$$

The leakage current is highly temperature-dependent and care needs to be taken in the design of common emitter transistor amplifiers.

Practical details of transistor amplifiers are given in Chapter 4.

2.6.6 Field effect transistor

The conventional transistor described in Subsection 2.6.5 has the disadvantage of being a low impedance device, and complex designs are needed to produce circuits with high input impedances.

The transistor is basically a current-operated device, but the conductivity of a semiconductor material can also be controlled by means of an electric field. A device using this principle is known as a field effect transistor (or FET).

The simplest FET is shown diagrammatically in *Figure 2.17(a)*. The FET is a three-terminal device comprising a slice of n-type silicon (called the channel) with a p–n junction diffused into it.

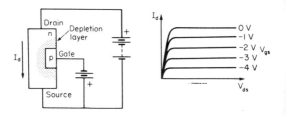

Fig. 2.17 Field effect transistor: (a) construction and bias; (b) characteristic curves

The drain is biased positive to the source, so current will flow from drain to source. If the gate is taken negative, however, a depletion layer will be formed at the p–n junction. This depletion layer will cause a decrease in the channel conductance and a decrease in the current I_d.

The conductance of the channel is thus controlled by the voltage on the gate; the more negative the gate, the less current flows. At all times the gate/channel junction is back-biased and negligible gate current flows.

If the gate voltage is taken further negative, the current I_d ceases altogether. The gate voltage at which this occurs is called the pinch-off voltage, and is typically around 5 V.

In many respects a FET resembles a thermionic valve, since it is a voltage-controlled device. Typical curves for a FET are shown in *Figure 2.17(b)*.

The FET has a very simple equivalent circuit, as shown in *Figure 2.18*. It consists of an input resistance and capacitance, a current generator and an output resistor. Typical values are:

R_{in}	1000 MΩ
C_{in}	30 pF
R_0	250 kΩ
g_m	2 mA/V

It can be seen that, for all practical circuits, the input impedance will be determined by C_{in}, and for reasonable values of R_L the voltage gain will be given by $g_m R_L$.

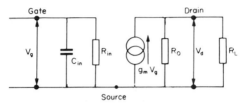

Fig. 2.18 FET equivalent circuit

The above FET is known as an n-channel JUGFET. It operates in the depletion mode, so called because the gate voltage depletes the conduction of the channel. By using p-type material, a p-channel JUGFET is produced. This operates in a similar manner, except that all polarities are reversed.

An alternative method of producing a FET is the so-called insulated gate FET (or IGFET), also known as the metal oxide semiconductor FET (or MOSFET). In this type of FET the gate is insulated from the channel.

The construction of an IGFET is shown in *Figure 2.19*. Two n-type regions are diffused into a p-type substrate. On top of this, an insulating layer of silicon dioxide is grown. An aluminium gate is then evaporated on to the oxide layer.

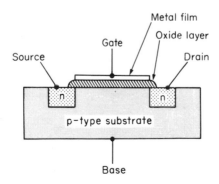

Fig. 2.19 Construction of enhancement mode IGFET

The device has four terminals. With the gate and base shorted, the only current flowing between drain and source is the negligible leakage current. If the gate potential is taken positive with respect to the base, electrons are attracted to the surface of the base, enhancing the conductivity between the two n-type regions. Drain current can now flow, the current being controlled by the gate/base voltage. This circuit operates by the gate voltage being used to enhance the conductivity between source and drain, and is hence known as an n-channel enhancement mode IGFET.

A depletion mode IGFET can be constructed as shown in *Figure 2.20*. A thin layer of n-type connects the source and drain regions. The gate is taken negative with respect to the base, in a similar manner to the JUGFET, to control the source/drain current. This type of device is known as an n-channel depletion mode IGFET.

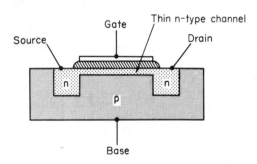

Fig. 2.20 Construction of depletion mode IGFET

As might be expected, enhancement and depletion mode IGFETs can be made with p- and n-channel material. Circuit symbols for all six basic FET types are shown in *Figure 2.21*.

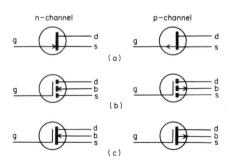

Fig. 2.21 The FET family: (a) JUGFET; (b) enhancement IGFET;
(c) depletion IGFET

2.6.7 Silicon-controlled rectifier (SCR) and family

The SCR is sometimes called a thyristor, although the latter term is also used to describe a whole family of devices. In essence, an SCR is a three-terminal, four-layer device as shown in *Figure 2.22(a)*; the corresponding circuit symbol is shown in *Figure 2.22(b)*.

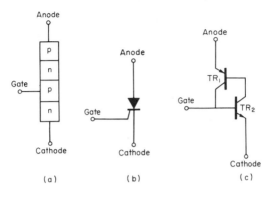

Fig. 2.22 Silicon-controlled rectifier: (a) construction; (b) symbol; (c) transistor analogy

If a positive voltage is connected between anode and cathode, negligible current will flow, since the central section is reversed biased. If the voltage is increased, the device will suddenly avalanche, passing current limited only by the resistance of the external circuit (cf. Subsection 2.6.2). Once avalanche has occurred, the current can only be stopped by reducing it to a value below a critical level called the 'holding current'.

Avalanching can also be initiated, however, by applying a positive pulse to the gate. As before, when current flow has been started, it can only be stopped by reducing the current below the holding current. A practical way to do this is to momentarily short the anode to cathode by means of a capacitor or a similar technique. The gate current required to turn on an SCR is small. A typical power SCR will control in excess of 50 A with gate currents of 20 mA.

The regenerative action of the avalanche effect can be considered as the action of the pnp/npn transistor pair in *Figure 2.22(c)*. Once a positive pulse is applied to the gate, transistors TR_1, and TR_2 will both turn hard on. The device in *Figure 2.22(a–c)* is called a cathode-controlled SCR. By utilising an npnp construction, an anode-controlled SCR can be made. This requires a negative gate pulse to turn it on.

SCRs can only pass current in one direction. By utilising a combined anode-controlled and cathode-controlled device in the one package, a bidirectional device called a triac is produced. The construction and circuit symbol are shown in *Figure 2.23*. The triac is widely used to control a.c. circuits.

A four-layer, two-terminal device can be made, utilising the avalanche effect described above. This device is called a diac. The device presents a high impedance between MT_1 and MT_2 until the

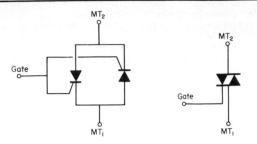

Fig. 2.23 Triac: (a) construction; (b) symbol

avalanche voltage is reached. Conduction then starts, the voltage falls
to a low value, and the current is limited solely by the external
resistance. As before, current only ceases when it is taken below the
holding value.

SCR circuits will be discussed further in Chapter 11.

2.6.8 Unijunction transistor (UJT)

The UJT is a three-terminal device consisting of an n-type bar
terminated in connections B_1 and B_2, *Figure 2.24(a)*. About halfway
along there is diffused a p-type region, called the emitter.

With the emitter open circuit, V_1 will be determined by simple
voltage division along the slice. This voltage is known as V_{EO}, *Figure
2.24(b)*. When V_{EB1} is made greater than V_{EO}, holes are injected into
the bar, causing increased conductivity, and RB_1 falls. This causes the
voltage at the junction of RB_1 and RB_2 to fall, initiating a cumulative
effect until RB_1 becomes negligibly small.

A relaxation oscillator using a UJT is shown in *Figure 2.24(c)*. UJT
oscillators are widely used in SCR firing circuits.

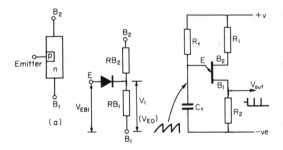

Fig. 2.24 Unijunction transistor: (a) construction; (b) operation;
(c) relaxation oscillator

3
Integrated circuits

Introduction 3.1

The past ten years have seen a marked change in the work of the average electronics engineer. When faced with the specification for a new electronic 'box', the engineer used to start designing transistor (or valve) amplifiers, oscillators and gates. Today he reaches for a catalogue of integrated circuits, and chooses one to suit.

In some respects it could be argued that this has lessened the skill of the designer, but there is no denying it has made his job easier. An added bonus is the wider horizons it gives the engineer. It is now relatively easy for one engineer to design the whole of a complex electronic assembly, and not just one small part.

Manufacture of integrated circuits 3.2

In Chapters 1 and 2 we saw how diodes and transistors could be manufactured from n- and p-type semiconducting materials. The actual semiconductor slice in fact occupies a very small proportion of the space inside a transistor 'can', and from the very early days of semiconductor technology efforts were directed at building complete circuits on a single semiconductor chip.

Small size is not, of itself, particularly important. What is significant, however, is the marked increase in speed and reduction in cost that the small size allows. In digital circuits operating at speeds above 1 MHz, the time taken for signals to pass down wires becomes critical, and this is reduced with the physical size of the circuit. A second constraint is stray capacitance, and this can be reduced if the circuit is built on a single silicon slice.

The initial design and manufacturing costs of an integrated circuit are very high, but once designed the circuit can be mass produced very cheaply. The main part of a user's costs is labour, and the construction of printed circuit boards using discrete components is very labour-intensive. If several transistors, diodes and resistors can be replaced by one integrated circuit, there will be considerable cost savings.

The theory behind the manufacture of integrated circuits is quite simple, but the practice is an operation requiring work at very fine tolerances. There are four basic mechanisms involved in the manufacture of an integrated circuit.

3.2.1 Oxidation
Integrated circuits are constructed on a slice of silicon, usually called a substrate. Silicon can be oxidised in a controlled manner by exposing it to an oxygen stream at a high temperature. The silicon oxide so formed appears as a thin layer on top of the slice.

The oxide is an excellent insulator and also acts as a seal, protecting the silicon below.

3.2.2 Photo-etching

In the manufacture of integrated circuits, parts of a silicon oxide layer are removed and parts left intact. The removal has to be done to a high degree of precision, and this can only be effected by photographic techniques.

The oxide layer is covered with a material called photoresist. This is similar to photographic film in some respects, although it is sensitive in the ultraviolet part of the spectrum. When exposed to light the photoresist becomes hard and impervious to solvents.

A piece of silicon which has been oxidised and covered with photoresist can thus be imprinted with a pattern from a photographic transparency. If the slice is then etched with acid, parts of the silicon oxide exposed to light will be protected, and parts not exposed to light will be etched away, exposing the silicon slice below the oxide.

The photoresist and the photographic transparency thus allow selective etching to take place.

3.2.3 Diffusion

We saw in Chapter 1 that a semiconductor can be made n-type or p-type by the addition of impurities. These impurity atoms can be introduced by heating silicon in an atmosphere of the correct chemical compounds. The impurity atoms (usually boron or phosphorus) diffuse into the silicon, forming layers of p- or n-type silicon at the top of the substrate. This process is called diffusion.

3.2.4 Epitaxy

Silicon is a crystalline material, and epitaxy is the name given to the mechanism of crystal growth. If a silicon slice is heated and then exposed to a gaseous silicon compound (such as silicon tetrachloride), the silicon crystal will grow as new layers of silicon are deposited.

These new layers will continue the original structure and will be an integral part of the crystal. This means that the layers we have added will behave, electrically, as part of the original structure.

The additional layers can, however, be doped as the crystal grows to form n- and p-type layers by the inclusion of suitable compounds in the atmosphere around the crystal. A transistor formed by this method is effectively a single crystal of silicon. Epitaxial methods are used almost exclusively for the manufacture of discrete transistors.

3.2.5 Manufacture of a bipolar integrated circuit

Figure 3.1 shows the stages in the manufacture of one npn transistor in an integrated circuit. In the circuit all the components are manufactured simultaneously on a single chip.

The production mechanism is a repetitive combination of the techniques described in Subsections 3.2.1–3.2.4 above.

At the end of the process, the chip contains all the required components, but these are unconnected. A thin layer of aluminium is evaporated on to the chip. The aluminium layer is covered with photoresist, exposed to light and then the unexposed aluminium etched away. The circuit is now complete and ready for encapsulation.

The manufacture is done to very fine tolerances, and failure rates are high. Rejection rates of over 90% are not uncommon in large-scale integration (LSI) chips such as microprocessors. Manufacturers

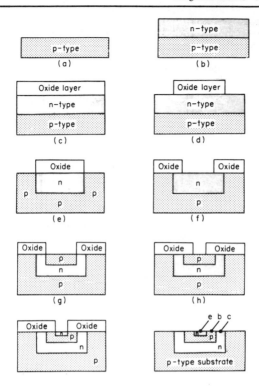

Fig. 3.1 Formation of an npn transistor in an integrated circuit:
(a) p-type substrate; (b) n-type layer grown epitaxially; (c) oxide layer formed; (d) oxide layer etched using photographic mask; (e) diffusion to form p-type material; (f) oxide layer reformed, and centre-etched using photographic mask; (g) p-type diffusion leaving n-type collector region; (h) oxide layer reformed and re-etched; (i) n-type diffusion forming base and emitter; (j) oxide layer removed and aluminium film evaporated on to form interconnection

usually have several production lines in parallel, so that in the not unlikely event of one line suddenly having a 100% rejection rate all production is not lost.

Diodes and resistors can easily be made by the processes described above. The absolute tolerance on resistors is poor, around 25%, but matching between resistors in the same chip is very good – better than 2%. Resistors take up more space than diodes and transistors, so their use is avoided where possible.

Capacitors can be made by using back-biased diodes, although they are limited to a few picofarads. Large values of capacitance have to be provided by discrete components external to the chip. It is not possible to form any useful inductance inside an i.c.

3.2.6 MOS circuits

The integrated circuits in Subsection 3.2.5 are described as bipolar because they rely on both n- and p-type material. Using techniques similar to those used in manufacturing FETs, it is possible to manufacture unipolar integrated circuits. This type of IC is known as a metal oxide semiconductor, or MOS.

A MOS transistor works by altering the conductivity of a silicon slice by means of an electric field. The construction of a MOS transistor is shown in *Figure 3.2*.

A thin slice of silicon has two p-type regions diffused into it, separated by a small gap. The two regions are known as the source and drain. The oxide between the source and drain is given an aluminium layer, and is called the gate.

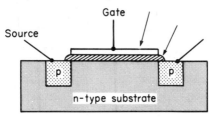

Fig. 3.2 A p-channel enhancement mode MOSFET

If a positive voltage is applied to either p-type region, there will be no current flow (other than leakage current through the gap). If we now apply a negative voltage to the gate, electrostatic forces will repel electrons away from the gate connection. This effectively converts the gap between the source and drain into p-type material, allowing conduction.

The size of the newly formed p-type material will depend on the applied voltage; hence the device behaves as a voltage-controlled resistor.

It is important to note that no current flows at the gate, since the oxide film is an excellent insulator. The MOS transistor thus has a very high input impedance.

The transistor in *Figure 3.2* is called a p-channel enhancement MOS transistor, and can be considered as a perfect switch, making it the ideal basis for a logic family.

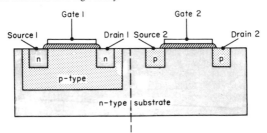

Fig. 3.3 N- and p-channel devices on the same substrate: left, n-channel MOSFET; right, p-channel MOSFET

Figure 3.3 shows a MOS transistor constructed in a similar manner, with two n-type regions diffused into a p-type substrate. This transistor is an n-channel enhancement MOS transistor, and requires a positive voltage at the gate to allow conduction.

3.2.7 CMOS circuits

It is possible to manufacture ICs with both p- and n-channel field effect transistors on the same slice. The family based on this technique is called complementary metal oxide semiconductor, or CMOS for short.

The attraction of CMOS is that the FETs can be considered as perfect switches in series with a low value resistor (typically a few hundred ohms) as shown in *Figure 3.4*. This allows very simple logic gates to be constructed, a topic discussed further in Subsection 7.9.2. Very few additional components (resistors, diodes etc.) are needed. An additional advantage is that gates using CMOS technology are about one-sixth the size of the equivalent bipolar device, making the family ideally suited for complex LSI ICs.

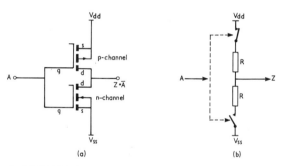

Fig. 3.4 CMOS logic gates: (a) CMOS inverter; (b) equivalent circuit

CMOS transistors also make good analog switches. *Figure 3.5(a)* shows a 4016 switch being used as an analog multiplexer to select one of four analog signals. The same device is used in *Figure 3.5(b)* to control digitally the gain of a d.c. amplifier. CMOS circuits used as analog switches are often called transmission gates.

CMOS can also be used to construct d.c. amplifiers with negligible input bias current and high input impedance. Because FETs do not saturate, CMOS d.c. amplifiers can be made to work at very low supply voltages (less than 3 volts) and often do not need a split supply.

The inputs to CMOS ICs are simply the gate of a FET, and consequently have a very high impedance, typically several megohms. Early devices were prone to damage from high voltage static electricity, but modern devices include protection.

3.2.8 Integrated injection logic (I^2L)

I^2L uses direct coupled transistors with current sources replacing the load resistors, and multiple collector transistors to simplify internal connections. A typical device is shown in *Figure 3.6*. This combines an OR function with inversion of the B input.

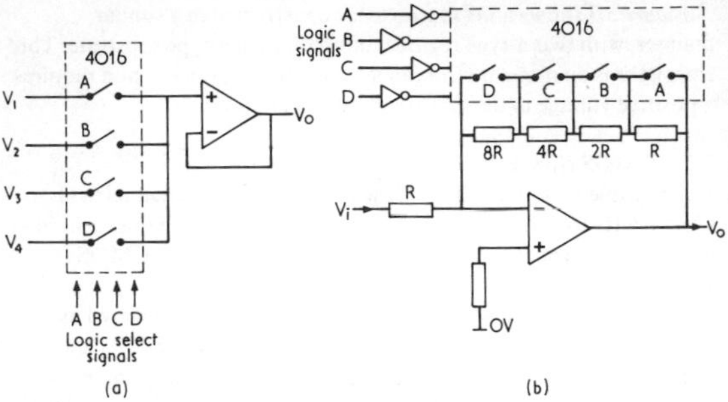

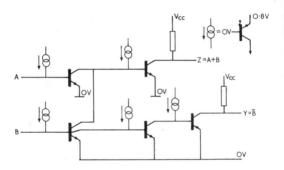

Fig. 3.5 Applications of transmission gates: (a) multiplexer circuit: ABCD are Select signals (one only energised); (b) amplifier with digitally selected gain: ABCD is a 4-bit binary number (A is LSB)

Fig. 3.6 Integrated injection logic

I^2L has a very small logic swing and poorly defined logic levels. It is not, therefore, a logic family in the same way that TTL or CMOS is. The technique, however, is well suited to the construction of complex LSI ICs as there is really only one type of component used. Many LSI devices use I^2L construction internally, coming to higher logic levels for connection to the outside world.

3.3 Integrated circuits in use

Integrated circuits have been one of the most spectacular successes of the past twenty years. ICs are now available to replace computers, amplifiers and logic gates.

One of the most impressive facets of ICs is the way that their price has continued to fall in actual terms, despite inflation. This has brought corresponding price falls in electronic items such as calculators, digital watches and televisions. The next decade will see a similar price fall in personal computers and information systems.

As integrated circuits become more complex, they inevitably become more specialised. The cost of producing the many photographic masks to make an integrated circuit is very high, but once the masks are available long production runs make it profitable; this is not possible, however, with specialist integrated circuits and a limited market.

This problem has been approached in several ways. The first is the microprocessor and its support devices, described in Chapter 8. The second approach is to make specialist circuits for industries with high turnovers, such as manufacture of domestic appliances and automobiles. The final approach is the introduction of the uncommitted logic array, or ULA.

A ULA is an LSI chip ready made with many logical functions (gates, storage, shift registers, etc.), but without the final interconnection layer. A user can draw up his required logical function, and the semiconductor manufacturer produces the necessary interconnection mask. Because only one specialised mask is involved and the interconnection procedure is the simplest of the IC manufacturing processes, the ULA becomes cost effective where few circuits are needed.

The range of ICs on the market is now so extensive that it is no longer possible to give a typical application. Almost every chapter in this book now contains a section on ICs relevant to the topic discussed.

4
A.C. amplifiers

4.1 Introduction

It is possible that the commonest types of electronic circuit are those covered by the term 'amplifier'. The description 'a.c. amplifier' covers a wide range of circuits, from the domestic hi-fi system to radio circuits operating at frequencies of over 1000 MHz. This chapter first describes the basic principles of a.c. amplification, then discusses specific amplifier types.

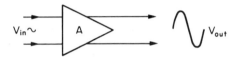

4.2 Basic principles

The basic requirements of an amplifier are simple. It is a circuit with two input terminals and two output terminals, as shown in *Figure 4.1*.

$V_{in} \sim$ A V_{out}

Fig. 4.1 Amplifier block diagram

An alternating voltage, V_{in}, is applied to the input terminals, and an amplified copy, V_{out}, appears at the output terminals. To describe the amplifier operation we need to define the following terms.

4.2.1 Frequency and period
The frequency of a signal is defined as the number of cycles of the signal occurring in 1s. The sine wave in *Figure 4.2* repeats every 1 ms. It therefore has a period of 1 ms and a frequency of 1 kHz.

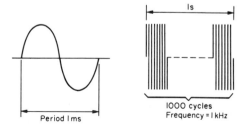

Period 1ms

1s

1000 cycles
Frequency = 1 kHz

Fig. 4.2 Frequency and period

4.2.2 Harmonic content

Most of the waveforms encountered in practice are vastly different
from a pure sine wave, and in many cases (such as speech) it is almost
impossible to define the fundamental frequency. It can be shown,
however, that any repetitive waveform can be constructed by the
addition of a series of sine and cosine waves at fundamental
frequency, 2 × fundamental, 3 × fundamental and so on. These are
known as the 'harmonics' of the waveform. It is the different
harmonic content that makes middle C on a violin sound different
from middle C on, say, a piano. In general, the higher the frequency of
the harmonic, the smaller its amplitude. There comes a point,
therefore, when the higher frequency components become so small as
to be negligible. The technique of splitting a complex waveform into
its component frequencies is called Fourier analysis. Examples are
shown in *Figure 4.3*.

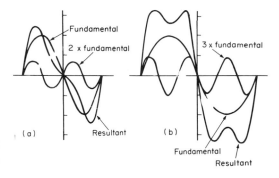

Fig. 4.3 Waveforms containing harmonics: (a) second harmonic;
(b) third harmonic

The technique has important implications for a.c. amplifier design.
If it is desired to amplify a complex signal, a Fourier analysis will
show the range of frequencies contained in the signal. If the amplifier
performance is consistent over this range, the output signal will be an
amplified true replica of the input signal. In an audio amplifier, for
example, we need to cover frequencies from 30 Hz to over 15 kHz if
we are to provide a true rendering of a musical performance.

4.2.3 Gain

The gain of an amplifier is simply defined as

$$\text{Gain} = \frac{V_{\text{out}}}{V_{\text{in}}}$$

The gain is defined for one specific frequency, since desired, and
undesired, effects will cause it to be different at other frequencies.

In many amplifier circuits, gains of several thousand are common,
and it is more convenient to express gains in logarithmic terms.

Amplifier gains are often expressed in decibels, defined as a power ratio

$$\text{Gain (dB)} = 10 \log_{10} \frac{P_{\text{out}}}{P_{\text{in}}}$$

The logarithm is taken to base 10.

If the source and load are of equal impedance, since

$$P = \frac{V^2}{R}$$

the gain in decibels can be expressed in terms of voltages:

$$\text{Gain (dB)} = 20 \log_{10} \frac{V_{\text{out}}}{V_{\text{in}}}$$

Although this expression is only strictly true if source and load impedance are equal, amplifier gains are often (incorrectly) expressed in decibels when source and load impedances are different.

4.2.4 Bandwidth

It was mentioned above that an amplifier's gain is specified at one particular frequency, and that the gain will be different at other frequencies.

At low frequencies, coupling capacitors between amplifier stages increase in impedance, causing loss of gain. At high frequencies the gain is reduced by stray capacitance and limitations of the transistors themselves.

It therefore follows that a graph of gain versus frequency would appear similar to that in *Figure 4.4*. It is usual to define the range of frequencies over which the amplifier can be used as the amplifier bandwidth. Normally this is taken between the two points at which the gain has fallen by 3 dB (i.e. the power gain has fallen by half).

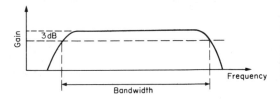

Fig. 4.4 Amplifier bandwidth

In many amplifier circuits (notably radio circuits) the bandwidth is deliberately designed to amplify, or reject, one particular range of frequencies.

Basic transistor amplifiers 4.3

A single transistor amplifier stage can be arranged in any of the three configurations in *Figure 4.5*. These are known as common emitter, common collector and common base, respectively.

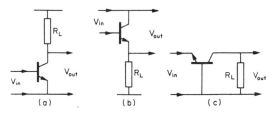

Fig. 4.5 Basic transistor amplifier configurations: (a) common emitter; (b) common collector; (c) common base

4.3.1 Common emitter amplifier

The most popular form of amplifier circuit is the common emitter. In its simplest form it is arranged as in *Figure 4.6(a)*. To keep a transistor conducting with current flow from collector to emitter, a much smaller current has to flow from base to emitter and under these conditions a voltage will exist between emitter and base of approximately 0·6 V.

The ratio of collector current to base current is called the common emitter current gain, and has the symbol h_{FE} (or sometimes the Greek letter β). Values of h_{FE} vary greatly, even within the same type of transistor. For example, the common audio transistor BC108 can have an h_{FE} in the range 100 to 800.

In *Figure 4.6(a)*, base current is provided by R_b and the base current is given by

$$I_b = \frac{(V_{cc} - 0\cdot6)}{R_b}$$

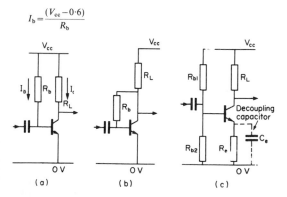

Fig. 4.6 Common emitter amplifier: (a) simple circuit; (b) temperature stabilisation; (c) practical amplifier

This causes a collector current to flow:

$$I_c = h_{FE} \cdot I_b$$

In turn ths causes a voltage drop across R_L: $V_L = I_c \cdot R_L$

Ideally R_L and R_b are chosen such that $V_L = 0.5 V_{cc}$, allowing an equal positive or negative swing of voltage at the collector.

If a small a.c. signal is now applied to the base, the base current will change in sympathy, causing a larger change in collector current. This, in turn, produces a large voltage change across R_L. Note that a positive increase in voltage at the base causes more base current to flow, causing more collector current to flow and the collector voltage to fall. The amplified output is the inverse of the input signal.

This simple amplifier circuit has many shortcomings. The values of R_b and R_L have to be adapted very precisely to the characteristics of the particular transistor. As mentioned before, h_{FE} varies widely from transistor to transistor, even of the same nominal type. Of more importance, however, is the sad fact that transistor characteristics are very temperature-dependent. A simple circuit such as in *Figure 4.6(a)* would not, in fact, work reliably over a temperature range of more than a few degrees Centigrade.

There are several transistor parameters that are temperature-dependent, but the most important are the current gain h_{FE} and the collector to emitter leakage current. The leakage current (denoted I_{ceo}) is the current flowing from collector to emitter with the base disconnected. This current is highly temperature-dependent and doubles for each 8 °C rise.

An improvement can be made with the circuit shown in *Figure 4.6(b)*. The base resistor R_b is now returned to the collector. Suppose we have chosen R_b and R_L such that the collector is sitting correctly at $0.5 V_{cc}$, and changes in temperature cause the leakage current to rise. The change in leakage current will cause more collector current to flow, causing the collector volts to fall. The fall in collector volts will reduce the base current flowing through R_b, reducing the collector current and compensating, to some extent, for the change in leakage current.

The circuit shown in *Figure 4.6(c)* gives almost perfect compensation for changes in transistor characteristics. Resistors R_{b1} and R_{b2} are a voltage divider defining the base voltage. The emitter voltage is thus defined, since the base emitter voltage is effectively constant at 0.6 V. Because the emitter voltage is fixed, the emitter current is given by

$$I_e = \frac{V_e}{R_e} = \frac{(V_b - 0.6)}{R_e}$$

In modern transistors, with high values of h_{FE}, it is a reasonable approximation to say that

$$I_c = I_e$$

Hence the voltage drop across R_L is defined.

In this particular circuit arrangement, variations in h_{FE} only affect the base current being drawn from the voltage divider R_{b1}, R_{b2}. The variation in base current will cause a negligible change in operating conditions if the standing bleed current through R_{b1}, R_{b2} is significantly larger than the base current. R_{b1} and R_{b2} must not be made too small, however, or the input impedance of the stage will be unacceptably low.

Calculation of the gain of a single-stage amplifier can be made very mathematical, with complex models. For most purposes, however, simple approximations will give adequate accuracy. To define the gain of our single-stage amplifier we need two parameters.

The first is h_{fe}. This is similar to the d.c. gain h_{FE} above, with the exception that it is the small signal a.c. gain (or a.c. β), i.e.

$$h_{fe} = \frac{\Delta I_c}{\Delta I_b}$$

where Δ denotes 'small change'. The parameter h_{fe} is a ratio (and hence is dimensionless) and has a typical range of 50 to 800.

The second parameter is h_{ie}. This relates the variation of base current to small signal changes in base emitter voltage. It is defined as

$$h_{ie} = \frac{\Delta V_{be}}{\Delta i_b}$$

The parameter h_{ie} has the dimensions of resistance, and has a typical value of several hundred ohms.

In the equations below, the load resistor R_l is not simply the collector load resistor; it is the effective parallel resistance of the collector resistor R_c and the input resistance R_{in} of the stage following, i.e.

$$R_L = \frac{R_c \cdot R_{in}}{R_{in} + R_c}$$

For the voltage amplifier of *Figure 4.6(c)*, we can use the following equation to give an adequate approximation of performance:

Input impedance, $Z_{in} = h_{ie} + h_{fe} R_e$ (1)

Output impedance, $Z_{out} = R_L$ (2)

Voltage gain $= \dfrac{R_L}{(h_{ie}/h_{fe}) + R_e}$ (3)

In equation (1), the effect of R_e is to raise the input impedance. In equation (3), the effect of R_e is to lower the gain. In most circuits the value of h_{ie}/h_{fe} will be much less than R_e, so equation (3) can be simplified to

$$\text{Voltage gain} = \frac{R_L}{R_e}$$

In most amplifier circuits, however, the degradation of gain due to R_e is not acceptable. If an emitter decoupling capacitor C_e is added, as shown in *Figure 4.6(c)*, the d.c. conditions necessary to give stable operation are unchanged, but the effective emitter impedance to a.c. signals becomes almost zero.

Substituting $R_e = 0$ into equation (3), we get

$$\text{Voltage gain} = h_{fe} \cdot \frac{R_L}{h_{ie}}$$ (4)

The ratio h_{fe}/h_{ie} is sometimes given the symbol g_m.

Equation (4) assumes that the decoupling capacitor C_e has negligible impedance compared with h_{ie}/h_{fe}. The impedance of a capacitor increases with decreasing frequency; hence the requisite value of C_e must be calculated for the lowest frequency to be amplified.

Transistor characteristics vary greatly from device to device, so the above formula can only be used as a guide to expected results. In practical amplifier designs it is usual to design an amplifier with very high gain, and then use feedback (to be described later) to define the gain. In this way, consistent amplifier performance can be obtained over the full tolerance of characteristics.

4.3.2 Common collector amplifier (emitter follower)

The second most popular transistor amplifier stage is the common collector arrangement shown in *Figure 4.5(b)*. The input signal is applied to the base and the output taken from the emitter. A practical version is shown in *Figure 4.7(a)*.

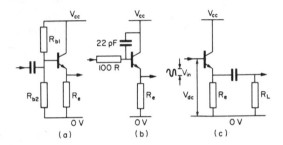

Fig. 4.7 Common collector amplifier (emitter follower): (a) practical circuit; (b) prevention of oscillation; (c) signal clipping

Resistors R_{b1}, R_{b2} and R_e specify the d.c. operating conditions as before, and give consistent performance with variation in transistor characteristics. Because the transistor is always conducting, there will be approximately 0·6 V between emitter and base. The output signal will be almost identical to the input signal in both amplitude and phase. Because the emitter follows the base, the circuit is sometimes known as an 'emitter follower'.

The emitter follower has a very low output impedance, typically less than 100 Ω, and an input impedance given by

$$Z_{in} = h_{ie} + h_{fe} \cdot R_e$$

The input impedance can be very high, typically 100 kΩ, although it will be lowered to some extent by R_{b1} and R_{b2}.

With high input impedance, low output impedance and unity gain the emitter follower makes a useful buffer stage.

Emitter followers can exhibit some peculiar effects. It is quite common for an emitter follower to burst into high frequency oscillations. The cure is to insert a low value (less than 100 Ω) resistor into the base lead or connect a small (about 22 pF) capacitor from collector to base, local to the transistor, *Figure 4.7(b)*.

The second problem occurs where an emitter follower is capacitively coupled to a load in the manner of *Figure 4.7(c)*. If R_L is less than R_e and the d.c. bias determined by R_{b1}, R_{b2} is only slightly greater than the signal amplitude, clipping of negative portions of the signal may occur. This is purely a question of design, the criteria being that

$$V_{in} < \frac{R_L}{R_e + R_L} \cdot V_{dc}$$

4.3.3 Common base amplifier

The final configuration is shown in *Figure 4.5(c)*. The input signal is applied to the emitter, and the output signal taken from the collector. The input impedance is very low, typically 15 Ω, whereas the output impedance is high, usually in excess of 1 MΩ. To a certain extent the output looks like a constant current source. These factors tend to limit the usefulness of a common base amplifier. The circuit, will, however, give voltage amplification and is sometimes used with low impedance sources such as microphones, transducers and aerials.

The general arrangement of a common base amplifier is shown in *Figure 4.8*. D.C. conditions are set by the base resistors R_{b1}, R_{b2}. The base is decoupled to a.c. signals by C_1. The common base circuit is less prone to stabilisation problems, as the leakage current I_{cbo} is usually only a few microamperes.

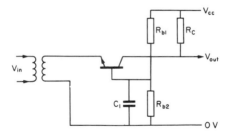

Fig. 4.8 Common base amplifier

The input signal needs to be fed from a low impedance source, usually the secondary of a transformer. If capacitance coupling is used, the value of the capacitor must be extremely large before its impedance is sufficiently low.

A positive input signal will cause the collector current to fall and the collector voltage to rise. With the common base circuit, therefore, there is no phase change between input and output.

Multistage amplifiers 4.4

Usually an a.c. amplifier is required to have a gain considerably higher than that obtained with a single transistor stage. Amplifier stages can be cascaded to give the required gain, the overall gain being given by

$$G = G_1 \times G_2 \times G_3 \times \ldots$$

Where G_n is the gain of stage n. If the decibel notation is used:

$$G(\text{dB}) = G_1 + G_2 + G_3 + \ldots$$

The design of multistage amplifiers needs some care if problems are not to be encountered with oscillations. Many a multistage amplifier has turned into a multistage oscillator.

Figure 4.9 shows a multistage amplifier. Transistor TR_3 will be causing quite major current variations in the supply current, and if the supply regulation is poor or the supply leads have significant inductance the supply volts will be varying in sympathy. These variations will be fed back to the first stage, where they will be treated as signal and amplified. If conditions are right, oscillation of the amplifier will occur.

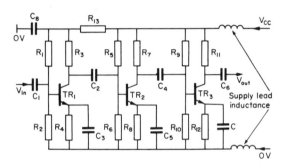

Fig. 4.9 Decoupling of multistage amplifier

To overcome this problem, supply decoupling for the first few stages is usually included. In *Figure 4.9*, resistor R_{13} and C_8 provide supply decoupling for TR_1.

The second problem with multistage amplifiers is oscillations induced by stray capacitance. This is a layout problem, and should not arise if early stages are kept clear of the large amplitude signals in the later stages, and interconnecting wires are kept short and tidy. Oscillations caused by stray capacitance are normally very high, and if the frequency of oscillation is above the desired amplifier bandwidth, a cure can be effected by deliberately reducing the high frequency gain.

One final point to note with multistage amplifiers is the problem of self-induced noise. Transistors produce white noise, partly due to irregularities in the electron flow (shot noise) and partly from thermal agitation of the electrons in the circuit impedances. Transistor noise has two components; intrinsic noise which depends on emitter current and excess noise which depends on collector volts.

Any noise occurring in the early stages of a multistage amplifier will be amplified by successive stages, to the detriment of the amplifier performance. To reduce the noise, early stages should be run at low currents and low voltages. The noise can also be reduced by the use of special low noise transistors (e.g. BC149).

It is unusual to find multistage amplifiers without overall feedback to determine the gain (see below). It was shown earlier that variations in transistor characteristics cause wide variations in the gains of apparently identical single-stage amplifiers. In multistage amplifiers, the effect is multiplied. For example, if an amplifier is constructed of three stages, each of which can have a gain variation of 5 to 1, the total variation in gain could be as much as 125 to 1.

Multistage amplifiers are normally constructed such that the minimum possible gain (calculated with the worst transistor characteristics) is more than adequate. The overall gain is then determined by negative feedback, giving an amplifier whose performance is consistent regardless of the transistors used in the circuit.

Negative feedback 4.5

Variation in transistor characteristics will give large differences between the gains of apparently identical amplifiers. Negative feedback is widely used to produce amplifiers with predictable gains and low distortion.

In the circuit of *Figure 4.10* we have a high gain amplifier A. The output voltage is attenuated by B and subtracted from the input voltage. Simple analysis will show that

$$\text{Overall gain} = \frac{V_{\text{out}}}{V_{\text{in}}} = \frac{A}{(1+AB)}$$

If, for example, A is 100 and B is 0·1, the overall gain is 9·1. If A is doubled to 200, and B remains at 0·1, the overall gain is 9·5, a negligible change. If A is large the overall gain becomes $1/B$.

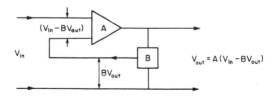

Fig. 4.10 Negative feedback

Negative feedback is also useful in reducing distortion, although this may not be immediately obvious. If an amplifier has $N\%$ distortion in its open-loop state, the distortion with negative feedback will be

$$\text{Distortion} = \frac{N}{(1+AB)}\%$$

The term $(1 + AB)$ is sometimes called the gain reduction factor, and the term AB the open-loop gain. The overall gain $A/(1 + AB)$ is called the closed-loop gain.

If the feedback block B is made frequency-dependent, the frequency response of the amplifier can be designed as required. An example of this technique is illustrated in the tone control circuit described below.

4.6 Amplifier types

In the sections following, the basic requirements and designs for various types of a.c. amplifiers are described.

4.6.1 Audio amplifiers

Audio amplifiers are designed to be used over the range 30 Hz to around 20 kHz. Over this range the gain has to be constant if the reproduction is not to exaggerate one particular range of frequencies. The human ear is very sensitive to distortion, so the output stage has to be designed for minimum distortion.

Audio amplifiers receive their input from microphones, record, cassette and tape decks and radio tuners. These are all low level signals, so care has to be taken in the design of the input stages to minimise noise from external sources and noise from the circuit itself. Low noise transistors are usually employed in pre-amplifier stages.

Classically, audio amplifiers have been designed in two blocks. A pre-amplifier (or control) stage is used to amplify the input signal to a level of around 1 V. This stage will also contain the user's volume and tone controls and the input and mode selection switches.

The second block is the power amplifier, which is used to deliver considerable power to the speakers. This usually has no user controls.

Most amplifiers now contain a pre-amplifier and power amplifier in a single case, but it is still convenient to deal with them as separate topics. The remainder of this section will therefore discuss pre-amplifier design, while the following section will deal with power amplifier design.

The input stage has to accept an input from a wide range of sources and at levels from a few millivolts for a magnetic pick-up to several hundred millivolts for an input from a radio tuner. The mode selection switch must therefore not only select the input, but must also select a suitable gain.

Further complication is added by the response of a magnetic cartridge. This is not flat, but has a rising response defined by the RIAA (Record Industry Association of America) standard. The selected gain for a magnetic cartridge has to be 'equalised' to give a flat response.

A typical input stage is shown in *Figure 4.11*. TR_1 and TR_2 form a simple two-stage amplifier, with d.c. stabilisation provided by R_3. The mode switch SW_{1a} selects the required input and the ganged SW_{1b} the feedback to give the correct gain. In the magnetic pick-up positions R_6, C_3, C_4 give the RIAA equalisation.

TR$_1$ and TR$_2$ will be specially chosen for their low noise characteristics, and care taken with the wiring to SW$_1$ to obviate the possibility of interference from mains transformers or RF pick-up.

The input stage will be followed by tone controls. These are usually some form of bass/treble–lift/cut circuit. A typical passive circuit is shown in *Figure 4.12(a)*, and an active circuit using negative feedback in *Figure 4.12(c)*. These have the basic response of *Figure 4.12(b)*.

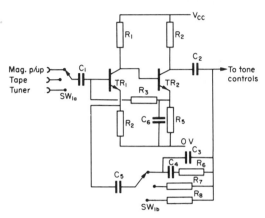

Fig. 4.11 Audio pre-amplifier

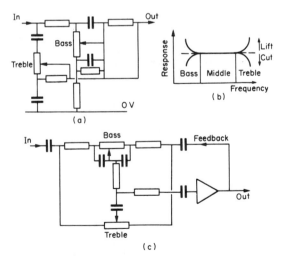

Fig. 4.12 Tone control circuits: (a) passive circuit; (b) response; (c) active (Baxendall) circuit

The human ear has a very nonlinear response, and at low volumes it is less sensitive to low frequencies. On some amplifiers a 'loudness control' is used in place of a simple attenuator volume control. A loudness control provides progressive bass lift as the volume is reduced, to compensate for the response of the ear. Hi-fi purists tend to decry the loudness control and prefer a simple volume control.

4.6.2 Power amplifiers

A power amplifier is designed to deliver power to a load. Usually the term is applied to the output stage of an audio amplifier, but similar design techniques are used in many other applications.

Power amplifiers are classified according to the bias condition of the output stage. The simplest arrangement is known as Class A, and is shown in *Figure 4.13(a)* and *4.13(b)*. The transistor is biased such that collector current flows at all times. The stage has low distortion, but poor efficiency – at best 50%. Class A is therefore best suited for low power amplifiers for portable radios and similar circuits.

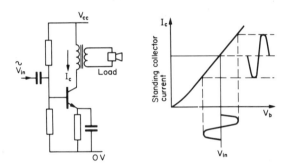

Fig. 4.13 Class A power amplifier: (a) circuit diagram; (b) relationship of I_c and V_b

A Class B amplifier is biased at cut-off, as shown in *Figure 4.14(b)*. By its very nature, Class B assumes push-pull operation with one transistor for positive half-cycles and one transistor for negative half-cycles. A typical output stage is shown in *Figure 4.14(a)*. The trim pot RV_1 sets the bias for TR_1 and TR_2, and D_1 and D_2 provide compensation for variation in V_{be} of TR_1 and TR_2 with temperature. Class B amplifiers have high efficiency because the quiescent current is small.

The nonlinear curves of *Figure 4.14(b)* cause severe distortion at low volume levels. This is known as crossover distortion and is particularly irritating to the ear. Pure Class B is seldom used in audio circuits, and it is usual to arrange a small standing current. This mode is known as Class AB, and is shown in *Figure 4.14(c)*. Both transistors are biased just beyond the nonlinear region, thereby reducing distortion considerably at the expense of a small decrease in power efficiency.

Class C amplifiers are only found in RF applications. The output stage is biased well beyond cut-off and only conducts on the peaks of

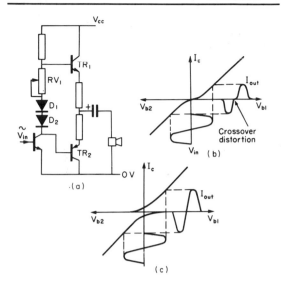

Fig. 4.14 Class B and Class AB amplifiers: (a) circuit diagram; (b) Class B, I_c/V_b curves; (c) Class AB, I_c/V_b curves

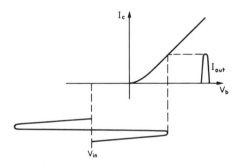

Fig. 4.15 Class C amplifier

the input signal. This produces the highly distorted waveform shown in *Figure 4.15* which is useless for audio circuits. In RF circuits, however, the use of a tuned load will restore the correct shape. Class C amplifiers are very efficient and are widely used in RF transmitters.

The final type of amplifier is Class D. These utilise the output transistors as switches, which are either on or off (*Figure 4.16*), and the output is achieved by varying the mark-space ratio of a square wave. The dissipation of the output transistors is low, since they are either on (low volts, high current) or off (high volts, zero current).

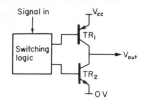

Fig. 4.16 Class D amplifier

Class D amplifiers are very efficient, but few practical designs have been produced.

All power amplifiers dissipate a fair amount of heat, the majority of it coming from the output transistors. Heat sinks are used to remove the heat and ensure that the transistors operate at a safe temperature.

4.6.3 Video amplifiers

An amplifier whose bandwidth extends from a frequency in the low audio range to a frequency in the megahertz range is generally termed a video amplifier, regardless of use. The term originates from television circuits where wideband amplifiers are needed, although video amplifiers are used in other equipment such as radar and ultrasonics.

The design of video amplifiers is superficially similar to audio amplifiers. The bandwidth is limited at high frequencies by stray capacitance and the fall of h_{fe} in the transistors. The lower limit is determined by the rising impedance of interstage coupling capacitors and emitter decoupling capacitors.

Stray capacitance can be reduced by careful layout and choice of components, but it can never be completely removed. Stray capacitance of 20 pF will have an impedance of about 4 kΩ at 2 MHz, and 1 kΩ at 5 MHz. This means that very low values of resistance would need to be used to swamp the stray capacitance by the rest of the circuit. The transistor equations of Subsection 4.3.1 show that low values of collector resistance will give low gain, so this approach is not very practical.

A practical solution is to use a series inductor and resistor as a collector load. The value of L is chosen with a knowledge of the stray capacitance, such that together they form a resonant circuit at the maximum required frequency (usually around 5 MHz). Since the value of R is quite high, the circuit is highly damped and the gain is fairly constant over the required frequency range.

The gain at low frequencies is largely determined by interstage coupling. Capacitance coupling and transformer coupling both have poor low frequency characteristics, and it is usual for video amplifiers to employ d.c. coupling.

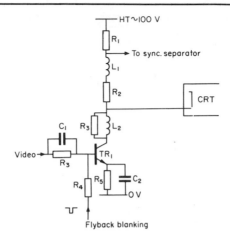

Fig. 4.17 Video amplifier stage

A typical video stage is shown in *Figure 4.17*. This stage amplifies a video signal from a few volts to around 60 V to drive a TV tube. Note the use of d.c. coupling and the compensating inductor in the collector circuit.

4.6.4 Frequency selective amplifiers

In RF amplifiers, a circuit is often required to amplify a very narrow band of frequencies and reject all others. Frequency selective amplifiers (often called tuned or simply RF amplifiers) usually use LC circuits to provide the necessary tuning.

The circuit of *Figure 4.18(a)* is known as a series tuned circuit. The inductor and capacitor have exactly opposite phase effects, and resonance occurs when their reactances are equal, i.e.

$$2\pi f L = \frac{1}{2\pi f C}$$

or

$$f = \frac{1}{2\pi\sqrt{(LC)}}$$

At resonance the impedance is determined solely by r. The circuit thus exhibits a low impedance at resonance.

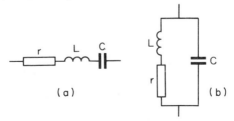

Fig. 4.18 Tuned circuits: (a) series circuit; (b) parallel circuit

The circuit of *Figure 4.18(b)* is known as a parallel tuned circuit, and is more common in RF amplifiers. The circuit again exhibits resonance when the reactance of the inductor and capacitor are equal, and the formulae above apply.

The parallel tuned circuit exhibits a very high impedance at resonance. It is, in theory, infinite, but practical components exhibit series resistance, denoted by *r* in *Figure 4.18(b)*.

If a parallel tuned circuit is used as the collector load of a transistor amplifier, the gain will vary with the impedance of the tuned circuit, being a maximum at resonance (*Figure 4.19*).

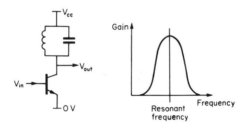

Fig. 4.19 Transistor amplifier with tuned load

The maximum gain is determined mainly by the series resistance of the coil *r*. A 'magnification factor', denoted by Q, is defined for a coil at resonance, where

$$Q = \frac{2\pi f L}{r} = \frac{\omega L}{r}$$

where $\omega = 2\pi f$ and *f* is the resonant frequency. The higher the value of Q, the higher will be the gain of the amplifier. Typical values for Q are in the range 100–500.

At resonance the parallel LC circuit looks like a pure resistance, R, given by any of the formulae;

$$R = \frac{\omega^2 L^2}{r} = \frac{L}{Cr} = \frac{Q}{\omega C}$$

It might be thought that Q should be designed to be as high as possible, since an RF amplifier is used to select one particular radio station. This is not quite true. As we shall see in Chapter 10, a radio signal does not occupy one specific frequency. It consists of a centre carrier frequency and a band of side frequencies. An RF amplifier is thus required to amplify a fairly narrow band of frequencies, and the ideal response would be that of *Figure 4.20(a)*.

The higher the value of Q in a tuned circuit, the narrower the band of frequencies that can be amplified. *Figure 4.20(b)* and *4.20(c)* compare the response of identical circuits with Q of 100 and 500. The high Q circuit is very narrow, and would not amplify the required band of frequencies. The low Q circuit will pass too large a range of frequencies. The shape of a resonance curve, in fact, means that there is no value of Q which will give a reasonable approximation to *Figure 4.20(a)* in a single-stage amplifier.

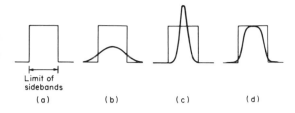

Fig. 4.20 Amplifier response in radio receivers: (a) ideal response; (b) single stage with $Q = 100$; (c) single stage with $Q = 500$; (d) multistage, each stage, $Q = 100$

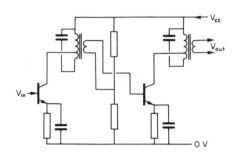

Fig. 4.21 Transistor RF amplifier

If, however, a multistage amplifier is constructed, and each stage has a Q of 100, we get the response of *Figure 4.20(d)*. This has the required width and reasonably sharp sides, approximating fairly well to *Figure 4.20(a)*. In RF amplifiers, multistages are used primarily to improve selectivity and not necessarily for more gain.

A transistor RF amplifier usually has a high output impedance and a fairly low input impedance. Transformers are therefore used to obtain the correct matching between stages, as shown in *Figure 4.21*. A tapped primary is used to allow L and C to have convenient values.

The techniques described above allow RF amplifiers to be constructed up to the bottom of the VHF band (about 40 MHz). Above this frequency, special techniques are needed which are somewhat beyond the scope of this book. The topic of communications is discussed further in Chapter 10.

4.6.5 Integrated circuit amplifiers

Integrated circuits are, of course, being used for a.c. amplifiers but not quite to the same extent as for d.c. amplifiers and logic circuits. Initially ICs were used for audio amplifiers, and today simple IC high power audio circuits can be built with a minimum of external components. A typical circuit, complete with tone control, is shown in *Figure 4.22*. The majority of television and 'middle market' music centres use IC amplifiers. Hi-fi purists tend to prefer transistor pre-

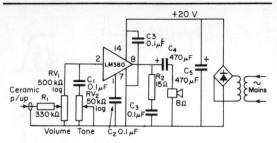

Fig. 4.22 Integrated circuit audio amplifier for cheap record player

amplifiers, and there is some justification for this view as the noise
performance of most integrated circuit pre-amplifiers cannot yet
match good transistor circuits.

Integrated circuits are also used in RF and IF circuits, although the
component count is not reduced as dramatically as for audio
amplifiers. Tuning components still have to be provided, and this is
likely to remain unchanged. Many ICs are being specially designed
for specific domestic applications, and the majority of modern colour
TVs use ICs for the IF, sound detector and colour demodulator. A
unique single-chip TRF radio receiver is available from one
enterprising manufacturer.

Integrated circuit a.c. amplifiers will doubtless increase in
versatility and the day will probably come when circuit designers
select an a.c. amplifier from a catalogue in much the same way as they
select d.c. amplifiers and logic gates.

5
D.C. amplifiers

Introduction 5.1

Until recently, descriptive texts on d.c. amplifiers would go into great detail on their design using discrete devices. Integrated circuit technology has provided the designer with excellent amplifiers at a cost similar to an individual transistor. D.C. amplifiers are now regarded as a building block and it is very unusual for an engineer to design one. This chapter reflects this change in attitude, and will mainly be concerned with applications.

Basic principles 5.2

In conventional a.c. amplifiers, capacitors and transformers are used to couple successive stages. This a.c. coupling allows the bias conditions for each stage to be totally independent. In a d.c. amplifier such techniques obviously cannot be used, and it is necessary to use direct coupling between stages.

Direct coupling brings problems, however. A first attempt at d.c. amplification could look similar to the circuit shown in *Figure 5.1*. Unfortunately there are several good reasons why this simple approach will not work.

Transistor characteristics vary widely, both with temperature and from device to device. Two characteristics are of particular importance in d.c. amplifiers: the base emitter voltage and the collector leakage current.

The base emitter voltage changes by 2 mV for every degree Centigrade change in temperature. The amplifier is unable to distinguish between V_{be} changes brought about by temperature, and V_{be} changes brought about by the input. In most applications, the input to the amplifier will be of the order of a few millivolts, and a simple amplifier could not be used if the ambient temperature changed.

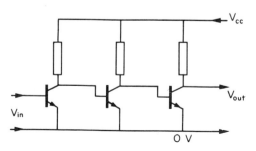

Fig. 5.1 Single d.c. amplifier

The collector current leakage will cause shifts in the collector voltage, which will be treated as signal by successive stages. This leakage current is again temperature-dependent. The simple circuit of *Figure 5.1* would thus make a reasonable thermometer, but a very poor amplifier.

5.2.1 The long-tail pair

The circuit arrangement in *Figure 5.2* is used almost universally for d.c. amplifiers. Transistors TR_1, TR_2 are specially chosen to have identical characteristics and, more importantly, these characteristics vary identically with temperature. With discrete components, the two transistors would be specially selected and fastened to a heat sink to maintain temperature equality. In an integrated circuit, the characteristics match automatically, and the encapsulation ensures temperature stability.

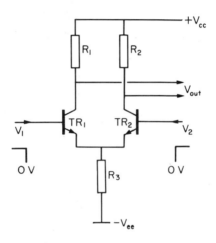

Fig. 5.2 The long-tail pair

Changes in V_{be} will thus affect the emitter voltages identically, and as R_3 can be considered to supply a constant current, the collector currents and voltages will be almost unaffected. Moreover any changes that do occur will be the same for TR_1 and TR_2, leaving the differential output voltage unchanged.

Changes in leakage current will affect both transistors similarly, again causing little change in the output voltage.

Suppose that the two input signals are equal in both amplitude and phase. This will cause equal variations at the two collectors, and the output voltage will be zero.

If the input voltages are different, the collector currents will be different, and the output voltage will be an amplified version of the difference between the two input voltages. The circuit is therefore sometimes referred to as a differential amplifier.

The important characteristic of a differential amplifier is its ability to amplify differences between signals, but not amplify the signals themselves. Suppose

$$V_1 = 0 \cdot 1 \text{ mV and } V_2 = 0 \text{ V}$$

and we find that $V_{out} = 50$ mV. The amplifier has a differential gain of

$$A_d = \frac{50}{0 \cdot 1} = 500$$

If we increase V_1 and V_2 by 1 mV, i.e.

$$V_1 = 1 \cdot 1 \text{ mV and } V_2 = 1 \text{ mV}$$

we might find that $V_{out} = 52$ mV. The common mode gain is thus

$$A_c = \frac{52 - 50}{1} = 2$$

The ability of an amplifier to amplify differential signals while rejecting common mode signals is called its common mode rejection ratio, or CMRR for short. It is defined as

$$\text{CMRR} = \frac{A_d}{A_c}$$

The above example has a CMRR of 250. In integrated circuits, the CMRR is so large that it is usually expressed in decibels. A 741, for example, has a CMRR of 90 dB.

The CMRR is improved by making R_3 closer to a constant current generator. This can be done by increasing its value which implies that V_{ee} is made more negative. Usually, d.c. amplifiers work on a ± 15 V supply, so there are practical limits as to how high R_3 can be made. A technique widely used is to replace R_3 with the transistor current source shown in *Figure 5.3*. The zener ZD_1 defines the emitter voltage of TR_3, which in turn defines the collector current. With constant current sinks on the emitters of long-tail pairs, very high CMRRs can be obtained.

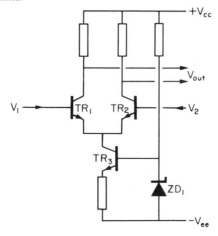

Fig. 5.3 Long-tail pair with high CMRR

5.2.2 Chopper amplifiers

An alternative technique for d.c. amplification is the use of transistor or CMOS switches to chop the input to give an a.c. signal which can be amplified by a cheap a.c. amplifier. At the output, another switch restores the d.c. level.

A block diagram is shown in *Figure 5.4(a)*. The two switches S_1 and S_2 are transistor or CMOS switches and operate alternately, i.e. when S_1 is closed, S_2 is open. Waveforms are given in *Figure 5.4(b)*. A chopper amplifier is usually followed by a filter to remove the a.c. component caused by the chopper switches.

Chopper amplifiers are also used where a high degree of isolation is required between the input and the rest of the circuit. A typical example is found in industrial data logging systems, where plant faults could cause high voltages to appear on transducer inputs. The use of isolation amplifiers prevents damage beyond the input of the amplifiers themselves.

Commercial isolation amplifiers are available in encapsulated form, with isolation voltages in excess of 1 kV. It is usually more economic for the engineer to purchase a ready-made amplifier than design his own.

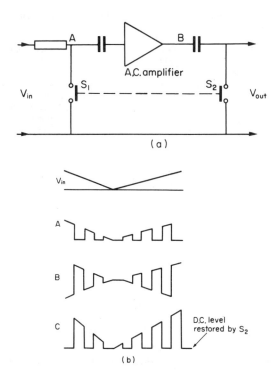

Fig. 5.4 Chopper amplifier: (a) block diagram; (b) waveforms

Integrated circuit operational amplifier 5.3

In the following sections the applications of operational amplifiers are discussed in some detail. Before these can be discussed it is necessary to describe the limits and restrictions pertinent to the design of the circuit.

The commonest operational amplifier is the 741, whose internal connections are shown in *Figure 5.5*. There are two inputs: the non-inverting (sometimes denoted by +) causes the output to move in phase with the signal; the inverting (sometimes denoted by −) causes the output to move in antiphase.

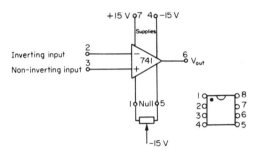

Fig. 5.5 The 741 operational amplifier

The first characteristic to be considered is the open-loop gain; for the 741 it is 200,000 (i.e. considerable). The second characteristic is the CMRR defined before. The data sheet gives the value of 90 dB.

To describe the next characteristics we must consider the internal workings of the amplifier.

If we connect both inputs to 0 V we would expect the output to sit at 0 V. Because of small differences in the V_{be} voltages of the input transistors and the high gain, the output voltage will certainly not be zero. To bring the output to 0 V we have to move one of the inputs away from zero. The voltage necessary is called the 'offset voltage', denoted by V_{IO}, and is usually around 10 mV, although offsets of less than 1 mV are possible with high quality 741s.

In itself the offset voltage is not particularly important, as it can be trimmed out. A very important factor is how V_{IO} varies with temperature. This is denoted by αV_{IO} and is usually about 5 μV/°C.

The two input transistors will require base current, denoted by I_b. This is usually very low, around 0·5 μA for the 741. To minimise the effect of I_b, the impedance in both input lines should be kept equal. The base current will then generate equal offsets which the amplifier will ignore.

Despite the close matching of transistors, the two base currents will not be equal. The inequality is denoted by I_{IO}, and is typically 0·2 μA. Unlike V_{IO}, I_{IO} does not vary greatly with temperature.

D.C. amplifiers are designed to work with low frequencies, and to minimise problems with stability when feedback is applied, the high frequency response of the 741 is deliberately limited by a strategically placed 30 pF capacitor on the chip. The gain falls to 60 dB at 1 kHz, 40 dB at 10 kHz and 0 dB at 1 MHz. The frequency at which the gain falls to unity is defined (oddly enough) as the 'unity gain bandwidth'.

D.C. amplifiers without internal compensation are available, an example being the 531 amplifier. This has a unity gain bandwidth in excess of 10 MHz, and gives 40 dB of gain up to 500 kHz. The use of uncompensated amplifiers requires some care if instability is not to be a problem.

A second method of describing the amplifier response is the slew rate. This measures the response of the amplifier to a step input. It is defined as the rate of change of the output and is measured in volts/unit time. The slew rate for the 741 is 0.5 V/μs.

5.4 Applications of d.c. amplifiers

D.C amplifiers are always used with feedback to determine the gain and response. The circuits below illustrate various types of feedback.

5.4.1 Inverting amplifier

The circuit is shown in *Figure 5.6*. Since the gain of the amplifier is very high, it can be assumed that the junction of R_1 and R_2 will be within a few millivolts of 0 V.

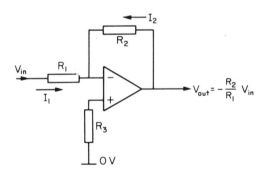

Fig. 5.6 Inverting amplifier

We then have

$$I_1 = \frac{V_{in}}{R_1}$$

$$I_2 = \frac{-V_{out}}{R_2}$$

If I_b is insignificantly small (as it usually is)

$$I_1 = I_2$$

$$\frac{V_{in}}{R_1} = \frac{-V_{out}}{R_2}$$

or

$$V_{out} = \frac{-R_2}{R_1} V_{in}$$

The gain is thus the ratio of R_2/R_1. The input impedance is simply R_1.

To minimise offsets due to I_b, the impedance at both inputs should be equal, i.e.

$$R_3 = \frac{R_1 \cdot R_2}{R_1 + R_2}$$

The amplifier can be zeroed for V_{IO} and I_{IO} by either of the two methods shown in *Figure 5.7(a)* and *5.7(b)*. *Figure 5.7(a)* uses the null facility on the chip (pins 1 and 5 on the 741). The method shown in *Figure 5.7(b)* uses an additional resistor, R_4, to add or subtract current to I_1. This method has slightly better temperature stability.

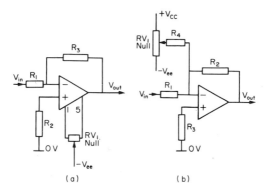

Fig. 5.7 Zeroing of d.c. amplifiers: (a) using null pins; (b) using summing junction

5.4.2 Adder

The circuit shown in *Figure 5.8* can be used to add several voltages. By a similar analysis to that above,

$$V_{out} = -\left(\frac{R_4}{R_1} V_1 + \frac{R_4}{R_2} V_2 + \frac{R_4}{R_3} V_3 \right)$$

and the value of R_5 is the parallel resistance of R_1, R_2, R_3 and R_4.

The adder circuit is used in analogue computers and as the basis for audio mixers.

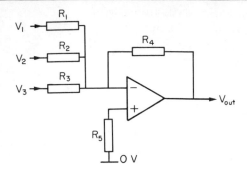

Fig. 5.8 Adder

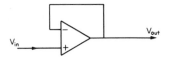

Fig. 5.9 Voltage follower

5.4.3 Voltage follower

The circuit in *Figure 5.9* applies 100% feedback. Since there can be only a millivolt or so between the inputs,

$$V_{out} = V_{in}$$

The input impedance is very high (typically several megohms), and the output impedance very low (typically a few ohms).

The circuit is a very useful buffer stage and can be considered as an exceptionally efficient emitter follower.

5.4.4 Non-inverting amplifier

Analysing *Figure 5.10(a)*, we see that the voltage at the inverting input is given by

$$V_1 = V_{out} \frac{R_2}{R_1 + R_2}$$

By similar reasoning to that outlined before,

$$V_1 = V_{in}$$

$$V_{out} \frac{R_2}{R_1 + R_2} = V_{in}$$

$$V_{out} = \frac{R_1 + R_2}{R_2} V_{in}$$

$$V_{out} = \left(1 + \frac{R_1}{R_2}\right) V_{in}$$

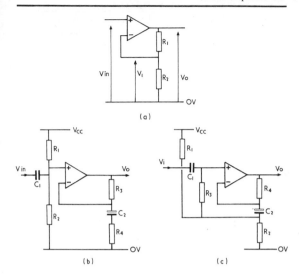

Fig. 5.10 Non-inverting amplifiers: (a) basic circuit; (b) a.c. amplifier; (c) bootstrapped a.c. amplifier

A.C. audio amplifiers are commonly based on the circuit of *Figure 5.10(a)*. In *Figure 5.10(b)*, C_1 and C_2 provide a.c. isolation, and R_1, R_2 define the d.c. level of the non-inverting input and the output. The amplifier has unity d.c. gain from its non-inverting input to the output so no zeroing adjustment is needed. The a.c. gain is determined by R_3, R_4.

The input impedance of *Figure 5.10(b)* is given by R_1 in parallel with R_2. The 'bootstrapped' circuit of *Figure 5.10(c)* gives a very high input impedance. The d.c. levels are set by R_1 and R_2 as before.

5.4.5 Differential amplifier
It is frequently required to measure the difference between two voltages. An example is the strain gauge bridge shown in *Figure 5.11*. X_1 and X_2 are two strain gauges to be measured, arranged such that X_1 increases in resistance for increasing stress and X_2 decreases. Y_1 and Y_2 are identical strain gauges not under stress to provide temperature compensation.

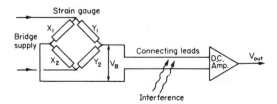

Fig. 5.11 Introduction of common mode noise

The voltage V_B is the bridge voltage, which will in practice be very small. When it arrives at the amplifier, the voltage at each input will be

$$V_{in} = \frac{\pm V_B}{2} + V_{cm}$$

where V_{cm} is common mode noise induced on the lines from external sources of interference.

If the leads are run from the bridge as a screened twisted pair, the common mode voltage will be the same at both inputs, allowing a differential amplifier to be used.

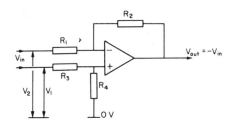

Fig. 5.12 Differential amplifier

A differential amplifier circuit is shown in *Figure 5.12*. It is very important, for correct operation, that $R_1 = R_3$ and $R_2 = R_4$. If these conditions are met,

$$V_{out} = \frac{R_2}{R_1} (V_2 - V_1)$$

For maximum CMRR, precision resistors should be used.

Differential amplifiers are widely used where low voltage signals (e.g. in thermocouples, strain gauges, medical electronics) have to be amplified in the presence of common mode interference.

5.4.6 Integrator circuits

Integration is a calculus operation that gives the area under a curve. More prosaically, it gives the result of time-dependent operations. The integral of acceleration, for example, is velocity, and the integral of velocity is distance. Integration is required in many systems and is, for example, one component of the three-term controller described in Subsection 11.3.3.

The theoretical circuit is shown in *Figure 5.13(a)*. By similar analysis to the inverting circuit, the current through the capacitor C and the resistor R must match.

$$I_1 = V_i/R$$

$$I_2 = C\frac{dV_0}{dt}$$

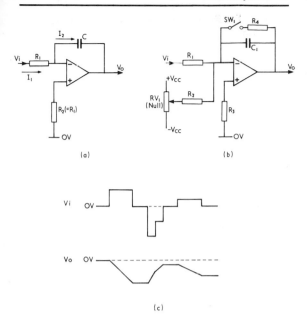

Fig. 5.13 Integrator circuit: (a) theoretical circuit; (b) practical circuit: SW1 is 'made' to reset and 'open' to integrate; (c) circuit response

These must be equal, so

$$\frac{V_i}{R} = -C\frac{dV_0}{dt}$$

or

$$V_0 = -\frac{1}{RC}\int V_i\,dt$$

A practical circuit is shown in *Figure 5.13(b)*. The potentiometer RV_1 adjusts for input current offset, which causes the amplifier output to drift slowly into saturation. Resistor R_4 and the switch discharge the capacitor to initialise the circuit.

The response of the circuit is shown in *Figure 5.13(c)*. For a step input of V volts, the output is a ramp rising (or falling) at V/RC volts per second.

5.4.7 Differentiator circuits

Differentiation gives the instantaneous rate of change of time-varying signals. The differential of distance, for example is velocity, and the differential of velocity is acceleration. The theoretical circuit is shown

in *Figure 5.14(a)*. By similar analysis to the previous section it is
found that:

$$V_0 = -RC \frac{dV_i}{dt}$$

In practice a perfect differentiator has a frequency response that
rises with frequency, giving impossibly high gains at high frequencies.
This is undesirable as it makes the circuit very prone to high
frequency noise. A practical circuit, shown in *Figure 5.14(b)*,
incorporates a limit on the high frequency response.

The differentiator is formed by R_1/C_1, giving a response identical
to the theoretical circuit at low frequencies. At high frequencies,
however, R_2 and C_2 cause the gain to fall. Values are chosen such that
$R_1.C_1 = R_2.C_2$. The point at which the gain reaches a maximum and
starts to fall is given by:

$$f = \frac{1}{2\pi R_1 C_1}$$

The maximum gain is R_1/R_2, the response being shown in *Figure
5.14(c)*.

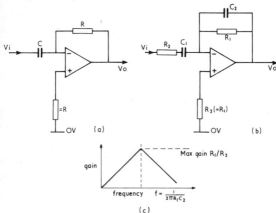

Fig. 5.14 The differentiator: (a) theoretical circuit; (b) practical circuit;
(c) frequency response

5.4.8 Filters
Filters are used to shape the frequency response of a circuit. There are
basically four types of filter. A low pass filter blocks frequencies above
some fixed value. Low pass filters are used to remove noise in audio
circuits, and is often called a scratch filter.

High pass filters only pass frequencies above some particular value.
They are used as rumble filters in audio circuits to block out noise
coupled from record player mechanics into the pick-up.

Bandpass filters pass frequencies in a specified range, and notch
filters block frequencies in a specified range. A 45–55 Hz notch filter is
widely used in instrumentation to block mains-induced noise (which
occurs at 50 Hz).

Figure 5.15 shows a range of op-amp-based filter circuits along
with their design criteria. It should be noted that the cut-off

frequencies are the point at which the response starts to fall, and not the point above (or below) which frequencies are blocked. *Figures 5.15(a)* and *(c)* are single-stage filters with a roll-off of 20 dB per decade. *Figures 5.15(b)* and *(d)* are two-stage filters with a roll-off of 40 dB per decade. The latter two circuits can have their damping adjusted by varying the component ratios as shown.

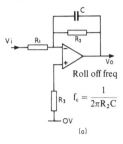

Roll off freq
$$f_c = \frac{1}{2\pi R_2 C}$$

(a)

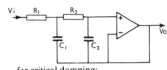

for critical damping:

$$R_1 = R_2 = R, C_2 = C, C_1 = 2 \times C$$

cut off frequency $f_c = \frac{1}{2\pi R \sqrt{C_1 . C_2}}$

if $C_1 > 2C_2$, circuit has resonant peak

(b)

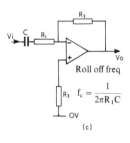

Roll off freq
$$f_c = \frac{1}{2\pi R_1 C}$$

(c)

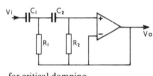

for critical damping

$$C_1 = C_2 = C, R_1 = R, R_2 = 2R$$

cut off frequency, $f_c = \frac{1}{2\pi C \sqrt{R_1 . R_2}}$

If $R_2 > 2R_1$ circuit has resonant peak

(d)

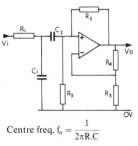

Centre freq, $f_o = \frac{1}{2\pi R.C}$

$$Q = \frac{R_5}{2.R_5 - R_4}$$

Providing $R_1 = R_2 = R$, $R_3 = 2R$
and $C_1 = C_2 = C$.

(e)

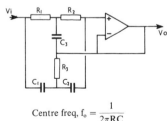

Centre freq, $f_o = \frac{1}{2\pi RC}$

Providing $R_1 = R_2 = R$, $R_3 = R/2$

$$C_1 = C_2 = C, C_3 = 2C$$

(f)

Fig. 5.15 Op-amp filter circuits: (a) simple low pass filter; (b) classical low pass filter; (c) simple high pass filter; (d) classical high pass filter; (e) bandpass filter; (f) notch filter

5.4.9 Schmitt trigger

The Schmitt trigger is widely used to convert slowly changing signals into crisp signals with fast edges that can be used in digital circuits. They also exhibit hysteresis, as shown in *Figures 5.16(a)* and *(b)*. The trigger points are defined by the upper trigger point (UTP) and the lower trigger point (LTP) Hysteresis is a form of backlash and is desirable to reduce jitter on the output if the slowly varying input has noise superimposed on it.

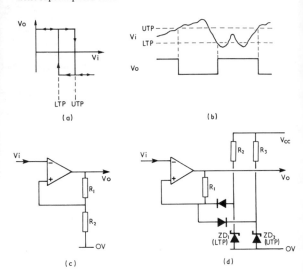

Fig. 5.16 Op-amp Schmitt trigger circuits: (a) circuit response (hysteresis); (b) effect of hysteresis; (c) basic circuit; (d) Schmitt trigger with trigger points set by zener diodes

An op-amp-based Schmitt trigger is shown in *Figure 5.16(c)*. The output will be either saturated positive or saturated negative. Suppose the input is above UTP; the output will be at $-V_{cc}$ and the non-inverting input will be at:

$$-V_{cc}\frac{R_2}{R_1+R_2}$$

This is the LTP. As long as V_{in} stays above LTP the output will not change. If V_{in} goes below LTP, the output will start to rise, taking the non-inverting input with it. Positive feedback takes place; the output rises rapidly to $+V_{cc}$ and the non-inverting input rises to:

$$+V_{cc}\frac{R_2}{R_1+R_2}$$

This is UTP, and the output will stay positive until V_{in} rises above UTP.

The circuit of *Figure 5.16(c)* has UTP and LTP symmetrical about 0 V. There are many variations on the circuit to give asymmetrical trigger points. *Figure 5.16(d)*, for example, has UTP and LTP of the same polarity (and the circuit will work with a single supply).

Most logic families include Schmitt trigger chips: the 7414 in the TTL family or the CMOS 4093 (quad NAND with Schmitt inputs). These ready-made Schmitts, however, have fixed trigger points and restricted input voltage range. Op-amp-based Schmitts allow the user to design a circuit when the standard chips are not suitable.

5.4.10 Positive/negative amplifier

The circuit of *Figure 5.17* has unity gain with switchable sign. When the contact is open the amplifier is effectively a voltage follower ($V_0 = V_{in}$). When the switch is closed the amplifier acts as a simple inverting circuit, again with unity gain ($V_0 = -V_{in}$). The state of the switch determines the sign of the gain.

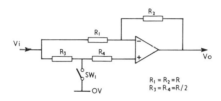

$R_1 = R_2 = R$
$R_3 = R_4 = R/2$

Fig. 5.17 Positive/negative amplifier

Although *Figure 5.17* shows a mechanical switch, in practice a CMOS analog switch (such as the 4016) allows the circuit to be switched at high speed with logic level signals. The circuit is useful in instrumentation circuits and is the basis of the phase sensitive rectifier circuit of *Figure 12.2*, described later.

5.4.11 Current/voltage conversion

Conversion between current and voltage signals is often required. A standard analog instrumentation signal, for example, uses a range of 4–20 mA and this often has to be converted to a voltage for display purposes. Similarly, a voltage may be required to be converted to a current for use with a signal transmission system.

Where analog information has to be transmitted over long distances, current signals are generally preferred to voltage signals as they are less affected by noise and line resistance. *Figure 5.18* shows circuits for conversion between voltage and current analog signals.

Figure 5.18(a) is a variation on a voltage follower. As usual, $V_1 = V_{in}$, but $V_1 = IR$ where I is the current flowing through the load. I is therefore set by V_{in} and is totally independent of the load resistance (provided the amplifier output does not saturate).

To go from a current signal to a voltage signal, *Figure 5.18(b)* can be used. The current passes through a load resistance across the input of a standard differential amplifier. The voltage across the load resistance is simply IR volts; the output voltage is determined by the differential amplifier gain, as described earlier in Subsection 5.4.5.

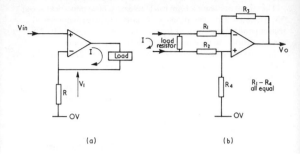

Fig. 5.18 Voltage/current/voltage conversion: (a) voltage to current; (b) current to voltage

If both circuits of *Figure 5.18* are used together, with the resistors of *Figures 5.18(a)* and *(b)* equal and the differential amplifier set for unity gain, the resulting circuit becomes a unity gain transmission link, which can be used to pass analog values through an electrically noisy area.

5.4.12 Ramp circuit

Figure 5.19(a) shows a circuit whose output changes at a fixed rate. The output voltage follows the input voltage (albeit inverted), but the rate of change is limited. Such circuits are used to limit the acceleration of, say, electric motors, to reduce wear.

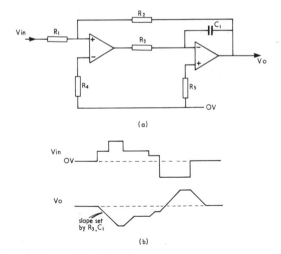

Fig. 5.19 Ramp circuit: (a) circuit diagram; (b) operation

Amplifier 1 acts as a comparator, comparing V_0 with V_i. The output of amplifier 1 will therefore be saturated either positive or negative if V_0 does not equal V_i.

Amplifier 2 is an integrator, and integrates the output of amplifier 1. If the output of amplifier 1 is positive, V_0 will ramp negative. The values of R and C determine the ramp rate. Similarly, if the output of amplifier 1 is negative, V_0 will ramp positive at a fixed rate.

If V_i changes, V_0 will ramp in the required direction at a fixed rate until V_0 again equals V_i. *Figure 5.19(b)* shows the action of the circuit. When input and output are equal the output of amplifier 1 is nominally zero, but in practice it tends to dither about randomly. This does not affect the output.

5.4.13 Peak picker circuit

A peak picker holds the maximum value of a signal. The circuit is shown in *Figure 5.20*. If V_i is greater than V_0, the output of amplifier 1 (which acts as a comparator) will go positive, charging C until V_0 equals V_i. As V_i falls again, the voltage on the capacitor is held, and the output of amplifier 1 swings negative as V_i falls below V_0. The diode is back-biased, so there is no route for the capacitor to discharge (except through the high input impedance of amplifier 2, which will normally be a FET amplifier).

The output voltage therefore holds the highest value of V_i. If the diode is reversed, the output voltage is the lowest value of V_i. A 'sample and hold' circuit can be formed by replacing the diode with a switch (either a physical contact or a CMOS transmission gate). V_0 now holds the value of V_i at the instant the switch was last opened. Sample and hold circuits are used to freeze the value of an input to a digital to analog converter. (See Section 7.10.)

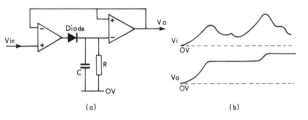

(a) (b)

Fig. 5.20 Peak picker circuit: (a) circuit diagram; (b) operation

6
Oscillators

6.1 Introduction

An oscillator is an electronic circuit which converts power from a d.c. supply into alternating power. Basically, oscillators fall into three classes: sine wave, square wave and other waveforms.

The conditions for maintaining oscillations are that the loop gain is equal to (or greater than) unity, and feedback exists with a loop phase shift of zero (or some multiple of 360 degrees) at the oscillator frequency.

Sine wave oscillators can be constructed using the resonant properties of an LC circuit, deliberately using an RC network to induce phase shift around an amplifier, or by using the piezoelectric effects of a quartz crystal. These methods allow sine wave oscillators to be built from frequencies below 0·1 Hz to frequencies over 400 MHz.

6.2 LC circuits

The resonant properties of LC circuits can easily be calculated from a.c. theory. Two arrangements are possible. The series arrangement in *Figure 6.1* exhibits a minimum impedance at resonance, since the inductive and capacitive reactances are equal at the resonant frequency, but have opposite phase effects and hence cancel. As mentioned in Chapter 4, resonance therefore occurs when

$$2\pi f L = \frac{1}{2\pi f C}$$

or

$$f = \frac{1}{2\pi\sqrt{(LC)}}$$

The series resonant circuit is sometimes called an acceptor circuit.

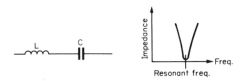

Fig. 6.1 Series LC circuit

The parallel arrangement in *Figure 6.2* is more widely used in oscillators. This exhibits maximum impedance at resonance, and the resonant frequency is again given by

$$f = \frac{1}{2\pi\sqrt{(LC)}}$$

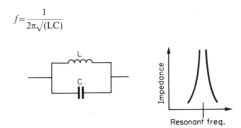

Fig. 6.2 Parallel LC circuit

The simplest form of LC oscillator is the arrangement shown in *Figure 6.3*. The tuned circuit is connected in the collector and feedback to the base is provided by R_{b1} and R_{b2} and R_e.

Once oscillations start, the amplitude increases until TR_1 either comes out of conduction on the positive cycle, or bottoms on the negative cycle. Under either of these conditions the loop gain (over a full cycle) is unity. It follows that there will be slight distortion on the peaks of the output waveform. This is normally unimportant.

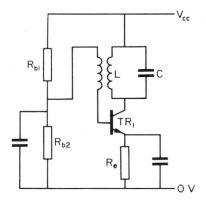

Fig. 6.3 Simple LC oscillator

Transformers are quite expensive to manufacture, and it is difficult to wind them with the degree of precision required for some oscillator applications. Oscillator circuits have evolved, therefore, using simple coils, and most are variations on the Colpitts and Hartley oscillators described below.

6.2.1 Colpitts oscillator

The resonant components in a Colpitts oscillator consist of a coil and two capacitors in series. A typical Colpitts oscillator is shown in

Figure 6.4. The tuned circuit consists of the coil L and the capacitors C_a, C_b. The resonant frequency is given by

$$f = \frac{1}{2\pi}\sqrt{\left[\frac{1}{L}\left(\frac{1}{C_a} + \frac{1}{C_b}\right)\right]}$$

Capacitor C_1 is simply a coupling capacitor.

Normally C_a is chosen such that its reactance is small at resonance, ensuring that the transistor input impedance does not load the circuit. This means that $C_a \gg C_b$; hence to a first approximation:

$$f = \frac{1}{2\pi\sqrt{(LC_b)}}$$

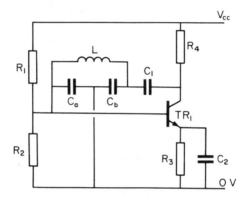

Fig. 6.4 Colpitts oscillator

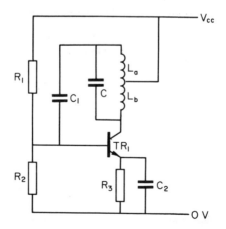

Fig. 6.5 Hartley oscillator

6.2.2 Hartley oscillator

The Hartley oscillator uses a centre-tapped coil. A typical arrangement is shown in *Figure 6.5*. The tuned circuit consists of the capacitor C and the two coil sections L_a and L_b. Capacitor C_1 is again a coupling capacitor.

The resonant frequency is given by

$$f = \frac{1}{2\pi\sqrt{[(L_a + L_b)C]}}$$

The values of inductance and capacitance become prohibitively large at frequencies much below 50 kHz, and this really limits the use of LC oscillators to RF applications. Fortunately for the circuit designer, the phase shift oscillator circuits are well suited to frequencies below 50 kHz.

Phase-shift oscillators 6.3

Phase-shift oscillators consist of an amplifier with feedback incorporating a deliberate phase shift. At one specific frequency the total phase shift is some multiple of 360 deg., and if the loop gain is then greater than unity oscillations will occur.

The phase shift is usually introduced using RC networks, allowing cheap components to be used. At frequencies above about 100 kHz, stray capacitance becomes a problem and it becomes easier to use the LC oscillators described earlier.

6.3.1 Three-stage RC filter oscillator

A single common emitter transistor oscillator has, effectively, a phase shift of 180 deg. at all frequencies from base to collector. If the collector is connected back to the base by a network having a phase shift of 180 deg., the total phase shift will be 360 deg. and oscillation will occur.

The three-stage filter in *Figure 6.6(a)* is arranged such that each stage has a phase shift of 60 deg., and a total phase shift of 180 deg. For each stage, the required 60 deg. phase shift occurs at a frequency

$$f = \frac{1}{4\pi RC}$$

In a series of stages, the reactance is modified by the succeeding stages, and for three stages 180 deg. phase shift occurs at

$$f = \frac{1}{2\pi RC\sqrt{6}}$$

Figure 6.6(b) shows a practical phase-shift oscillator. Resistors R_{b1}, R_{b2} and R_{in} of the transistor, all in parallel, form the third resistor. As the input resistance of the transistor is subject to wide variation, it is common for the actual oscillation frequency to be different from the theoretical frequency.

The three-stage filter attenuates the signal from collector to base, but this is more than compensated for by the voltage gain of the

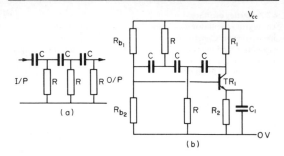

Fig. 6.6 Phase-shift oscillator: (a) three-stage filter; (b) phase-shift oscillator

transistor. The amplitude of the output is again limited by the transistor coming out of conduction or going into saturation. Some distortion of the output waveform therefore occurs.

6.3.2 Wien bridge oscillators

The Wien bridge is an a.c. version of the well-known Wheatstone bridge, and is shown in its basic form in *Figure 6.7*. If analysed by a.c. theory, it is found to balance at a frequency of

$$f = \frac{1}{2\pi RC}$$

and at balance the output voltage is in phase with the input voltage (but one-third of the amplitude).

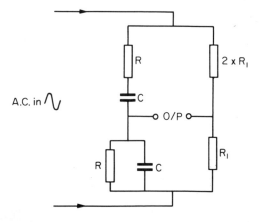

Fig. 6.7 The Wien bridge

The phase shift at balance is zero, so the Wien bridge has to be used with a non-inverting amplifier if oscillation is to occur. This can be done either by using a two-stage transistor amplifier, as shown in *Figure 6.8(a)*, or an integrated circuit operational amplifier, as in *Figure 6.8(b)*. As we saw in Subsection 6.3.1, other circuit components may modify the balance condition, and in *Figure 6.8(a)*, R_1 has to be chosen to take account of the parallel resistance of R_{b1}, and R_{in} of transistor TR_1.

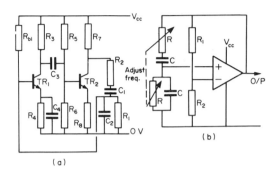

Fig. 6.8 Wien bridge oscillator: (a) transistor circuit; (b) op-amp circuit

One advantage of the Wien bridge oscillator is the simplicity of tuning. This can be achieved by a means of a two-track (double-ganged) potentiometer.

The amplitude is limited by events similar to those described in earlier sections. If R_1 in *Figure 6.8(b)* is replaced by a thermistor, however, the amplitude can be made reasonably constant. If the oscillation amplitude increases, the temperature of the thermistor will increase and its resistance reduce. This increases the negative feedback and reduces the amplifier gain. The circuit stabilises at the correct gain to maintain oscillation (i.e. the open-loop gain is unity).

Crystal oscillators 6.4

All the oscillators so far described have one major shortcoming; their frequency is dependent on circuit characteristics outside the direct control of the designer. Outside events such as temperature and supply variations will cause the frequency of oscillation to vary from day to day.

In many applications a precise frequency is not important, but there are several circuits where accuracy is important. A UHF mobile radio, for example, working on 460 MHz has to keep its carrier constant to a few kilohertz despite temperature changes, varying battery voltages and mechanical vibration.

Oscillators designed to these tight specifications use the properties of quartz crystals. These crystals are capable of vibrating up to high frequencies, and as they do so the piezoelectric effect develops an alternating voltage across the two opposite faces. The crystal then behaves as a tuned circuit having a very high L/C ratio and very high Q.

Typical crystal oscillators are shown in *Figure 6.9(a)*, and *6.9(b)*. The coupling capacitor C_1 in *Figure 6.9(b)* is sometimes implemented by the transistor collector/base capacitance.

The highest natural frequency it is possible to attain with a crystal is of the order of 1 MHz. For frequencies above this, it is usual to drive the crystal at a harmonic frequency, the choice of harmonic being determined by some external LC circuit such as the collector load in *Figure 6.9(a)*.

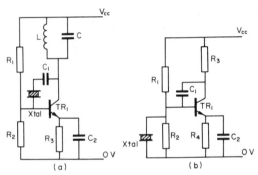

Fig. 6.9 Crystal oscillators: (a) Pierce oscillator; (b) Miller oscillator

A very limited amount of tuning can be done by shunting the crystal with a low value capacitor. The range available is less than 0.01%, so the tuning can only be a fine trim. Once set, the frequency stability is excellent, and stabilities of 1 part in 10^8 are easily obtained. If care is taken, and the circuit kept in a temperature-controlled environment, stabilities better than 1 part in 10^{10} are attainable.

6.5 Square wave oscillators

If a Fourier analysis is done on a square wave it is found that the waveform is composed of many harmonics of the fundamental frequency. This rich harmonic context makes the square wave particularly useful as a quick test of amplifier performance. Examples of possible results are shown in *Figure 6.10*.

The simplest way to produce a square wave is to make a sine wave oscillator in one of the ways described earlier, then feed the output to some form of squaring circuit such as a Schmitt trigger. This is the method adopted in most commercial sine/square wave generators.

There are, however, several circuits for square wave oscillators and the commonest is described below.

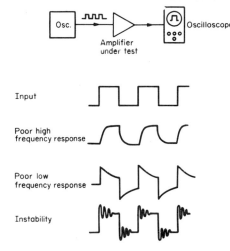

Fig. 6.10 Square wave oscillator used to test an amplifier

6.5.1 Multivibrator

Technically the multivibrator is a relaxation oscillator, working on the charging of a capacitor through a resistor. If a negative edge is applied to the circuit of *Figure 6.11(a)*, transistor TR_1 will turn off for the time taken for the base voltage to return to 0 V. If the voltage step was the same magnitude as the supply voltage, the time that TR_1 is turned off for will be given by

$$T_1 = 0 \cdot 7 C_1 R_1$$

The output will be a positive pulse of period T_1.

We now connect TR_1 to another transistor through the capacitor/resistor $C_2 R_2$, as shown in *Figure 6.11(b)*, and again apply a negative edge to C_1. Transistor TR_1 again turns off for T_1, but as T_1 ends, the negative edge turns TR_2 off in a similar manner, for time T_2 given by

$$T_2 = 0 \cdot 7 C_2 R_2$$

If the output of TR_2 is now connected back to C_1, as shown in *Figure 6.11(c)*, when TR_2 turns back on the negative edge will turn TR_1 off again, repeating the cycle. The circuit will continue to oscillate, giving complementary square waves from TR_1 and TR_2. The circuit is usually drawn similar to *Figure 6.11(d)*.

It can be a problem deciding how a multivibrator actually starts (and it should be said that they sometimes do not!). Starting is usually brought about by differences in the transistor gains at first turn-on. When a multivibrator does not start, both transistors end up turned on, with base current provided through the base resistors. This can be avoided by deliberately having an asymmetrical waveform with T_1 and T_2 different values.

Because of its simplicity, the multivibrator has many shortcomings.

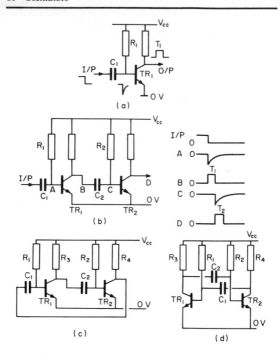

Fig. 6.11 The multivibrator

The major problem is the poor positive edge. The collector resistors are loaded by the timing capacitors, giving a marked exponential shape to the waveform.

The other problem is that the bases of the transistors are taken negative to a voltage equivalent to the supply. Most transistors have a maximum reverse V_{be} of about 5 V, implying that the simple circuit can only be used on 5V supplies. In practice, higher supplies can be used, but the transistor base emitter junction acts as a zener, limiting the base to around 6 V negative. This does not appear to harm the transistor, but causes the actual frequency to differ widely from the theoretical value.

6.5.2 Op-amp square wave oscillator

The circuit in *Figure 6.12* is a useful oscillator where a large voltage swing is required. Referring to the timing diagram in *Figure 6.12*, at time $t = 0$ the amplifier is in negative saturation and

$$V_A = K \times V_0 - \text{ve sat.}$$

where

$$K = \frac{R_2}{R_1 + R_2}$$

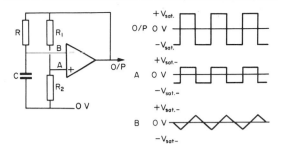

Fig. 6.12 Operational amplifier oscillator

Point B charges towards the negative supply rail via the timing resistor R. When points B and A are the same voltage, V_0 switches to positive saturation. Point A is now at

$$V_A = K \times V_0 + \text{ve sat.}$$

and point B charges towards the positive rail. When points B and A are at the same voltage, V_0 switches back to negative saturation, recommencing the sequence.

The output thus oscillates between $V + \text{ve}$ and $V - \text{ve}$, point A between $KV + \text{ve}$ and $KV - \text{ve}$, and point B rises and falls exponentially between the same voltages as point A.

Calculation of the period is somewhat lengthy, but may be given by

$$T = 2CR \log_e \left(1 + \frac{2R_2}{R_1} \right)$$

6.5.3 Blocking oscillator

At first sight the blocking oscillator might be mistaken for the LC, oscillator shown earlier in *Figure 6.3*. The operation is, however, completely different. A typical blocking oscillator circuit is drawn in *Figure 6.13*. The sequence starts with the timing capacitor, C, charged negative and transistor TR_1 turned off. The timing resistor, R,

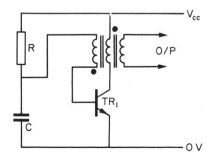

Fig. 6.13 Blocking oscillator

charges C and the base voltage starts to rise towards V_{cc}. At about 0·5 V, TR_1 turns on, and current flows through the primary of the transformer. This couples back into the base, causing more current to flow. Regenerative action takes place, and the increased base current flows through C, driving the RC junction quickly negative, cutting TR_1 off. The sequence now starts again.

The output consists of short negative pulses (with width determined by the transistor and transformer) occurring at regular intervals (with time determined by RC).

6.5.4 Integrated circuit astables for digital circuits

Control circuits using TTL and CMOS logic gates frequently require oscillator circuits to act as system clocks. These can easily be implemented using specially designed ICs. A typical example is the 555 timer chip shown in *Figure 6.14(a)*.

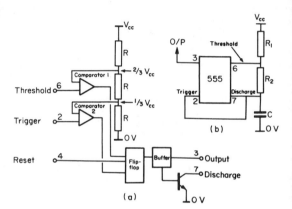

Fig. 6.14 The 555 timer: (a) internal logic; (b) 555 astable

This consists of a memory flip-flop, and two comparators set at two-thirds and one-third of V_{cc}. To construct an astable we add two resistors and a capacitor, as shown in *Figure 6.14(b)*. Assume that the memory has been set, and the voltage on the capacitor is approximately $\frac{1}{2}V_{cc}$. The capacitor will charge via $(R_1 + R_2)$. When the voltage reaches $\frac{2}{3}V_{cc}$, comparator 1 will reset the memory. The capacitor now discharges via R_2 to pin 7. When the voltage reaches $\frac{1}{3}V_{cc}$, comparator 2 sets the memory and the sequence starts again.

Oscillators for use with digital circuits need fast falling and rising edges if problems are not to be encountered with noise. Counter circuits, in particular, are prone to double counts on slow edges. Oscillator circuits with very fast edges can be built using Schmitt trigger gates, and a circuit for a gated CMOS oscillator is shown in *Figure 6.15*.

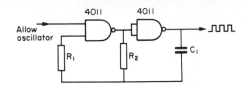

Fig. 6.15 Gated CMOS oscillator

7
Digital circuits

7.1 Introduction

Many control schemes rely on decisions that can only be in one of
two states. A contact can be open or closed, for example, or a gas
flame lit or not lit. The electronic version of this type of circuit is
known as a digital circuit, and signals inside the circuit can only be at
one or other of two voltages. These two voltages are usually referred
to as a '1' or a '0'. In TTL, for example, a '1' is represented by 3·5 V
and a '0' by 0 V.

Digital circuits can be classified into two main groups. The first
group is concerned with control of objects (e.g. start drill, advance
chuck-head at low pressure until limit switch A makes, open high
pressure valve, advance until limit switch B makes, then retract at
high speed). The second group is concerned with numbers, and digital
circuits are used for arithmetic and counting purposes.

7.2 Basic principles

7.2.1 Basic logic gates

It is convenient to compare many of the basic logic gates with relay
circuits. The first gate is the AND gate. This is represented by the
symbol in *Figure 7.1(a)*, and is equivalent to the relay circuit in *Figure
7.1(b)*.

The output C is at a '1' if, and only if, both inputs A and B are at a
'1'. Otherwise the output is at a '0'. A so-called 'truth table', listing all
possible input combinations, is given in *Figure 7.1(c)*.

The second gate is an OR gate, shown in *Figure 7.2(a)*. The output
C is at a '1' if ANY input is at a '1'. It is thus similar in operation to the
relay scheme in *Figure 7.2(b)*, and its truth table is shown in *Figure
7.2(c)*.

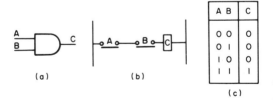

A B	C
0 0	0
0 1	0
1 0	0
1 1	1

(a)   (b)   (c)

Fig. 7.1 The AND gate

Although the AND and OR gates are shown in *Figures 7.1* and *7.2*
with two inputs, they can have any number of inputs. An 8-input
AND gate, for example, will have its output at a '1' if, and only if, all 8
inputs are at a '1'.

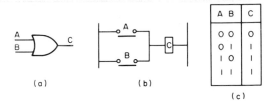

A B	C
0 0	0
0 1	1
1 0	1
1 1	1

Fig. 7.2 The OR gate: (a) OR gate symbol; (b) relay equivalent; (c) truth table

The next gate is the inverter. This has one input and one output and is shown in *Figure 7.3(a)*. The output is the opposite state to the input; a '1' in gives a '0' out and vice versa. This is similar to the normally closed contact in *Figure 7.3(b)*.

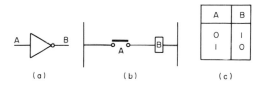

A	B
0	1
1	0

Fig. 7.3 The inverter: (a) inverter symbol; (b) relay equivalent; (c) truth table

Where possible, logic designers tend to build logic schemes around the next two gates described. Of all the gates these are probably the most versatile.

The NAND gate shown in *Figure 7.4(a)* is simply an AND gate followed by an inverter, as redrawn in *Figure 7.4(b)*. The output is thus a '0' when all inputs are at a '1'.

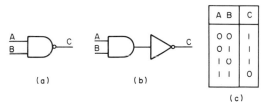

A B	C
0 0	1
0 1	1
1 0	1
1 1	0

Fig. 7.4 The NAND gate: (a) NAND gate symbol; (b) equivalent logic; (c) truth table

The NOR gate shown in *Figure 7.5(a)* is an OR gate followed by an inverter. The output is a '0' when any input is a '1'.

The final gate is not particularly common. It is called the exclusive OR gate, or XOR for short. It has only two inputs, and checks for these being the same (i.e. both '1' or both '0').

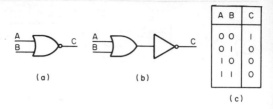

A B	C
0 0	1
0 1	0
1 0	0
1 1	0

(a)   (b)   (c)

Fig. 7.5 The NOR gate: (a) NOR gate symbol; (b) equivalent logic; (c) truth table

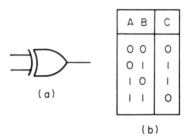

A B	C
0 0	0
0 1	1
1 0	1
1 1	0

(a)   (b)

Fig. 7.6 The XOR gate: (a) XOR gate symbol; (b) truth table

The gate is shown in *Figure 7.6(a)*, with its truth table in *Figure 7.6(b)*. There is no simple relay equivalent to a XOR gate.

7.2.2 Positive and negative logic

If the '1' voltage is more positive than the '0' voltage the logic is said to be positive logic. Consider for a moment the circuit in *Figure 7.7(a)*. If you followed the logic you would find that the output is a '1' when inputs A and B are both '1' or inputs C and D are both '1'. It has thus behaved like the circuit in *Figure 7.7(b)*, and the right-hand NAND gate has somehow behaved like an OR gate.

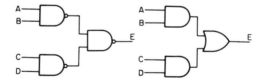

Fig. 7.7 Positive and negative logic: (a) original logic; (b) equivalent logic

The truth table for a NAND gate is shown in *Figure 7.4(c)*, and it can be seen that the output is at a '1' if any input is at a '0'. A positive logic NAND gate is thus also a negative logic NOR gate.

Similar interchangeability exists between all the logic gates, and these are summarised in *Figure 7.8*.

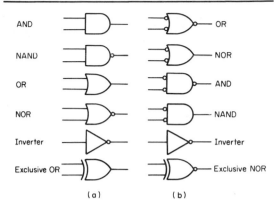

Fig. 7.8 Interchangeability of (a) positive logic and (b) negative logic

Combinational logic 7.3

7.3.1 Truth tables

Circuits built purely around logic gates are called combinational logic circuits. These have no storage, counter or timer elements and can be represented as shown in *Figure 7.9(a)*. This has N inputs labelled 1 to N and Z outputs labelled 1 to Z. In systems with multiple outputs, as in *Figure 7.9(a)*, it is usually easier to consider it as Z separate, and different, circuits each of which can be represented as shown in *Figure 7.9(b)*.

The design of a combinational logic circuit consists first of defining in some way the relationship between inputs and output. This is then converted into a corresponding circuit built from the logic gates described in the preceding sections.

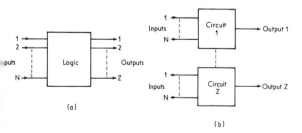

Fig. 7.9 Combinational logic circuits: (a) generalised representation; (b) redrawn as Z separate circuits

One useful way of achieving this is via a truth table, in which all possible input states are tabulated along with the required output states. Suppose we wish to build a majority vote circuit where the output Z takes a majority vote of three inputs A, B, C. This would have the truth table:

A	B	C	:	Z	
0	0	0	:	0	
0	0	1	:	0	
0	1	0	:	0	
0	1	1	:	1	*
1	0	0	:	0	
1	0	1	:	1	*
1	1	0	:	1	*
1	1	1	:	1	*

It can be seen that Z is 1 for the four conditions marked with an asterisk, namely:

Not A & B & C
A & Not B & C
A & B & Not C
A & B & C

allowing us to build a circuit which is a series of AND gates whose outputs are OR'd together as in *Figure 7.10*.

Designs with truth tables always give an AND/OR solution that will work (called a sum of products, or S of P, circuit). What is not known, however, is whether the solution uses the minimum number of gates. To get to a minimal circuit other techniques must be used. Truth tables also tend to become rather unwieldy with more than four inputs (which have 16 possible input combinations).

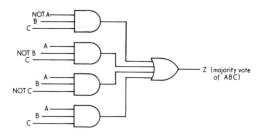

Fig. 7.10 Sum of products (S of P) majority vote circuit

7.3.2 Boolean algebra

In the nineteenth century a Cambridge mathematician and clergyman, George Boole, developed an algebra to express and manipulate logical expressions. His algebra can be used to design combinational logic circuits.

The AND function is represented by a dot (.), the OR function by a + symbol. The inverse (NOT) function is represented by a bar above the signal, so NOT A is represented by $\overline{A}$. Using this notation the circuit of *Figure 7.11* can be represented by:

$$Z = (\overline{A}.B.C) + (A.\overline{B}.\overline{C}) + D$$

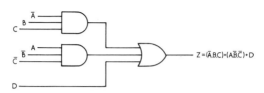

Fig. 7.11 Circuit represented by Boolean equation

Boolean algebra allows complex expressions to be written in a simple and concise form, but it also contains rules to allow expressions to be manipulated and a minimal form found. To do this, a series of rules is used. The first eleven of these are really self-evident:

(1) $A.A = A$
(2) $A + A = A$
(3) $A.1 = A$
(4) $A.0 = 0$
(5) $A + 1 = 1$
(6) $A + 0 = A$
(7) $\overline{\overline{A}} = A$
(8) $A.\overline{A} = 0$
(9) $A + \overline{A} = 1$
(10) $A + B = B + A$
(11) $A.B = B.A$

The next two laws are concerned with the operation of brackets:

(12) $(A + B) + C = A + (B + C) = A + B + C$
(13) $(A.B).C = A.(B.C) = A.B.C$

The next two laws are called the absorbtive laws:

(14) $A + A.B = A$
(15) $A.(A + B) = A$

In both cases the B term has no effect.

The next two laws (called the distributive laws) allow us to factorise Boolean equations:

(16) $A + B.C = (A + B).(A + C)$
(17) $A.(B + C) = A.B + A.C$

We have already encountered the S of P representation of a logic circuit. It is also possible to form a Product of Sums circuit which consists of a series of OR gates whose outputs are AND'd together, as shown in *Figure 7.12*.

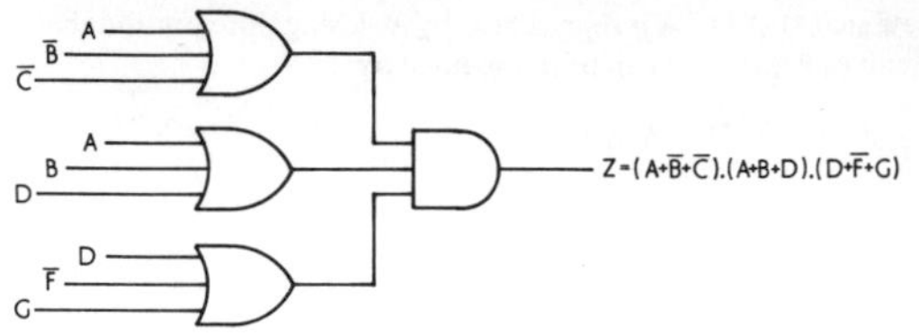

Fig. 7.12 Product of sums (P of S) representation

The last two laws, known as De Morgan's theorem, give ways to go from S of P to P of S forms, and also how to form the inverse of any given expression:

(19) $\overline{A.B.C\ldots N} = \overline{A} + \overline{B} + \overline{C} + \ldots + \overline{N}$

(20) $\overline{A+B+C+\ldots+N} = \overline{A}.\overline{B}.\overline{C}\ldots\overline{N}$

As written out above, De Morgan's theorem appears of little use. It can be more easily expressed in English:

'To form the complement of an expression there are two steps:
   (a) Replace each + by a . and each . by a +
   (b) Complement each term in the original expression.'

For example, to complement $\overline{A} + B.C$:

Step 1 gives $\overline{A}.(B+C)$

Step 2 gives $A.(\overline{B} + \overline{C})$ which is the complement of the original expression (as can be verified by constructing the corresponding truth tables).

Boolean algebra can be used to minimise expressions, but it relies on intuition and there is no logical procedure. It is easy to make errors on double or triple inversions, and also in the swapping of the 'dot' and 'plus' symbols. As an example of the use of Boolean algebra to minimise an expression, consider:

$$Z = A.B.C + A.\overline{B}.(\overline{A.C})$$

Applying De Morgan gives

$$Z = A.B.C + A.\overline{B}.(\overline{\overline{A}} + \overline{\overline{C}})$$

But $\overline{\overline{A}} = A$ and $\overline{\overline{C}} = C$, giving

$$
\begin{aligned}
Z &= A.B.C + A.\overline{B}.(A+C)\\
&= A.B.C + A.A.\overline{B} + A.\overline{B}.C\\
&= A.B.C + A.\overline{B} + A.\overline{B}.C
\end{aligned}
$$

But $A.B.C + A.\overline{B}.C = A.C.(B + \overline{B}) = A.C$, so

$$Z = A.C + A.\overline{B}$$

which is the minimal form.

7.3.3 Karnaugh maps

A Karnaugh map is an alternative way of representing a truth table in the form of a two-dimensional grid. Two-, three- and four-variable maps are shown in *Figure 7.13*. Each square on the table represents one line of a truth table. For example:

X represents $A = 1$, $B = 0$ or $A.\overline{B}$

Y represents $A = 0$, $B = 0$, $C = 1$ or $\overline{A}.\overline{B}.C$

Z represents $A = 0$, $B = 1$, $C = 1$, $D = 0$ or $\overline{A}.B.C.\overline{D}$

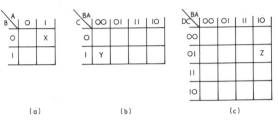

(a)   (b)   (c)

Fig. 7.13 Karnaugh maps: (a) two-variable; (b) three-variable; (c) four-variable

The axes on a Karnaugh map are labelled so that a move between adjacent squares vertically and horizontally results in the change of only one variable. For example, the map of *Figure 7.14* represents the four lines of a truth table:

$$A.\overline{B}.C.\overline{D} \quad A.B.C.\overline{D} \quad A.\overline{B}.C.D \quad A.B.C.D$$

In its Boolean form we could write:

$$Z = A.\overline{B}.C.\overline{D} + A.B.C.\overline{D} + A.\overline{B}.C.D + A.B.C.D$$

The map, however, reveals that both B and D can change without affecting the output. The marked squares in fact represent A.C so the above Boolean expression simplifies to:

$$Z = A.C$$

DC\\BA	OO	OI	II	IO
OO	O	O	O	O
OI	O	I	I	O
II	O	I	I	O
IO	O	O	O	O

Fig. 7.14 Simplifying with a Karnaugh map

The rules for minimising an expression with a Karnaugh map are simple:

(a) Plot the expression on the map either from a Boolean equation or truth table.

(b) Form new groups of 1's. Groups must be rectangular and as large as possible. Groups can overlap and go round the tops and sides.

(c) From the map, read off the new groups of 1's, which can be directly implemented in S of P form.

By way of an example, consider the majority vote circuit from Subsection 7.3.1. This is plotted on the Karnaugh map of *Figure 7.15(a)*. Following the above rules gives the grouping of *Figure 7.15(b)* and the simpler expression:

$$Z = A.B + A.C + B.C$$

This is redrawn, in its minimal form, in *Figure 7.15(c)*. Karnaugh mapping is the simplest way of minimising combinational circuits, as the eye can easily see the largest possible groups that can be formed on the map.

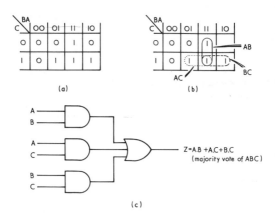

(a)

(b)

(c)

Fig. 7.15 Simplifying a majority vote circuit: (a) original plot; (b) new grouping; (c) simplified circuit diagram

7.4 Storage

7.4.1 The S–R memory

Control schemes often need to remember that some event has occurred. This can be implemented in relays by the latching circuit in *Figure 7.16(a)*. The logic equivalent is shown in *Figure 7.16(b)*.

Suppose both inputs are at a '0' and output X is at a '1'. Output X goes to NOR gate 2, so output Y will be at a '0'. Both inputs of NOR gate 1 are at a '0', so the output X will be at a '1' as we originally stated.

If input A is now taken to a '1', output X will go to a '0'. This in turn will cause output Y to go to a '1'. The outputs have changed over. If input A goes back to a '0' now, output X will stay at a '0' until input B goes to a '1', when the outputs will change over again.

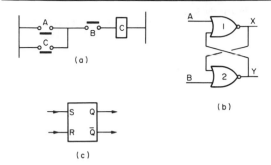

Fig. 7.16 Storage: (a) relay latch; (b) logic S–R memory; (c) S–R memory symbol

The circuit thus memorises which input went to a '1' last. If it was input A, then X is a '0' and Y is a '1'. If it was input B, then X is a '1' and Y is a '0'. Obviously it is not permitted for both inputs to be at a '1' together.

The circuit of *Figure 7.16(b)* is the simplest form of memory, and is called an S–R (for set-reset) memory. The output X and Y are usually denoted by Q and $\overline{Q}$ (pronounced 'Q bar'). The S–R symbol is shown in *Figure 7.16(c)*.

7.4.2 D-type flip-flop

The next type of flip-flop is the D-type. This has two inputs labelled D and CK (for clock); the two outputs are labelled Q and $\overline{Q}$ as before, *Figure 7.17(a)*.

The output Q takes up the state of the input D when a pulse is applied to the clock input. Output $\overline{Q}$ goes to the opposite state. The operation is summarised on the timing chart, *Figure 7.17(b)*.

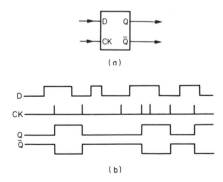

Fig. 7.17 The D-type flip-flop: (a) symbol; (b) timing chart

7.4.3 JK-type flip-flop

The JK flip-flop has three inputs (J, K and the clock), and the usual two outputs. The symbol is shown in *Figure 7.18*. The operation is controlled by the clock in a similar manner to the D-type flip-flop, although the JK is similar to the S–R in some respects.

The circuit responds similar to an S–R memory for

$J = 1, K = 0$
$J = 0, K = 1$
$J = 0, K = 0$

except that the changes occur at the clock pulse. One major difference, however, is that if $J = 1$ and $K = 1$ when a clock pulse occurs, the outputs change over. The state $J = K = 1$ was not allowed in the simple S–R memory.

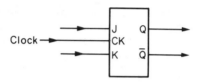

Fig. 7.18 The JK flip-flop

7.5 Timers and monostables

Control circuits often need time delays (e.g. open gas valve, run igniter for 5 s, check for gas flame). Delays are provided by circuits called monostables. In its simplest form, a monostable is as shown in *Figure 7.19*. It has one input and the usual Q and $\overline{Q}$ outputs. In addition there are the two components determining the period of the delay. Usually the period, *T*, is given by approximately $0.7RC$.

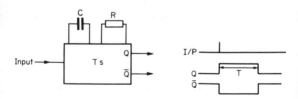

Fig. 7.19 Simple monostable

Every time the input goes from a '0' to a '1' the output Q goes from 0 to 1 for *T* seconds, then back to '0' again. $\overline{Q}$ does the opposite.

There are many variations on the design of monostables. Common variants are shown in *Figure 7.20*. The delay on and delay off are obvious. The re-triggerable variant restarts the timing period for each '0' to '1' transition at the input.

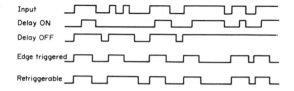

Fig. 7.20 Monostable variants

The period of a monostable is of the order of RC seconds where R and C are the value of the timing components. Delays in excess of about 30 seconds consequently need large values of R or C. Practical limits for R are around 1 megohm or leakage becomes a problem. Large values of capacitance imply the use of electrolytics. These are bulky, have high leakage current and low accuracy.

The technique shown in *Figure 7.21* allows long delays (up to years!) to be constructed with reasonable value components. An oscillator produces a free-running pulse train. This can be built around a normal timer IC and run at a relatively high frequency. The pulses are normally blocked by the AND gate.

To start the timer a pulse is applied to the input. This sets the S–R flip-flop and resets the counter. Pulses are now allowed to pass to the counter. When the counter reaches some predetermined value, the S–R flip-flop is reset, blocking further pulses. The Q output of the flip-flop is high for a time:

$$T = NP \text{ secs}$$

where N is the counter preset and P the oscillator period. The time is accurate to one cycle of the oscillator.

The circuit of *Figure 7.21* is available in IC form, typical of which is the Ferranti ZN1034 which includes the RC oscillator and a divide by 4096 counter.

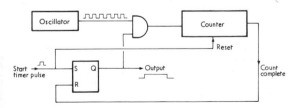

Fig. 7.21 Long-period timer

7.6 Event-driven logic

Most logic systems are not pure combinational logic, but incorporate storage and timer devices. Although such systems can be represented as shown in *Figure 7.9*, the output states are not determined solely by the input conditions but also by what has happened previously. The simple motor start/stop circuit of *Figure 7.22(a)*, for example, has two inputs (start and stop buttons) and one output (motor run relay). The condition with no inputs present can, however, have the motor running or stopped according to which input was last present. Systems incorporating storage are often called event-driven or sequencing circuits.

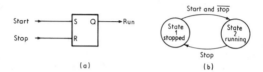

Fig. 7.22 Simple event-driven system: (a) motor starter using S–R flip-flop; (b) state diagram

Event-driven systems are designed around the concept of 'state diagrams'. These show all the possible conditions that can exist for the system, identify the conditions that cause a change, and detail outputs in each state. The very simple state diagram for the motor starter is shown in *Figure 7.22(b)*, which shows that it has two states, with transitions between them being determined solely by the buttons. Note that with no button pressed the system can be in either state as explained before.

A more complex system for the control of a lift is shown in *Figure 7.23*. This has eight inputs (two lift call buttons on the floors, two floor buttons in the lift, two limit switches saying the lift is at a floor, a door-closed limit switch, and a door-obstructed photocell) and four outputs (drive up/down, door open/close). There are eight possible states that the system can be in (states 3 and 7, for example, cover the condition where the lift is requested to move and someone is standing in the door).

The easiest way to go from the state diagram to a circuit is to assign a flip-flop to each state. Each is set by the entry conditions to the state, and reset by succeeding states. *Figure 7.23(c)*, for example, is the flip-flop for state 1. Outputs are energised via OR gates. The door-open output, for example, is required in states 1, 3, 5, 7 and is given by the circuit of *Figure 7.23(d)*.

State diagrams often incorporate timers. States 3 and 7 both start a five-second timer which initiates a retry at closing the door. Note that a given state may have routes to more than one succeeding state.

Event-driven systems are usually far more complex than that shown in *Figure 7.23* (and there are many safety defects in the described lift control scheme!) but most can be converted to a circuit via a state diagram. The technique is also useful for the design of event-driven computer and programmable controller-based schemes.

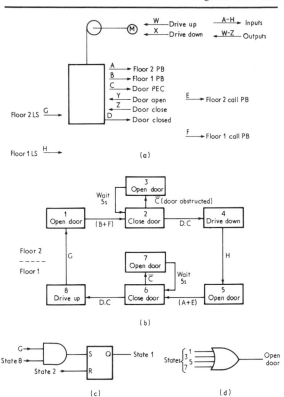

Fig. 7.23 Analysing a lift circuit with state diagrams: (a) lift schematic; (b) state diagram; (c) state circuit (one of eight); (d) output circuit (one of four)

Arithmetic and computing circuits 7.7

7.7.1 Numbers and bases

Human beings count to a base of ten. This means that each digit in a decimal number represents a power of ten. The number 74057, for example, means;

7×1	7
plus 5×10	50
plus $0 \times 10 \times 10$	0
plus $4 \times 10 \times 10 \times 10$	4 000
plus $7 \times 10 \times 10 \times 10 \times 10$	70 000
	Total 74 057

The reason we count to a base of ten is, of course, because we have ten fingers. Number systems can be constructed to any base; there is nothing magic about ten. If we had twelve fingers we would probably have counted to a base of twelve.

Of particular interest in electronics and computing is the number system to a base of two, called binary. In binary, each digit represents a power of two (1, 2, 4, 8, 16, 32 etc.). Each digit is called a 'bit'. Using the same approach as we did for the decimal number above we can therefore evaluate a binary number, 11010 say, as:

0×1	0
plus 1×2	2
plus $0 \times 2 \times 2$	0
plus $1 \times 2 \times 2 \times 2$	8
plus $1 \times 2 \times 2 \times 2 \times 2$	16
Total	26

The binary number 11010 is therefore decimal 26.

A more complex example, 11011101, noting that $2 \times 2 = 4$, and $2 \times 2 \times 2 = 8$ and so on:

1×1	1
plus 0×2	0
plus 1×4	4
plus 1×8	8
plus 1×16	16
plus 0×32	0
plus 1×64	64
plus 1×128	128
Total	221

The binary number 11011101 is thus decimal 221.

Any decimal number can be represented as an equivalent binary number, but the resulting binary representation is confusing for human beings. Binary is however ideal for digital circuits as a number can be represented as a combination of on/off states.

Conversion from binary to decimal is done by repeated division by two and noting the remainders (which will be 0 or 1). This is best shown by example. To convert decimal 23:

11 r. 1 (Least significant bit)
 5 r. 1
 2 r. 1
 1 r. 0
 0 r. 1 (Most significant bit)

Decimal 23 is therefore binary 10111. The technique can be used for any size of decimal number.

In computing, the engineer often has to deal with binary numbers and these are difficult to interpret directly. Number systems based on 16 (called hex) and 8 (called octal) are a useful halfway house between binary and decimal.

Hex uses letters A, B, C, D, E, F to cover the decimal numbers 10 to 15 (D is decimal 13 for example). Octal omits numerals 8 and 9. The counting sequence is thus:

Decimal	Hex	Octal
0	0	0
1	1	1
2	2	2
3	3	3
4	4	4
5	5	5
6	6	6
7	7	7
8	8	10
9	9	11
10	A	12
11	B	13
12	C	14
13	D	15
14	E	16
15	F	17
16	10	20
etc.		

The convenience of hex and octal is that conversion to and from binary is simple because a hex number is represented by four binary bits, and an octal number by three binary bits. For example, the number 10110101 can be represented in hex as:

1011	0101
B	5

or in octal as:

10	110	101
2	6	5

The hex representation B5 and the octal representation 265 are found much easier than conversion to decimal (to give 181). Hex representation is common in computing.

7.7.2 Encoders and decoders

These devices convert between decimal and binary for interfacing to decimal devices such as thumbwheel switches and decade displays. An encoder converts ten decimal input lines to 4-bit binary, and a decoder converts 4-bit binary to ten decimal output lines, as shown on the logic symbols in *Figure 7.24(a)* and (c).

Construction of encoders and decoders is a simple, if somewhat lengthy, combinational logic design problem. A part of an encoder (for the bit representing 2) and a decoder (for the decimal output 7) are shown in *Figure 7.24(b)* and (d).

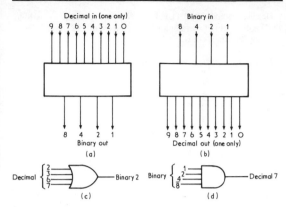

Fig. 7.24 Binary/decimal conversion: (a) part of encoder circuit; (b) part of decoder circuit

7.7.3 Counters

A binary counter will count pulses at its input. A four-bit counter is shown in *Figure 7.25(a)*. Its output will thus go:

	D	C	B	A
0	0	0	0	0
1	0	0	0	1
2	0	0	1	0
3	0	0	1	1
4	0	1	0	0
5	0	1	0	1
6	0	1	1	0
7	0	1	1	1
8	1	0	0	0
9	1	0	0	1

etc.

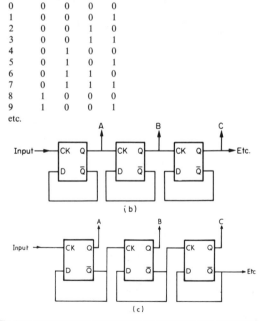

Fig. 7.25 Binary counters: (a) counter symbol; (b) D-type counter; (c) down counter

It will be seen from *Figure 7.25(a)* and the above table that a bit changes from '0' to '1' or '1' to '0' each time its predecessor goes from '1' to a '0'. If negative edge-triggered D-types are connected, as in *Figure 7.25(b)*, they will behave as counters. Counters can also be implemented using JK flip-flop, with $J = K = '1'$.

Figure 7.25(b) is called an up-counter, for obvious reasons. If the coupling between stages is taken from the $\overline{Q}$ pins, as in *Figure 7.25(c)* (with the output still being taken from the Q pins), the counter will count down. This arrangement is known as a down-counter. By selecting the interstage coupling a bidirectional counter can be constructed.

7.7.4 Synchronous counters

The counters in *Figure 7.25* are called 'ripple-through' or 'non-synchronous' counters because the change of state of the counter ripples through from the least significant end and the counter outputs do not change simultaneously. In slow applications this is of little import, but at high speeds the time taken to go, say, from 01111111 to 11111111 can be significant. Problems can also arise if the counter outputs are being decoded, as false glitches can appear on the decoder outputs while the count change ripples through.

These problems can be overcome by constructing a synchronous counter circuit, a JK form of which is shown in *Figure 7.26*. This uses combinational logic to look at preceding stages and set the JK inputs to a '1' if a toggle is required. With this arrangement, all counter outputs change together and the counter can be safely decoded without producing any glitches.

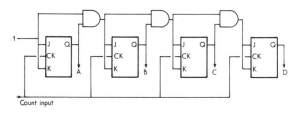

Fig. 7.26 4-bit synchronous counter

7.7.5 Counters to non-binary bases

Counters are often required to give non-binary counts. A BCD counter, for example, omits the counts for 10, 11, 12, 13, 14, 15. Such counters can be designed around state diagrams, described earlier in Section 7.6.

Figure 7.27(a) shows the general principle. The Q and $\overline{Q}$ outputs from the counter flip-flops are fed to a combinational logic circuit which sets up the correct D-input levels for the next counter state. This technique inherently gives a synchronous counter circuit.

The design procedure thus involves producing a state diagram for the counter, identifying which outputs are required to change at each count, and designing the (probably involved) combinational logic circuit to give these transitions.

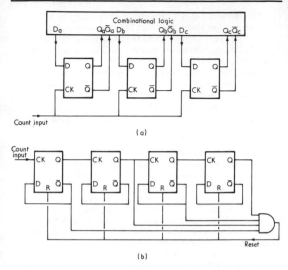

Fig. 7.27 Non-binary counters: (a) synchronous counter for any count sequence; (b) BCD ripple-through counter using reset inputs

The above technique can be used to design any count sequence, however odd, with D-type and JK flip-flops. If the required count sequence is a truncated binary count, however, it is often simpler to force a reset or set of individual bits at the required point. *Figure 7.27(b)* shows the circuit for a BCD counter where a single gate detects a count of ten (1010) and forces a counter reset.

7.7.6 Arithmetic units

The first arithmetic unit we need is an adder. This is shown diagrammatically in *Figure 7.28*. It will be seen that this is constructed using multiple identical blocks, each block adding one bit. The block is called a one-bit adder. It has three inputs, the 'A' and 'B' number inputs and the 'carry in' from the previous stage. It has two outputs, the bit sum and the 'carry out' to the next stage.

A one-bit adder is easy to construct with gates, and has the following truth table:

A	B	Carry in	Sum	Carry out
0	0	0	0	0
0	0	1	1	0
0	1	0	1	0
0	1	1	0	1
1	0	0	1	0
1	0	1	0	1
1	1	0	0	1
1	1	1	1	1

As with most common logic assemblies, adders are available in integrated circuit form.

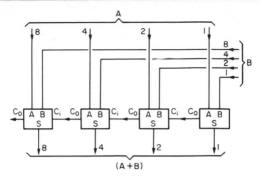

Fig. 7.28 Binary adder

Subtraction is done by a specialised form of addition. Suppose we are adding two numbers in decimal, but we can only represent numbers up to 999. We add

$$\begin{array}{r} 47 \\ 994 \\ \hline \end{array}$$

lost → ⚡ 041

The top 1, representing 1000, is lost leaving us with 41. The number 994 thus looks like − 6, and is called the complement of 6.

Similar methods are used to subtract binary numbers. This is known as twos complement arithmetic.

The formation of a twos complement is achieved by inverting each bit and adding 1. To form the twos complement of 5 to a length of 5 bits, for example:

00101 Binary 5
11010 Inverted
11011 Plus one gives complement 5.

We can now use the complement 5 to perform the subtraction (14 − 5) = 9:

$$\begin{array}{r} 0\,|1\ 1\ 1\ 0 \quad 14 \\ 1\,|1\ 0\ 1\ 1 \quad \text{complement 5} \\ \hline \text{lost} \rightarrow 1\ 0\,|1\ 0\ 0\ 1 \quad 9 \\ \uparrow \\ \text{sign bit} \end{array}$$

It is usual to represent the sign by the most significant bit; '1' denotes a negative number, '0' a positive number.

It might be thought that the next blocks we need will be multiply and divide. In fact, multiplier and divider logic blocks are practically unknown, these functions being easier to implement by computer. The shift register circuit given below does limited multiplication and division by two.

7.7.7 Shift register

A shift register moves a binary number by one column for each input pulse. It can be designed to shift to the left or to the right. Shifting to the left (shift up) multiplies by two, whereas shifting to the right (shift down) divides by two:

	Up	*Down*
Start	10111011	10111011
1	01110110	01011101
2	11101100	00101110
3	11011000	00010111
4	10110000	00001011

Shifts can be 'logical' in which case the bit pattern is simply moved, or 'arithmetic', in which case the sign is maintained.

A shift register constructed with D-types is shown in *Figure 7.29*. As might be expected, IC shift registers with facilities such as preload, bidirectional shift, etc., are readily available.

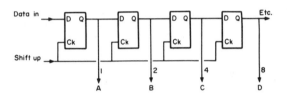

Fig. 7.29 Shift register

7.8 Practical considerations

The design of any logical system needs care. Practical points that need consideration are speed, noise and power consumption.

The speed of a logic gate is defined as the propagation delay; this is the time a signal takes to travel from the input of a logical unit to the output, *Figure 7.30(a)*. Allied with this is the rise time, defined roughly as the time taken for a signal to travel from one state to another, *Figure 7.30(b)*. These two factors determine the maximum speed at which the system can operate. Normal 'cooking' logic can operate up to around 5 MHz and high speed logic can operate at 50 MHz.

Noise is often a major problem, particularly in industrial systems. Noise causes memories to set, monostables to trigger and counters to count. Broadly speaking there are four classes of noise:

(1) Pick-up on signal inputs.
(2) Supply-borne externally generated.
(3) Supply-borne internally generated.
(4) Cross-talk and reflections.

Pick-up on signal inputs can be avoided by avoiding cable runs shared with high current cables and the use of opto-isolators on all inputs and outputs (see Subsection 9.4.2). Cables should be screened and the screen earthed at one end only to avoid earth loops.

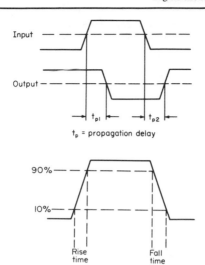

Fig. 7.30 Speed parameters of logic elements: (a) propagation delay;
(b) rise and fall times

External supply noise is caused by the switching of heavy loads. It
can be avoided by the use of mains filter and constant voltage
transformers. In extreme cases, the logic can 'float' on a battery which
is charged from the mains.

Internal supply noise is quite a common problem. As gates switch
their load current changes very quickly, and the di/dt, combined with
the inductance of the supply leads, causes voltage spikes. TTL (see
next section) is particularly notorious for this effect. The cure is to
adopt a sensible supply layout and to liberally decouple the supply
with $0.01 \, \mu F$ capacitors on every other IC package.

Cross-talk and reflections have a common cause. The logic signals
have fast edges, and line lengths over a few hundred centimetres need
to be treated as transmission lines. There are special line driver gates
and receivers available, and their use should be considered for lengths
of over a few metres. Cross-talk can be minimised by avoiding lengthy
parallel tracks.

Logic families have their noise immunity defined in their data
sheets. Somewhat simplified, it is the disturbance that has to be added
to a logical state before the signal might be detected as a signal of the
opposite state under the worst conditions of supply and load.

Digital systems operate at high speed, and to do this some logic
families use low value resistances internally to minimise the effects of
stray capacitance. This tends to lead to quite high supply currents.
Large logic systems using tens of amps at 5 V are by no means
uncommon. Supply layout obviously needs care in the design to

avoid voltage drops, and adequate protection should be given to harness wiring to ensure that faults do not lead to overheating of cables.

Gate outputs and inputs cannot be connected together indefinitely, and the loading of each output must be considered. An output has a defined 'fan-out', which is the number of standard gate inputs it can drive (typically 10 for TTL and 50 for CMOS).

Inputs have a defined load (called the 'fan-in') which relates to the number of equivalent gate inputs. Most simple inputs have a fan-in of 1, but some complex clock inputs on microprocessor ICs can have fan-ins of 2 or 3. To ensure correct operation the sum of all the fan-ins connected to a gate output must be less than or equal to its fan-out capability.

7.9 Logic families

7.9.1 Transistor-transistor logic (TTL)

TTL utilises a single 5 volt supply and is based on the NAND gate element of *Figure 7.31(a)*. The rather odd-looking dual-emitter transistor can, for analytical purposes, be considered as two transistors in parallel, as in *Figure 7.31(b)*.

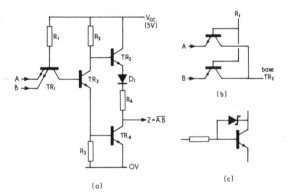

Fig. 7.31 Transistor-transistor logic: (a) circuit diagram of TTL gate; (b) addition of Schottky diode to prevent saturation

The two output transistors are known as a 'totem pole' output and serve to increase the gate speed. TR4 acts as a saturated transistor with a low impedance output and TR3 as an emitter follower. Logic states are well defined (3·5 V for a 1, 0 V for a 0) and the low output impedance in both states makes edge speeds relatively independent of load.

The totem pole output does, however, bring a few problems. As the output changes state, both transistors conduct together for a short time. This causes a brief large current pulse to be drawn from the supply. This can be as high as 100 mA, and can be a source of noise problems. Frequent decoupling of the supply rails with 0·01 μF capacitors is necessary.

TTL uses saturating transistors to define the logic levels, and as such suffers from a phenomenon called 'charge storage'. This causes a saturated transistor to hold on for a few nanoseconds when it is turned off. Hole storage can be overcome by the inclusion of a Schottky diode, as in *Figure 7.31(c)*, to prevent the transistor saturating. The low forward drop of the diode prevents the collector going more negative than the base.

There are three common TTL families. These differ in speed and power requirements (which is always a trade-off that needs to be made in digital circuits. Low impedances give fast speeds but high power consumption).

Family	Suffix	Tdp nS	Power mW
Normal	none	10	10
Schottky	S	3	19
Low power Schottky	LS	9·5	2

Other less common variations are 'high speed' (now really defunct, as it is slower than Schottky), 'low power' and 'advanced Schottky'.

TTL logic is almost universally based on the Texas Instruments' 74 series range, with device numbering of the form 74suffixNNN, where NNN defines the function (e.g. 74LS123).

TTL was once the most widely used logic family, but its requirements for expensive high-current 5 volt power supplies have led to it being overtaken by the next logic family, CMOS.

7.9.2 Complementary metal oxide semiconductor logic (CMOS)

CMOS is almost the perfect logic family. It requires no special power supplies and can operate from a single rail anywhere in the range 3 to 15 volts. It uses little power when operated at low speeds (typically 0·01 mW per gate) and is adequately fast for most applications (but not as fast as S series TTL). CMOS gates have high input impedances and this allows very high fan-outs, typically around 50 compared to 10 for TTL.

CMOS is built around the two types of field effect transistor described earlier in Subsection 2.6.6. These can be considered as a perfect switch in series with a resistor, as in *Figure 7.32(a)*. It is thus a straightforward job to construct logic gates, the circuits for an inverter, NAND and NOR gates being shown in *Figure 7.32(b–d)*.

A CMOS input is simply the gate of a FET, and has a very high impedance which, in early versions, allowed damage from high voltage static electricity during handling. More modern devices are well protected and can be handled almost like any other component. It is, however, still good practice to handle CMOS on an earthed sheet and use earthed wrist straps when inserting or removing CMOS ICs.

Although CMOS is a low powered family, power consumption does rise with increasing speed as stray capacitance is charged and discharged. Above toggle speeds of about 1 MHz, CMOS and LS TTL have similar power consumption. In any system, however, all the gates are not toggling at the same speed, and a CMOS circuit will

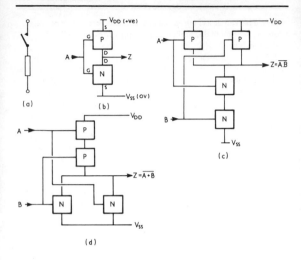

Fig. 7.32 Complementary metal oxide semiconductor (CMOS) logic:
(a) equivalent of FET; (b) CMOS inverter; (c) CMOS NAND gate;
(d) CMOS NOR gate

typically use one-tenth to one-quarter of the equivalent LS TTL
circuit.

CMOS ICs are based around the 4000 series, which is a rational
combination of the RCA COSMOS range and the Motorola
McMOS. Devices are coded 4NNNsuffix (e.g. 4002B) where the suffix
denotes a buffered (B) or unbuffered (A) device. B series should be
used for all new designs. A 74C series is available which is pin
compatible (but *not* electrically compatible) with 74 series TTL.

CMOS is well suited to the design of complex high density ICs.
Most microprocessor ICs and their support chips, such as memories,
are based on CMOS technology.

7.9.3 Emitter coupled logic (ECL)

ECL has the merit of being the fastest available logic family, with
propagation delays as low as 1 ns and operating speeds up to 500
MHz. The two main constraints on operating speed are charge
storage and stray capacitance. ECL overcomes the first problem by
using non-saturating transistors and the second by using low
impedances. Both of these solutions result in high power
consumption, typically over 30 mW per gate.

The circuit of an ECL OR/NOR gate is shown in *Figure 7.33(a)*.
This has the logic symbol shown in *Figure 7.33(b)*. The circuit
resembles a DC amplifier long-tail pair, with inputs A, B being
compared with the reference voltage on TR2 base. Emitter follower
outputs are used to give good drive capability.

ECL is not easy to use. Its logic swing is small and poorly defined
(-0.8 V and -1.6 V) so its noise immunity is poor. It needs three
high current stable power supply rails. Its biggest problem, however,

is inherent in its high speed. The very fast edges demand that interconnecting leads be dealt with as transmission lines, and hence much care must be put into the layout design. An ECL circuit cannot be thrown together; multilayer PCBs must be used.

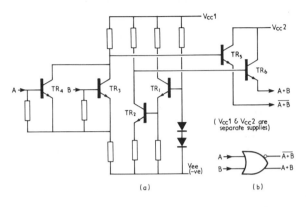

Fig. 7.33 Emitter coupled logic: (a) circuit diagram; (b) logic symbol

Analog interfacing 7.10

7.10.1 Digital to analog converters (DACs)

An 8-bit binary number can represent a decimal number in the range 0 to 255. It can also represent a voltage in the range 0 to 2·55 volts if one bit is said to represent 10 mV. Any other scaling could, of course, be chosen.

A device which converts a digital number to an analog voltage is called a digital to analog converter. *Figure 7.34* shows two common DAC circuits.

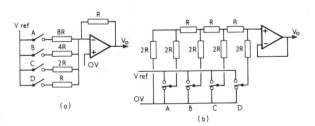

Fig. 7.34 Digital to analog converter (DAC) circuits: (a) summing op-amp; (b) R–2R ladder

Figure 7.34(a) switches different resistor values to the input of an inverting op-amp from a fixed reference voltage. If switches D and B are closed, for example, the output voltage will be 1·25 times V_{ref}.

Figure 7.34(b) is easier to construct in IC form as only two values of resistor are used, regardless of the number of bits. This circuit is known, for obvious reasons, as an R–2R ladder.

In both circuits CMOS transmission gates are used to perform the switching. DACs are readily available in IC form, typical devices having a resolution of 12 bits (one part in 4096).

7.10.2 Analog to digital converters (ADCs)

An ADC converts an analog voltage to an equivalent digital representation for use by a computer or logic system. There are many different circuits, but most work by comparing the output of a logic-driven DAC with the input voltage.

The circuit of *Figure 7.35* is called a ramp ADC and is one of the slower, but simpler, circuits. A binary counter is connected to a DAC. As the counter counts up from zero, the DAC output will be a ramp. This voltage is compared with the input voltage, and when the two are equal the counter is stopped. The count value is then a digital representation of the input voltage. The Q output of the flip-flop indicates 'ADC busy' and the $\overline{Q}$ output 'count complete'.

ADCs are, inevitably, most often used in IC form. Typical devices will give a 12-bit (one part in 4096) resolution. Conversion times of a few microseconds can be obtained with more refined circuits. The fastest ADCs, called Flash Converters, are used to digitise television pictures for units which convert between different TV standards and for TV special effects units.

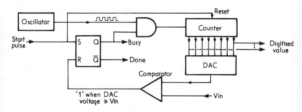

Fig. 7.35 Ramp analog to digital converter

8
Digital computers

Introduction 8.1

The growth of computer technology has been spectacular. Over a few decades computers have developed from massive multi-million pound monsters, used by universities and government research departments, to home computers that are readily affordable by small firms and private individuals. At the time of writing, it is estimated that in the UK a remarkable one home in six has a home computer.

Part of this rapid growth is due to the introduction of the microprocessor. This is often thought of as some form of super computer but, as will be seen later, a microprocessor is just one small part of a conventional computer. A computer based on a microprocessor (called a microcomputer) is usually less powerful than more conventional mini and mainframe machines. What microprocessors have given us, however, is reasonably powerful computers at very low cost.

There has been an interesting side-effect to this for the electronic engineer. As computing costs fall, it becomes more and more attractive to do any given project 'by computer', particularly if dedicated computers such as the Z-8 described in Section 8.9 are used. Increasingly, the role of the circuit and logic designer is being replaced by the skills of the computer architect and programmer.

Computer architecture 8.2

8.2.1 Introduction
Any computer can be represented by the block diagram of *Figure 8.1*. A computer is a manipulator of data, which is a loose term that varies according to the application. If the computer is being used for payroll calculations, the computer will accept data such as employees' details, hours worked and hourly rates, and produce data in the form of payslips. A home computer running a video game will accept data in the form of keyboard or joystick movements, and produce data in the form of television pictures and sound effects.

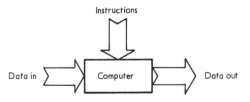

Fig. 8.1 Representation of a computer

The computer therefore accepts input data, manipulates it in some way, and as a result produces output data. To do this we need to provide it with the instructions necessary to perform the data manipulation.

It is important to grasp the essential difference between the computer and a calculator. There are obvious similarities: both are digital; both use large scale integrated circuits. But a calculator can be used immediately and does not require instructions. To add 4057 and 3220, one simply enters

$$4057 + 3220 =$$

and the calculator gives the result (7277) instantly. To perform the same sum on a computer one would need to write a small series of instructions, then instruct the computer to follow them. Part of the instructions would be an order to print the result.

In many respects, the operation of a computer is similar to the work performed by a clerk sitting at a desk, as in *Figure 8.2*. We can identify the essential components of a computer by seeing what tools the clerk needs to perform his job.

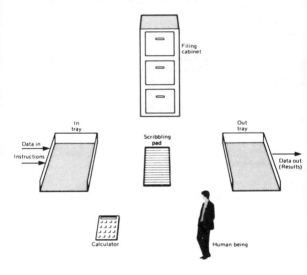

Fig. 8.2 The essential parts of a computer

The clerk needs to communicate with the outside world, so first we need an in-tray and an out-tray. The in-tray will be used to accept data for processing, and occasionally for receiving instructions. The out-tray, of course, will be used for output data (the results of the clerk's labours).

It is likely that some arithmetical operations will be needed, so the clerk will need a calculator. If complex calculations are being performed it is likely that he will need a scribbling pad to jot down part results and information that will be needed at some later time.

Finally, he will probably need a filing cabinet for storing records that need to be accessed occasionally. Note that the scribbling pad and the filing cabinet are both forms of storage, but data on the scribbling pad can be retrieved quickly, whereas more time is needed to access the filing cabinet. There is also a difference in the quantity of data that can be stored. The scribbling pad is limited in size, whereas the filing cabinet can be extended indefinitely, being limited only by the time taken for the clerk to walk to the correct unit.

We have identified six essential items for the clerk's job, summarised in *Figure 8.3*. These are:

(a) An input device to receive data and instructions.
(b) An output device for completed work.
(c) A calculator.
(d) A fast, but limited, storage system.
(e) A slower, large, organised mass storage system.
(f) Some form of control system.

The last item should not be overlooked, and is the clerk himself. His job is to read the next step in the instruction list and manipulate the other five items to obey the instructions.

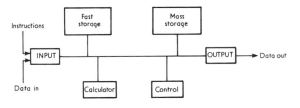

Fig. 8.3 Block diagram of a computer

8.2.2 Data representation

Although a computer works with a variety of data, text, numerals, video displays etc., internally it deals solely with binary numbers. Anything can be represented as a number. Text, for example, can be represented in the ASCII code of *Table 10.1*, where decimal 65, for example, represents A.

Statistical information can also be represented as a binary number by allocating one bit to each Yes/No statement as in *Figure 8.4(a)*. A similar representation could also be used in industrial control to store the state of on/off signals such as switches and indicator lamps.

The basic size of binary number that a computer deals with is called its word size. Most microcomputers use an 8-bit word (called a byte) or a 16-bit word. Larger computers use 24-, 32- or even 48-bit words. An 8-bit word can hold a number in the range 0–255. This is not, however, the restriction that it might seem, as larger numbers can be held by using several words together, as shown in *Figure 8.4(b)*.

The computer manipulates the data held in numerical form in words. To the computer, all data is binary numbers and it cannot distinguish between ASCII coded text, multi-word precision numbers of bit-by-bit statistical representation. It is up to the programmer to make this distinction.

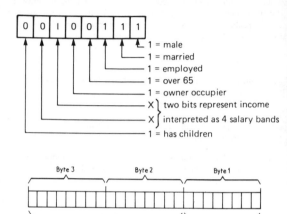

Fig. 8.4 An 8-bit word does not limit a computer to 8-bit numbers. Examples of different representations: (a) Non-numerical data held in binary; (b) Representation of large numbers by using several bytes

8.2.3 The store

Section 8.3 deals with details of the construction of computer stores, but it is useful at this point to deal with a simple picture of how the fast store is used. It can be visualised as a collection of pigeonholes similar to *Figure 8.5*. A typical machine would have from 16 000 to 64 000 pigeonholes (1024 being termed 1 k).

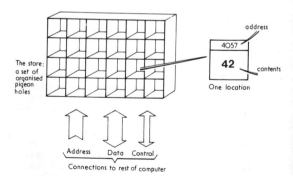

Fig. 8.5 The fast store

Retrieval of data from the store (or 'fetching' or 'reading' as it is often called) is a slightly misleading term as it implies that the data is removed and the store location left empty. In reality, retrieval is more of a copying process; a copy of the store location contents is taken when data is retrieved, and the store contents are unaltered. The only way to alter the contents of a location is to write new data to it.

If data is to be put into the store for later retrieval, each and every location must be individually accessible. This is achieved by giving each and every store location a unique numerical address. Each store location therefore has an address, and can hold one word. Data can be sent to, or retrieved from, each and every store location. The store therefore has the following connections to the outside world:

(a) A bidirectional group of lines for carrying data to and from the store, the number of lines being the same as the word size.
(b) A group of lines carrying the address being accessed.
(c) Sundry control signals indicating whether we are writing to or reading from the store, plus timing and strobe signals.

These groups of signals are known as 'buses' (short for busbars) and are called, respectively, the data bus, the address bus and the control bus.

The store is used not only to hold data but also to hold the program instructions. These, like everything else, are held as numbers in the store. The hex number C7, for example, tells the computer to stop, on a Z-80 microprocessor-based machine. The computer only distinguishes between instructions and data in the store by the point in its cycle of operation at which the store is accessed. We will return to this distinction shortly.

8.2.4 Input and output connections

Even a simple computer has many possible peripheral devices with which data can be exchanged. These are identified by an address usually called a port number, allowing program instructions to say, for example, 'Get a word from the tape reader on port 3 and put it into store location 3FF7', or 'Take a word from store location 1C50 and put it to the printer on port 7', and so on.

Conceptually, we can visualise the input/output connections as shown in *Figure 8.6*. Note that these use the same bus structure as the store, with data transfers taking place on the data bus, and ports being identified on the address bus. The control bus again carries timing and direction signals.

8.2.5 Control and arithmetic

The control unit is required to read the next instruction from the store, and set up the internal routes inside the machine that cause the instruction to be obeyed. To do this it needs to keep track of where the next instruction is kept. This is held in a one-address word store called the program counter, or PC for short.

Unless special instructions called jumps or subroutines (described later) are being obeyed, the instructions are held sequentially in the store. The PC can therefore be literally a counter that is incremented each time an instruction is completed.

The control unit also contains some word storage itself. These are called registers. If the arithmetic unit can send results to them, the

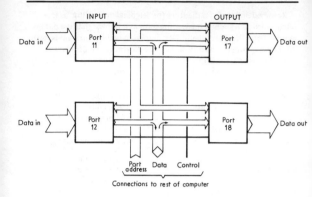

Fig. 8.6 Input/output connections

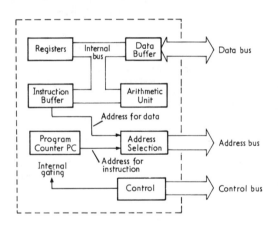

Fig. 8.7 The central processor unit (CPU)

term accumulator is used. These provide yet another fast storage area which can be accessed quicker, and easier, than the store itself as no addressing is needed. Some computers have as few as one register, some have 32.

The arithmetic unit generally operates on the contents of one of the registers and on the contents of another register or a store location. In most machines the result goes to one of the registers. In 8-bit machines the arithmetic unit can only perform addition and subtraction, plus logical operations AND, OR and XOR between words. The more powerful 16-bit machines often include multiply and divide, giving a 32 bit result in the same way that a two-decimal digit multiply gives a four-digit result, e.g. $99 \times 99 = 9801$.

Where multiply and divide are not provided, the programmer can write suitable instruction routines. A simple, but not very fast, multiplication, for example, can be achieved by repetitive addition.

To see how the control unit operates, let us follow the sequence through one instruction. The PC contains OC50, which is the address of the next instruction. The sequence is shown in *Figure 8.8*.

(a) The contents of the PC (OC50) are put on the address bus, and a READ initiated from the store. The number read indicates the instruction required. Let us assume it is: 'Add the contents of store location 2FFE to the contents of register B, result to go to register A'. The instruction is decoded by the control unit.

(b) 2FFE is put on the address bus and a READ initiated from the store. The contents of address 2FFE (hex 27, say) is brought to the arithmetic unit.

(c) The contents of register B (hex 15, say) is also brought to the arithmetic unit and added to the number hex 27 from the store. The result (hex 3C) goes to register A, as required (overwriting any number already in there).

(d) The program counter is incremented ready for the next instruction.

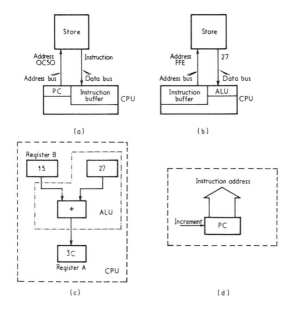

Fig. 8.8 The steps in obeying an instruction: (a) instruction address (OC50) sent to store with Read command on control line. Instruction brought to CPU; (b) instruction decoded as 'Add contents of location 2FFE to Register B contents, result to Register A.' Address 2FFE put on address line with Read command on control line. Contents of 2FFE (27) brought to ALU; (c) contents of ALU and Register B added, result to Register A; (d) program counter incremented for next instruction

On older computers, there was a tendency to construct a computer as four separate cubicles. These held the store, the I/O circuits, mass storage and the control. The latter was often called the Central Processor Unit, or CPU. Although modern computers are usually built in one cubicle, the term CPU is still used for the control and arithmetic circuits.

8.2.5 Bus structure and tristate gates

It will be noted that each of the three units in *Figures 8.5, 8.6* and *8.7* are interconnected by a common bus structure, allowing us to visualise the computer as in *Figure 8.9*. The bus structure is a fundamental part of computer design, as it allows the computer to be easily expanded with more memory, additional I/O ports etc.

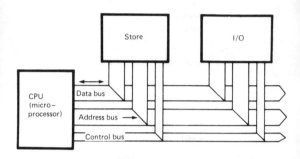

Fig. 8.9 The highway structure of a computer

The data bus will have as many lines as the word size being used (8, 16, or 32 bits etc.). The address bus will be determined by the amount of store being addressed; 16 bits for a 64K, for example. The control bus carries directional, timing and control signals, and will typically contain six to 12 lines according to the complexity of the computer.

Bidirectional buses and control lines can have logic states that can originate in several places. The data bus, for example, sends data from the CPU to the store or I/O, but can also carry data from the I/O or store to the CPU. Several of the control bus lines may also be bidirectional.

This bidirectionality is achieved by the use of tristate gates. These have the logic symbol shown in *Figure 8.10(a)* (shown for an AND gate) and do not, as the name might imply, have three logic states. With the enable input at a '1', the gate acts as a normal AND gate, with the output state ('1' or '0') being determined by the A, B inputs. With the enable input at a '0', the gate output goes to a floating (high impedance) state. The action of a tristate gate is shown in *Figure 8.10(b)*.

Figure 8.10(c) shows the applications of tristate gates. One bus line is shown; in practice, of course, there are several. To send data from the CPU, gate 3 is enabled, and gates 1, 2 disabled. To send data from the store, gate 1 is enabled and gates 2, 3 disabled. In this way there is no clash where two units are trying to put different voltage levels on the same line.

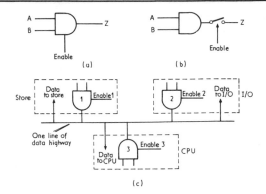

Fig. 8.10 The tristate gate: (a) logic symbol; (b) representation of circuit action; (c) operation of data bus

8.2.6 Simple programming

The art of programming will be discussed in Section 8.4, but it is useful to have a preview as part of the discussion of the way a computer is constructed.

A program is a sequence of instructions that will be followed by the machine. At the level of the machine itself there are really very few types of instruction. These are:

(a) Input a word from a port to a store location or a register.

(b) Output a word from a store location or register to a port.

(c) Copy a word from a store location to a register (usually called a Read or a Fetch), overwriting the previous register contents.

(d) Copy a word from a register to a store location, overwriting the previous store location contents. (Usually called a Write, Load or Put.)

(e) Perform arithmetical operations between the contents of a store location and the contents of a register, the result usually going to a register.

(f) Perform logical operations (AND, OR, XOR) between the contents of a store location and the contents of a register, the result usually going to a register.

(g) Conditional and non-conditional jumps. This group of instructions is what makes a computer particularly useful. It was said earlier that the instructions are held sequentially in the store and are obeyed by increasing the PC. Jump instructions direct the computer to a new set of instructions by altering the contents of the PC. Conditional jumps perform a jump only if some condition is true (e.g. Jump to instruction 1FE7 if register A contains zero). These instructions are very powerful because they allow the computer to change its route according to outside events (e.g. 'If last bill has not been paid then send a reminder', or 'If stock in stores bin is less than 5 then order a new batch'.

(h) Control instructions (such as HALT).

Most of these instructions have the form

WHAT is to be done
WHERE the data is to be found
WHERE the result is to go.

Programming at this level is called machine code programming and is very tedious. Most programs are written in high level languages, a topic covered further in Section 8.4.

8.2.7 The microprocessor

The manufacturers of LSI chips in the mid-1970s had a problem. The more complex a chip, the more limited the market. One solution to this problem was the ULA, described in Chapter 3. Another was the microprocessor.

The microprocessor is simply, and no more than, the CPU of a small computer, i.e. the registers, and the arithmetic and control unit. A computer built around a microprocessor is called a microcomputer. There is nothing particularly special or powerful about microcomputers; they are, in fact, decidedly inferior to many machines built in the 1970s from discrete components.

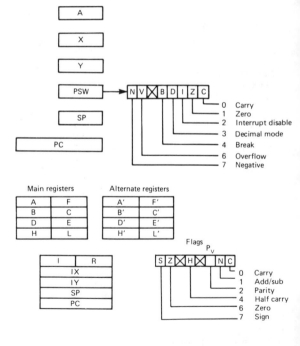

Fig. 8.11 Typical 8-bit microprocessors: (a) the 6502. PSW stands for Processor Status Word, which is another name for the flag register; (b) the Z-80 has two main register sets, each with seven registers plus flag register

Above all, however, the microprocessor, along with easily usable support chips for I/O, disc access and cheap storage ICs (described in the next section), has brought cheap computing, and it is this cheapness that has had such an impact. Small, cheap, easy to manufacture machines have allowed computers to be used in applications that would have been uneconomic a few years ago.

Typical 8-bit microprocessors are the 6502 (used in the BBC Micro), *Figure 8.11(a)*, and the Z-80 (used in most Sinclair machines), *Figure 8.11(b)*. These are shown as programmers' models, which is the most useful visualisation. The registers, PC, etc. operate as described above. The F, or flag register, hold bits which indicate the result of the last instruction (positive, negative, zero) for use by conditional jumps. The Z-80 has two register sets, which can be switched by a control instruction.

The two microprocessors of *Figure 8.11* are not 'state of the art'. The 6502 and the Z-80 both work with 8-bit data words and 16-bit (64K) addresses. More modern microprocessors, described later, work with 16-bit and 32-bit data words and can address megaword storage. Surprisingly however, many microcomputers still use simple 8-bit microprocessors for reasons of simplicity and cost.

Storage circuits 8.3

The store in a modern computer is invariably constructed from LSI storage ICs. Early computers used ferrite beads which were magnetised to store bits, but these have largely been superseded. The term 'core store' may still be encountered; this is a throwback to magnetic cores.

The store may be visualised in either of the forms shown in *Figure 8.12*. In *Figure 8.12(a)* the store is represented as a 'tower block', with each floor representing one location (of eight bits in the example).

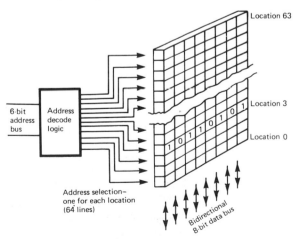

(a)

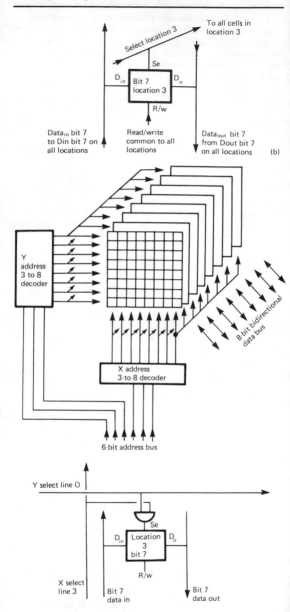

Fig. 8.12 Arrangement of a typical store. A 64-word store is shown for simplicity. Although (a) is conceptually simpler, (c) is how a store is constructed with one IC for each plane

Figure 8.12(c), although less obvious, is a closer representation of how a store is actually built.

Storage ICs are usually built of ICs arranged in planes, i.e. one IC represents one bit. Typical ICs are arranged as, say, 16K × 1 bit, so eight such ICs would give an 8-bit 16K store. A 64K, 16-bit store could be constructed from 16 ICs, each 64K × 1 bit.

Storage is based around storage cells similar to *Figure 8.13*. Gates 6 and 7 form an S–R flip-flop. Data In, Data Out and R/W are common to all cells in the IC. The select line comes from the address decode logic to say that it is this cell that is to be used. One store location can then be represented as shown in *Figure 8.14*. Note that this one location uses eight (say) ICs, one for each data word.

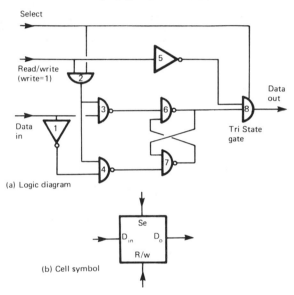

(a) Logic diagram

(b) Cell symbol

Fig. 8.13 A memory cell for storing one bit: (a) logic diagram; (b) cell symbol

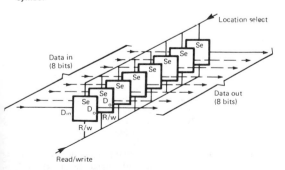

Fig. 8.14 A store location

Figure 8.15 shows the construction of a typical 8-bit 4K store using 4K × 1 bit ICs. A 4K store uses 12 address lines, so separate page decode logic decodes the top four bits to select this 4K block.

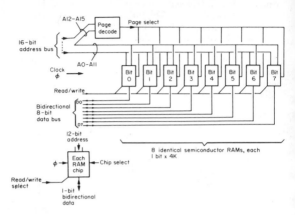

Fig. 8.15 Organisation of 4k semiconductor RAM

Store ICs are described as static or dynamic. A static store uses simple S–R flip-flops, as in *Figure 8.16(a)*. This is wasteful of power. Dynamic stores hold the data as charges on capacitors, as in *Figure 8.16(b)*. This conserves power, but the charges slowly leak away. Dynamic stores have to be continually refreshed about every 2–5 ms. Refreshing is done automatically by some microprocessors. (This is the function of the R register in the Z-80 block diagram of *Figure 8.11(b)*.)

Store contents are lost if the power is removed. The store is said to be 'volatile'. Stores can be made immune to power failure by the use of batteries. The one advantage of the early core memories was that they were inherently non-volatile.

The term RAM is often encountered. This simply stands for Random Access Memory, and means that it takes the same time to access any location (i.e. all are equally accessible). Data stored on magnetic tape, for example, is said to be serially accessed, and the time taken to get to the data varies according to where it is stored and the current tape position.

The store also holds instructions as well as data. If the instructions are fixed they can be held in form of store called a ROM, or Read Only Memory. To the computer, a ROM looks like the rest of the store, but the contents cannot be altered. Obviously ROMs are inherently non-volatile. Various techniques are used for storage in ROMs, common being the burning-out fusible links, or by storing charges on capacitors. ROMs required in large quantities are manufactured by a technique similar to that used in ULAs. These are known as Mask Programmable ROMs.

Erasable Programmable ROMs (EPROMs) allow the user to change the contents of a ROM (albeit with special equipment). The

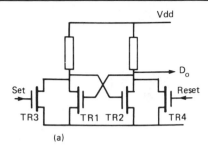

(a)

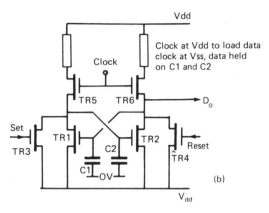

Vdd

Clock at Vdd to load data
clock at Vss, data held
on C1 and C2

(b)

Fig. 8.16 Static and dynamic memories: (a) static memory cell;
(b) dynamic memory cell

data is held as charges on capacitors and can be erased by exposure to
ultraviolet light through a quartz window in the top of the IC.
EPROMs are loaded via the PROM programmer.

An interesting development is the so-called bubble memory, which
fills the gap between large low speed storage such as discs or magnetic
tape, and fast but relatively small storage given by core and
semiconductor RAMs.

In certain materials, magnetic domains are formed which have a
preferred line of magnetisation, which we will call 'up' and 'down'.
Normally the material will have random stripes of magnetisation, as
shown in *Figure 8.17(a)*. If a magnetic field is applied, as shown in
Figure 8.17(b), the antiparallel regions shrink, until at a certain
critical field strength small magnetic bubbles are left; see *Figure
8.17(c)*. These bubbles are mobile and can be moved around the
material by suitable magnetic fields, since each acts as a small bar
magnet. It should be noted that the actual material does not move, it
is simply the magnetisation that is mobile.

To use these bubbles as a useful storage system, some method of
control is needed. This is commonly provided by the structure shown

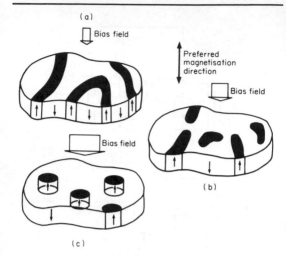

Fig. 8.17 Magnetic bubbles: (a) small field, stripes form; (b) islands formed; (c) islands become cylindrical bubbles

in *Figure 8.18*. Magnetically soft nickel iron is deposited on the surface of the material in the shape of alternate I and T formations. A bias field is applied perpendicular to the paper to allow formation of bubbles, as described previously, and a rotating field applied in the plane of the paper. As the field rotates, the I and T elements are magnetised in sympathy, and simple magnetic attraction and repulsion shifts the bubbles one place to the right for each field rotation.

The bubble memory thus approximates to a large shift store. Data is loaded in by simple current loop which produces a bubble, and the output data sensed by a Hall effect element (see Subsection 12.6.3); 16K devices are quite easily fabricated, and 64K devices have been made. Plans for megabit devices have been announced.

Because the bubble memory is a serially accessed device there is an inherent delay in reading data. The field rotation frequency is around

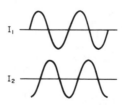

Fig. 8.18 T and I propagation elements

100 kHz, giving a delay of a few milliseconds for a 16K device. This can be improved by splitting the device into several smaller registers.

The construction of a typical device is shown in *Figure 8.19*. The bias field is provided by two permanent magnets, and the rotating field by two solenoid coils driven by sine waves 90 degrees out of phase. Unfortunately, drive currents of a few amps are needed, so the bubble memory is not, at present, as convenient as semiconductor RAMs. Bubble memories do, however, usefully fill the gap between fast access memories and the bulk storage devices and they are non-volatile.

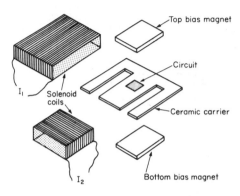

Fig. 8.19 Bubble memory chip

Programming 8.4

8.4.1 Assembly language and machine code
Subsection 8.2.6 showed that a computer obeys relatively few types of instruction. Programming at the level of the machine itself is called machine code programming and is very time-consuming and error-prone. To some extent it is made easier by the use of mnemonics instead of bald hex coding. This is called assembly language programming.

In Z-80 assembly language, for example, to put the number 8 in register B, we would write

LD B,8

where LD stands for Load. Similarly, to add the contents of registers A and B we would write

ADD A,B

This makes the program much easier to read than the straight hex coding (which for the above two instructions is 06 08 80). The mnemonics are converted to a machine code program by a special language called an assembler.

8.4.2 Subroutines

It is often found that a set of instructions is required at many places in a main program. Most 8-bit micros, for example, do not have multiply or divide instructions, and these have to be written into the program. It is wasteful to have to write such groups of instructions (called routines) each time they are used. A technique called subroutines allows commonly used instructions to be written once and then called as required.

The principle is shown on *Figure 8.20*. An instruction GOSUB, or CALL (e.g. CALL MULT) takes the program to the subroutine and a Return instruction in the subroutine takes the program flow back to the instruction following the subroutine call. Subroutines can call subroutines, as shown in *Figure 8.20(b)*. This is known as 'nesting'.

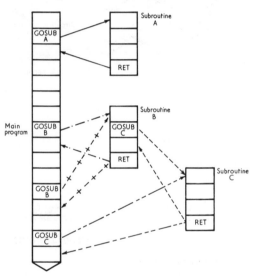

Fig. 8.20 Subroutines and their nesting. Subroutine C is nested with B, but can also be called from the main program

8.4.3 High-level languages

Most computer programs are written in a high-level language, which is similar to English. For example, a program written in the high-level language BASIC to print out a requested multiplication table could be:

```
10 INPUT "Which times table";N
20 FOR J = 1 TO 10
30 PRINT J;"Times";N;"is";J*N
40 NEXT J
50 INPUT "Another go";Q$
60 IF LEFT(Q$,1) = "Y" THEN GOTO 10
70 PRINT "Bye"
80 STOP
```

High-level languages allow the programmer to use names (N,J,Q$ above) instead of store numbers and write instruction types in an easy to read form (INPUT, PRINT, IF etc).

The user writes his program in the high-level form above, and this is converted to machine code by a special program usually supplied with the computer. There are two ways in which this conversion can be done. An interpreter converts each instruction as it is obeyed; a compiler converts the whole program before it is run.

Interpreters are easier and friendlier to use, as changes in the program are easy to make. Compiled programs run much faster, but changes are more difficult as a new compilation has to be made after each change.

BASIC is just one of many programming languages, but is the commonest on home and business microcomputers. Other languages commonly encountered are Pascal, Forth, Lisp, Comal, Fortran and many more. Each has its own advantages and disadvantages, and it is fair to say that there is no perfect all-purpose language.

Mass storage 8.5

Although various optical techniques have been tried, virtually all mass storage is done magnetically on suitably coated tapes or discs. The commonest method in business and home computers is the so-called floppy disc, shown in *Figures 8.21(a)* and *(b)*.

A disc is organised into concentric tracks, which are further subdivided into sectors. The example of *Figure 8.22* uses 35 tracks and 10 sectors. Sector identification is usually provided by an index hole to identify sector 0, other sectors being located by an angular position-measuring device in the hub drive shaft. This is called soft sectoring. Tracks are accessed by a movable read/write head, usually positioned by a stepper motor.

The disc rotates at 300 rpm, giving a data transfer rate of about 12·5K bytes per second. Discs come in 20 and 13 cm (8 and 5·25 inches) sizes, the latter being capable of holding around 200K bytes of data per side. Smaller 3-inch mini discs are also available.

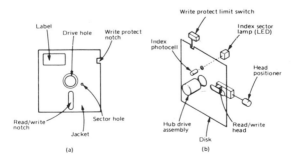

Fig. 8.21 Floppy disk schematic: (a) floppy disk; (b) disk-drive components

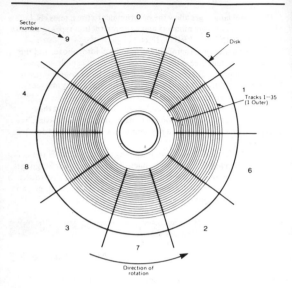

Fig. 8.22 Tracks and sectors on a disk

Larger storage capacity is given by so-called Winchester discs. The enemy of magnetic storage is dirt and grease. Winchester discs are based on a non-replaceable rigid metal disc which is sealed into its own housing along with the read/write head. Because the disc and its associated hardware are manufactured together and operate in a totally clean environment, tighter tolerances are possible. A typical Winchester disc can store 10 Mbytes of data.

Commercial mainframe computers rely on large rigid disc packs or magnetic tape. Storage capacity is only limited by space and finance.

Disc drives connect to computers via special parallel ports, which allow them direct access to the store without involving the CPU. This is known as Direct Memory Access or DMA. This operation is transparent to the user, and allows large programs or files of data to be loaded or saved quickly.

Most home computers use the humble domestic tape recorder. Data and programs are stored serially as a series of tones. A common standard uses 1200 Hz for a '0' and 2400 Hz for a '1'. Data transfer rates of 1200 baud are easily achievable. The main problem is time; 1200 baud is around 9K bytes per minute, so program and data loading takes minutes. There is also no automatic location of data as there is on disc drives; the user has to wind the tape to the right position. Despite these disadvantages, however, cassettes provide cheap and reliable mass storage for many users.

Peripherals 8.6

8.6.1 Printers
A printer is the first accessory bought by most computer users. Two types of printer have evolved. The dot matrix printer of *Figure 8.23* builds up characters as a matrix of dots. The print head consists of a column of needles which are driven by solenoids to strike the ribbon. As the print head moves across the page a complete matrix is built up for each character, a column at a time.

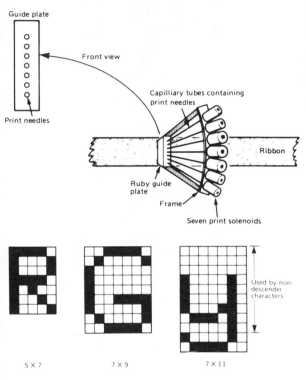

Fig. 8.23 The dot matrix printer: (a) construction of dot matrix head; (b) various dot matrices. 7 × 11 allows true descenders

The daisywheel printer in *Figure 8.24* is slower, but is quieter and gives a better print quality. The characters are embossed at the end of petals on a wheel which is spun at high speed. The solenoid strikes the back of the required letter. Control logic rotates the wheel to the correct position as the head moves to the next character position.

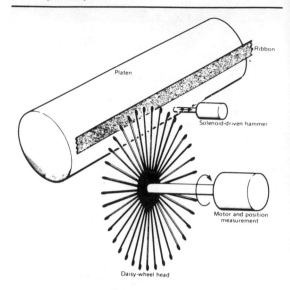

Fig. 8.24 Operating principles of daisywheel printer

Other printers are available (ink jet, laser scanners etc.) but at the time of writing these seem unlikely to replace the dot matrix or daisywheel where cheap, reasonable quality is required at no great speed.

Typical printer speeds are 300 baud (around 30 characters per second) but many incorporate internal storage that allows data to be sent much faster from the computer (providing, of course, the buffer store is not full). Printers can use serial or parallel data transmission, but the subject is confused by a lack of standards, even when RS232 protocol is supposedly being used.

8.6.2 Other devices

There are many peripheral devices that can be attached to a computer. Generally these are related to the input and output of data. A light pen, for example, is a device like a ball point pen with a photocell at the end. When held on a VDU screen, the computer detects the X,Y coordinates being indicated. Light pens can be used to select options from a menu or even drawing for computer-aided design (CAD).

Related devices are the graphics tablets (where the user draws on a special pad which again gives the computer the coordinates of the pen position) and the 'mouse'. The latter device is superficially similar to a toy mouse which the user moves over a desk. The movement is sensed by position transducers on the mouse and relayed to the computer. The mouse is mainly used for menu selection in business programs.

Drum and flatbed plotters are output devices used where high quality drawings are required (in CAD applications, for example).

The computer moves a felt-tip pen over the paper to literally draw the required image. A typical machine can handle up to A3 paper size and have four different pen colours.

Modems are peripherals that allow computers to communicate over long telephone lines. They give microcomputers access to large mainframes and their vast storage facilities. The topic of modems is covered in Chapter 10.

8.6.3 Interrupts

If a computer is required to input data from a keyboard, we would need it to respond within, say, $0 \cdot 1$ seconds. To do this while running another program, the computer would need to look at the keyboard every $0 \cdot 1$ s, a procedure that is wasteful of computer time because the keyboard might only be used for a few minutes each hour.

Most computers include an interrupt facility which allows a device to signal a request for attention to the computer. The computer then temporarily halts its current task to run a service routine for the interrupting device.

Usually an interrupt priority is established so that less urgent interrupt service routines can themselves be interrupted by more urgent requests, as in *Figure 8.25*.

Reading a keyboard is a typical interrupt-driven task. The action of pressing a key generates an interrupt that initiates a routine that scans the keys to see which has been pressed. The interrupt service routine then takes action suitable for the depressed key.

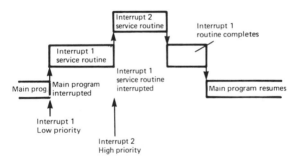

Fig. 8.25 Handling of interrupts according to priority

Graphics 8.7

Computer-generated graphics has been one of the major advances of the past decade. Applications as diverse as computer-aided design (CAD), arcade games, and graphs and charts packages for business analysis all rely on a good computer-generated display on a visual display unit (VDU). To understand the operation of computer graphics it is first necessary to understand how a television signal is produced. This background is given in Section 10.7.

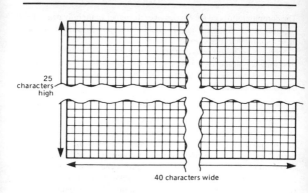

Fig. 8.26 Standard 40 × 25 character display

Before we can discuss graphics it is first necessary to describe how text is displayed. For this we will assume a standard 40 × 25 character display, as in *Figure 8.26*. We refer to this as a 40 column by 25 row display. One 8-bit computer store location can hold a number in the range 0–255 and hence represent one ASCII-coded character. To display 40 × 25 characters requires 1000 store locations. An area of memory is shared between the display logic and the computer, as shown in *Figure 8.27(a)*. To place a character on the screen, all that the computer has to do is place the correct ASCII code in the store location corresponding to the required screen position.

Figure 8.27(b) shows the scheme in more detail. Two multiplexers, MUX 1 and 2, swap the shared data and address bus between the computer (to load data) and the display logic (normal state, to display data).

Figure 8.28 shows the display logic in more detail. Characters are displayed on a dot matrix, 9 by 7 in our example. Because a TV picture is displayed a line at a time and is serial in nature, the ASCII data in the store has to be converted to a series of dots.

The heart of the circuit is the character generator ROM. This takes in data for the character (ASCII coded), and which line of the character is being displayed, and gives out the corresponding bit pattern. In the illustration, letter A (ASCII 65) is the data and we are displaying line 7, so the dot pattern is 0100010.

The dot pattern from the character generator ROM is converted to a serial bit stream via a shift register. The whole operation is controlled by a long timing chain driven by a master oscillator, which also drives the sync pulse generator. The timing chain brings data from the store via an X (horizontal, column) address and Y (vertical, row) address and provides load/shift pulses for the shift register.

Although a shared memory system (called a memory mapped display) is used on *Figures 8.26–8.28*, a VDU can also be used as a peripheral driven by a serial link. In this case the screen data store is separate from the computer store, and control characters are used to define where a character is to be placed (e.g. HOME (top left), Down 5 rows, Right 12 columns, Print 'A'). This is obviously slower.

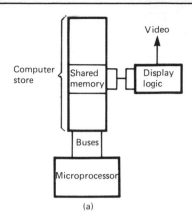

(a)

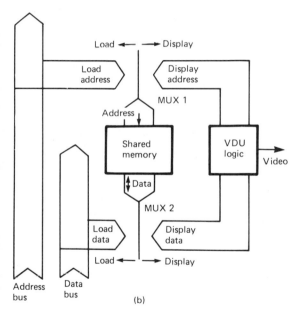

(b)

Fig. 8.27 (a) memory mapped VDU; (b) detailed diagram of memory mapped VDU

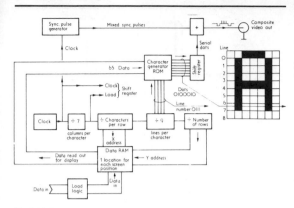

Fig. 8.28 Basic VDU block diagram

ASCII uses 128 characters but an 8-bit location can hold 0–255.
The simplest graphics schemes use the remaining 128 numbers to
define new block symbols as in *Figure 8.29*. This scheme was used on
many early microcomputers such as the TRS-80, PET etc. and is also
to be found on Teletext and Prestel displays. With imagination, very
impressive displays can be achieved. The use is still limited, however,
to the basic grid of *Figure 8.26*.

Line graphics, or high resolution graphics, allow the programmer
to control individual dots on the screen. In its highest resolution
mode, for example, the BBC Micro uses 640×256 dots. This is
approaching the limit of resolution of an average television.

In the text and so-called block graphics display of *Figures
8.26–8.28*, one location is needed per character, the dot pattern for the
display being determined by the character generator ROM. A line
graphics machine stores the *entire* screen dot pattern. This requires a
large store.

For the BBC machine, with 640×256 dots and eight bits per store
location, some 20 480 store locations are needed. This is a sizeable
reduction on a 32K machine, as the video RAM cannot be used to
store data.

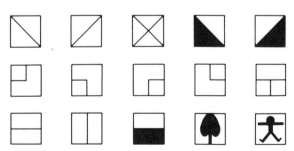

Fig. 8.29 A selection of block graphics symbols (most machines have
many graphics symbols)

Line graphics machines incorporate graphics instructions in their high level language. Typical are MOVE (X,Y), DRAW (X,Y), FILL (an enclosed area), CIRCLE (X, Y, R) and so on. These allow graphic displays to be quickly and easily constructed.

Colour adds more complications. In text and block graphic displays, the foreground and background colour for each character cell need to be defined. Section 10.7 shows how a colour picture is constructed from red, green, and blue primary colours. These three colours can be combined as pure colours to give eight colours:

R	G	B	Colour displayed
0	0	0	Black
0	0	1	Blue
0	1	0	Green
0	1	1	Cyan
1	0	0	Red
1	0	1	Magenta
1	1	0	Yellow
1	1	1	White

A single 8-bit store location can thus hold the six bits necessary to define foreground and background colour for one character cell. The two spare bits could be used for 'Bright' and 'Flashing'. A full-colour 40×25 text or block graphic display therefore requires 2000 store locations, 1000 for the text/graphics and 1000 for the colour definitions.

Teletext and Prestel use reserved control codes to change colours. Once a colour combination is defined, those colours are used until a new colour definition is sent. This keeps the store size for a 40×25 display at 1000 locations, at the loss of some ease of use. Similar control codes are used to generate flashing and double-height characters.

Colour extends the store size required for line graphics quite dramatically. To display eight colours with a 640×256 resolution display would require a staggering 81 920 locations, way beyond the addressing capability of an 8-bit micro and very expensive in memory. Stores of this (and larger) sizes are used on commercial CAD and graphics terminals, but smaller computers reduce the store requirements by having a trade-off between resolution and colour (BBC), or by restricting colour definitions to areas corresponding to one text character (Spectrum).

Store size and cost are the limiting factors in graphics. As memory ICs become cheaper and more complex the graphics capabilities of computers will improve still further.

Applications 8.8

Traditionally, computer applications have been split into three categories. The first of these is commercial computing, where large mainframe computers are used by companies such as banks, insurance offices and government organisations such as the DVLO. These applications require simple, but repetitive, calculations and vast amounts of storage for records.

The next category was scientific computing, where machines were used for complex scientific and engineering calculations. High-level languages such as FORTRAN evolved from this background. Finally, computers were used to control industrial plant, a topic covered further in Chapter 11.

The cheap microcomputer has blurred these distinctions somewhat, as the same machine can be used by a small engineering firm for design, book-keeping and playing games at home. The split of one machine/one job no longer applies.

Computers are good at storing and retrieving records so many applications are built around the so-called database. This is defined as an organised set of records. A doctor's patient records, or an estate agent's list of house details are typical databases. A database program allows records to be stored, amended, examined or searched for records meeting defined criteria.

Many computers are used for wordprocessing, where the text is displayed on a VDU screen. This allows easy correction of mistakes, simple text editing and facilities such as duplication of standard text. (This edition of the *Electronics Pocket Book* was revised on a BBC computer with the Wordwise wordprocessing program.) Standard letters can be merged with files of names/addresses on more complex wordprocessors to give 'personal' letters, all mass produced.

The business uses are legion. Stock control, invoicing, wages, VAT, customer records are all readily available. The ubiquitous spreadsheet can be used for financial modelling and prediction (and other less obvious applications; Lotus 123 is good at producing cable schedules). Graphical packages can be purchased to produce bar charts, graphs and pie charts.

Standard programs are now available for a wide range of applications; farming, plumbing, hotels, solicitors, dentists and many other professions have ready-made programs which can be bought off the shelf. It is perhaps trite, but true, to say that business applications are limited only by the imagination of the user.

Home uses are more restricted. You can use a computer to keep records, feed the fish or work the burglar alarm, but it really is not worth the effort. By all means buy a computer to learn about the subject, educate the children or play games, but be aware that for the average family with averagely complex affairs a notebook and a calculator are the best tools for keeping track of what is going on.

8.9 Future developments

Computer developments seem to hinge around three areas: cheap storage; more powerful microprocessors; and communications. Database programs rely on fast cheap storage, and these uses will undoubtedly increase as computer RAM and mass storage become larger and cheaper.

The 8-bit word size of early microprocessors was an undoubted handicap, and the norm at present is the 16-bit word. Typical of these is the Z-8000 shown in *Figure 8.30*. This device has 16 general-purpose 16-bit registers, all of which can be used to take results from

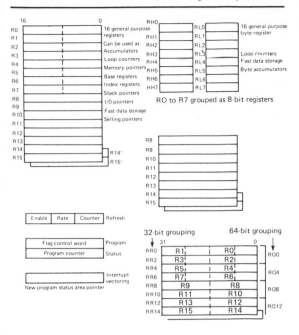

Fig. 8.30 The Z-8000 16-bit microprocessor

the arithmetic unit. They can, however, be grouped or split into 8-, 16-, 32- or 64-bit registers. The Z-8000 can address a remarkable 8 megabytes of memory, some of which is on disc (but appears to the CPU). This technique is known as virtual memory. Arithmetic functions are also upgraded; 32-bit multiplication and division are available.

The Z-8000 is by no means 'state of the art'; 32-bit microprocessors are already available, and the trend to larger words, more store addressing space and more programming facilities will continue.

One interesting development is the array processor. All computers described so far are based on the so-called Von Neumann model, which performs tasks in series. At any time a conventional computer is only obeying one instruction. An array processor does many tasks in parallel. Machines built to date utilise an array of processors (typically 64 × 64) to perform a task.

At the other end of the range, one-chip computers will become more common. Devices such as the Z-8 and TMS 1000 are true computers, with CPU, RAM and program ROM all on one IC. These are appearing in applications such as toys, white goods (washing machine programmers, for example) and intelligent instruments. Costs of these are very low, and most houses probably have a few computers without owners being aware of it.

Data communication will, however, have the most impact. Computers can already communicate via telephone lines, and it would seem that the future of computers lies in small computers on office desks linked into a network with the firm's mainframe (which need not be in the same building or even the same country). Ready access to any information is available to anyone. This could work as a force for good or for evil; which, remains to be seen.

9
Optoelectronics

Introduction 9.1

Light is an electromagnetic phenomenon, which exhibits many of the
properties of radio waves. Visible light is the part of the
electromagnetic spectrum covering wavelengths from about $0.4\ \mu m$
(violet) to $0.8\ \mu m$ (red) (400–800 nm). Optoelectronic devices cover a
far wider range than this, from the ultraviolet into the infrared. The
relevant parts of the spectrum are shown in *Figure 9.1*.

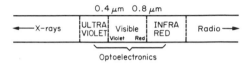

Fig. 9.1 The electromagnetic spectrum

Since there is a close family resemblance between optics and
electronics, it is not surprising that the multidisciplinary topic of
optoelectronics has become increasingly important in recent years.

Optoelectronic devices fall into three categories: (1) devices that
respond to light (sensors); (2) devices that emit light (emitters); (3)
devices that utilise light.

Sensor devices 9.2

9.2.1 Photoresistive cells (light-dependent resistors)

The simplest form of light sensor is the photoresistor, a common
example being the ORP12. Absorbed light produces electron-hole
pairs in the material of the photoresistor, causing the resistance to
decrease. A typical cell will have a resistance of around 2 MΩ in the
dark and 100 Ω in room lighting. This represents a change of 10 000
to 1, allowing very simple circuits to be used. *Figure 9.2* shows a
circuit for a light-operated relay.

Photoresistive cells normally have a peak response around 600 nm,
at the red end of the spectrum. The peak response frequency is
determined by the choice of semiconductor.

Photoresistive cells are slow devices, taking several milliseconds to
respond to step changes in light. The response is also non-linear and
temperature-dependent. They are thus best suited to on/off detector
circuits.

9.2.2 Photovoltaic devices (solar cells)

A photovoltaic device is a specially designed p–n junction which
generates a voltage across its terminals when illuminated with strong

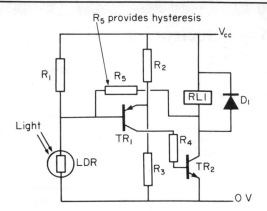

Fig. 9.2 Light-operated relay using LDR

light. The power generated is small; a single cell produces between 20 mA and 100 mA at 0·4 V in sunlight.

The open circuit voltage/incident light relationship is logarithmic, making them useful for photographic light meters. The short-circuit current/incident light response is linear, and this mode is used in some limited range light meters.

Photovoltaic cells are expensive, and this restricts their use to specialist applications. Unless a totally self-contained battery-less circuit is required, photodiodes or photoresistors are more cost-effective devices.

9.2.3 Photodiodes
The photodiode consists of a back-biased p–n junction. Under dark conditions the only current flowing will be the minority carrier leakage current. When the junction is illuminated, electron-hole pairs are generated and the current increases.

The changes in characteristics in a photodiode are not as marked as in a photoresistor. A typical photodiode will go from 10 μA dark current to around 100 μA in strong light. The photodiode is a low level, high impedance device, and requires more complex circuits than the photoresistor. *Figure 9.3* shows an operational amplifier used as a buffer amplifier.

The response of the photodiode is relatively linear, allowing it to be used in photometer applications. Its main advantage, however, is its high speed of operation. The response time of most photodiodes is under 200 ns, allowing them to be used in conjunction with high speed circuits. They are widely used in high speed tape readers and opto-isolators.

9.2.4 Phototransistors
The phototransistor can be considered as the combined transistor and photodiode shown in *Figure 9.4*. The photodiode replaces the normal base bias resistor, and the light-dependent leakage current supplies the base. This current is multiplied by the normal transistor

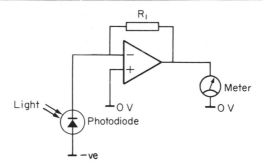

Fig. 9.3 Photodiode and amplifier

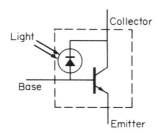

Fig. 9.4 The phototransistor

action. Unfortunately, the dark current of the diode is also multiplied, so the dark current of a phototransistor is rather high.

A typical phototransistor will have a dark current of several microamps. The current will rise to several milliamps when the device is illuminated. Although faster than photoresistors, the phototransistor is not as fast as a photodiode, and can only be used up to 100 kHz. The response is somewhat nonlinear, limiting its use to on/off detecting circuits.

9.2.5 Other devices
Theoretically, any semiconductor device can be made into a sensor. Photo-FETS, photo-darlingtons and photo-thyristors all exist, but these are rather rare.

An interesting recent development is the production of a combined photodiode and integrated circuit amplifier. These are combined in a small case and only require the two external components shown in *Figure 9.5*. These are designed for on/off applications, and are both fast and reasonably priced.

9.2.6 Comparison of devices
Table 9.1 gives a comparison of the characteristics of the four common sensor types: photoresistor, photovoltaic, photodiode and phototransistor.

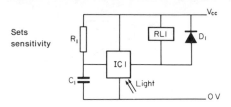

Fig. 9.5 Integrated circuit photocell

Table 9.1 *The four common sensor types*

Type	Advantages	Disadvantages
Photoresistor	Cheap Large change in characteristics Simple circuits	Temperature-sensitive Physically bulky Very slow Nonlinear
Photovoltaic	Linear or logarithmic response according to mode Can be used without external power source	Expensive Slow
Photodiode	Linear response Very fast Small size, can be used in multisensor applications (e.g. tape readers)	Small change in characteristics Low level output
Phototransistor	Can directly interface to small loads Reasonably fast	Nonlinear Temperature-sensitive

9.3 Emitters of light

9.3.1 Light-emitting diodes (LEDs)

An LED is a p–n junction diode which emits light when conducting. The mechanism by which the light is produced is somewhat complex. Basically, electron-hole pairs are formed which emit light as they recombine. Fortunately it is not necessary to have a detailed knowledge of how LEDs work in order to use them.

Electrically, an LED looks like a normal semiconductor diode having low resistance in the forward direction and high resistance in the reverse direction. The only major difference is the high forward drop of around 2 V and the low PIV of around 5 V.

An LED is a current-operated device, so it must always be operated with a series resistor (or driven from a constant current source). For most applications the current required will be between 5 mA and 30 mA. Because the eye has a logarithmic response to light, the apparent light output does not vary greatly with current once the LED has attained a reasonable intensity.

In the circuit given in *Figure 9.6(a)* the value of the series resistor, R, is given by

$$R = \frac{V - V_f}{I}$$

where V_f is the LED forward drop and I the required current. These are obtained from the data sheet.

The low PIV can present design problems. If an LED is to be driven from an a.c. source, the LED should be protected by a reverse diode, as shown in *Figure 9.6(b)*. Because the LED is being illuminated for only one half-cycle, a higher value of current is required.

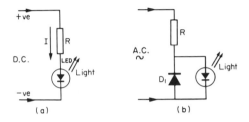

Fig. 9.6 Driving LEDs: (a) d.c. supply; (b) a.c. supply

LEDs are an almost perfect indicator lamp. They are very efficient, and run cool. Unlike normal incandescent light bulbs, they are immune to shock and vibration, have a long life and no surge current at turn-on.

LEDs can be obtained in a wide range of colours, the commonest being red, yellow and green (ideal for model railway enthusiasts). Special LEDs, working in the infrared region of the spectrum, are also available for use with photocells.

9.3.2 Incandescent bulbs

Normal lamp bulbs have almost entirely been superseded by LEDs for panel indicators. The maximum intensity available from an LED, however, does not yet match that available with bulbs. Where a high intensity is required, the designer therefore has little choice.

The life of a bulb is inherently limited to a few thousand hours. This can be extended in several ways. The first (and obvious) way is to underrun the bulb. Operating a bulb at 10–20% below its nominal voltage can double its life.

The cold resistance of a bulb is considerably lower than its hot resistance. At turn-on there is a considerable current surge which may fracture the bulb filament (and cause noise problems in the rest of the circuit). This current surge can be reduced by always keeping a small 'lamp warming' current flowing through the bulb, so that in the 'off' state it glows dimly. The absence of a current surge extends the life of the lamp considerably. *Figure 9.7* shows a typical indicator panel, with lamp warming resistors and a lamp test switch.

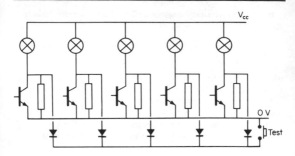

Fig. 9.7 Driving incandescent bulbs

9.3.3 Neons

The neon is a gas discharge device suitable for use with high voltages. Once common, it is now mainly used for 'mains on' indication. It is a current-operated device, and like an LED needs a series resistor. The value is obtained from the equation given for LEDs in Subsection 9.3.1. Typical values for V_f are around 100 V.

9.3.4 Liquid crystal displays

Liquid crystal displays (LCDs) are unique display devices, in that they require minimal power to operate. This makes them very popular for battery-powered devices such as calculators and digital watches.

LCDs are based on materials which exhibit regular crystal-like structures even in a liquid state. The material is normally transparent, but if an external electric field is applied, complex interactions between the internal molecules and free ions cause turbulence in the crystal. The liquid then turns an opaque milky colour.

In its simplest form an LCD cell consists of two glass plates separated by insulating spaces. The gap between the plates is filled with the liquid crystal (*Figure 9.8*). When an electric potential is applied across the plates, the cell becomes opaque.

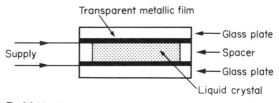

Fig. 9.8 Liquid crystal display

An LCD cell can be used in either of the two modes shown in *Figure 9.9(a)* and *9.9(b)*. *Figure 9.9(a)* is called a transmissive mode and requires an integral light source. *Figure 9.9(b)* is called a reflective mode and uses incident light. Obviously the reflective mode can only be used in good ambient light levels, but its exceptionally low current requirements (typically 1 μA) make it almost mandatory for battery-powered circuits.

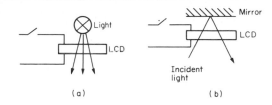

Fig. 9.9 Operating LCDs: (a) transmissive mode; (b) reflective mode

LCDs operate on a few volts, making them a natural companion to low power CMOS. Although LCDs will operate on d.c., the life expectancy is reduced by polarisation effects. This can be overcome by driving the cell segment and back-plane from a simple square wave generator. A circuit commonly used is shown in *Figure 9.10*.

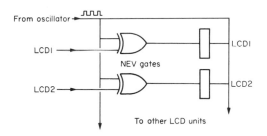

Fig. 9.10 A.C. drive to LCD units

9.3.5 Lasers
Lasers are commonly thought of as a kind of death ray, and have been described by some engineers as a problem in search of a solution. Over the past few years lasers have been emerging from the laboratories to become a useful tool for industry.

Light from a laser differs in two respects from light from a normal source. Firstly it is absolutely monochromatic; it consists of light of only one frequency. Secondly it is coherent. This term requires some explanation.

All light (because it is a form of electromagnetic radiation) is wave-like in nature. Light from conventional sources is emitted with random phase, as shown in *Figure 9.11(a)*, so even if it is monochromatic some cancellation will occur. All the light from a laser, however, is exactly in phase, as in *Figure 9.11(b)*, and reinforces rather than cancels.

Electron orbits were described in Sections 1.1–1.3. If an atom absorbs energy, say from being heated, electrons move out to larger radius orbits. The atom is then said to be in an excited state. Eventually the electrons return to a lower orbit, releasing energy in the form of a packet of light called a photon. Because the electron orbits are fixed, only certain energy gains and losses are allowed.

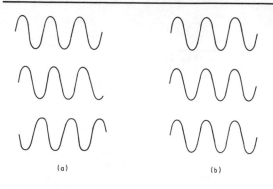

(a)   (b)

Fig. 9.11 Coherent and non-coherent light: (a) single-frequency, non-coherent light. Components out of phase, partial cancellation results; (b) coherent light. Components all in phase reinforce each other

Figure 9.12 shows the possible energy states for hydrogen; a minimum of 10 eV is required to lift it to state 1.

The frequency of the emitted light depends on the energy change, and is given by:

$$E_2 - E_1 = hf$$

where E_1 and E_2 are the energy states, f is the frequency and h is Planck's constant.

When a substance is heated, atoms are continually being excited into higher states, and falling back. Each transition, from higher state to lower state and from high states to base state, emits a different wavelength. We perceive the combination of all these as the object glowing.

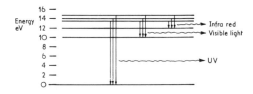

Fig. 9.12 Energy states of a hydrogen atom

Laser light, however, arises from just one transition, hence its monochromatic nature. A typical laser, shown in *Figure 9.13(a)*, consists of a ruby rod surrounded by a flash tube. The ends of the rod are machined parallel. One face is silvered to a mirror finish, and the other half-silvered.

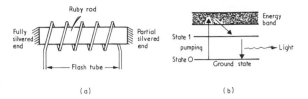

Fig. 9.13 The ruby pumped laser: (a) construction; (b) energy states for ruby

To start laser action it is necessary to get more atoms into an excited state than remain in the ground state. This is called a 'population inversion', and is obtained by firing the flash tube (called 'pumping'). Ruby has the energy states of *Figure 9.13(b)*. There is a state 1 at 1·8 eV above the base state, and several hundred closely spaced states forming a band just above state 1. Pumping takes a majority of the atoms into the energy band from where they fall back spontaneously into state 1. Here they are transiently stable.

Eventually (after a few microseconds) an atom returns to the ground state, emitting a photon as it falls. This photon strikes other excited atoms and triggers their return to the ground state. These also emit photons which are exactly in phase with the originator. A chain reaction effect now takes place, with a rapidly intensifying pulse of light reflecting up and down the tube, all photons in phase. Eventually a brief intense pulse of light, lasting about a millisecond, emerges from the half-silvered end of the tube.

The energy difference between state 1 and the ground state is 1·8 eV, which from the above equation corresponds to a wavelength of 6943 Å; that is, in the red part of the spectrum.

The ruby laser of *Figure 9.13* is called a pulsed laser, for obvious reasons. It is not possible to operate it continuously, as a permanent population inversion cannot be achieved. To get continuous laser action a four-level system is used, as in *Figure 9.14*. Atoms are excited into the high energy band, from which they fall spontaneously to state 2. Laser action takes place between states 2 and 1, from which atoms

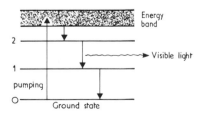

Fig. 9.14 Energy states of a continuous laser

return spontaneously to the ground state. Laser action occurs if there is a population inversion between states 2 and 1 and this is achievable with relatively low pumping energies. Continuous lasers are less powerful than pulsed lasers.

Laser applications are based on a laser beam's monochromaticity, its tight beam (a laser beam will spread by less than 0·001 radians) and its high concentration of power (because a laser beam is very narrow the energy is concentrated on a small area). Typical uses include accurate level-setting in civil engineering, and precision cutting and trimming (the lack of a flame means no contamination of the object being cut). Precision distance measurement can be made by interferometry techniques because of the monochromatic nature of laser light. Distances from a few millimetres to thousands of kilometres can be measured to a high degree of accuracy.

9.4 Applications

9.4.1 Photocells

A photocell is a device for detecting the presence (or absence) of an object by means of a light beam. Typical applications are counting of objects on a conveyor belt, burglar alarms and sequencing of automatic control.

There are basically three types of photocell:
(1) transmitter/receiver, (2) reflector, (3) incident light.

The transmitter/receiver uses a separate light source and photocell, *Figure 9.15* (*a*). The object to be separated breaks the beam. By careful design, beam lengths of over 1000 m can be obtained, although alignment can be a problem.

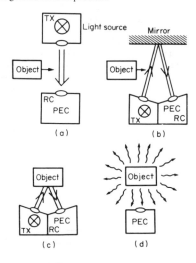

Fig. 9.15 Types of photocell: (a) TX/RC system; (b) reflective system 1; (c) reflective system 2; (d) incident light

A reflector system is shown in *Figure 9.15(b)*. The beam is a double (out and back) beam with an external mirror and an integral light emitter/sensor. This arrangement is simple to install. The mirror is usually a prismatic type (similar to rear reflectors on motor cars) to simplify alignment.

A second type of reflector system uses light reflected off the surface of the object to be detected. This is shown in *Figure 9.15(c)*. This obviously requires the object to have a reflective surface, and the range is limited to a few centimetres.

The final type of photocell uses light from the object itself, *Figure 9.15(d)*. A typical application using incident light is the tracking of red hot billets of steel in a rolling mill.

In Section 9.2 we saw that most sensor devices are temperature-sensitive, and this presents problems for the design of a stable photocell system. In addition, photocells are often required to operate in high ambient light levels that vary considerably, so a simple d.c. coupled amplifier/trigger circuit will not work reliably.

Most photocell systems use a modulated light source, usually at a frequency of a few kilohertz. This can easily be obtained by turning the transmitter on and off rapidly.

The receiver comprises an a.c. coupled bandpass amplifier tuned to the modulating frequency, followed by a rectifier and d.c. level trigger. A typical circuit is shown in *Figure 9.16*. The circuit will only respond to light modulated at the correct frequency, and the a.c. amplifier ensures that it is unaffected by temperature changes.

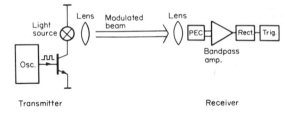

Fig. 9.16 Modulated photocell system

9.4.2 Opto-isolation

The designer of a logic scheme can face problems with noise if he is required to interface with equipment remote from the logic panel. In addition, there is always the possibility that some external fault will introduce mains voltages into the logic. These problems can be almost totally overcome by the use of opto-isolators.

An opto-isolator consists of a light-emitting diode and phototransistor coupled in one package, as shown in *Figure 9.17*. The operation is obvious, and the complete electrical isolation gives excellent protection from common mode noise.

Opto-isolators are normally used for digital inputs and outputs (e.g. push buttons, limit switches, etc.), but it is possible to use them for isolation of linear signals by encoding the analog signal into some digital form (e.g. pulse width or pulse code modulation).

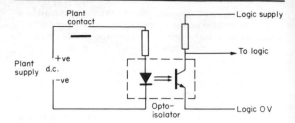

Fig. 9.17 Opto-isolation

An opto-isolator is specified by its isolation voltage (usually 1–2 kV) and its current transfer ratio, defined as the ratio of phototransistor current to LED current. This is typically 20%, although higher values can be obtained by the use of photodarlington transistors.

Opto-isolators are quite fast devices, allowing data transmission to take place at frequencies of over 100 kHz.

9.4.3 Numerical indicators

If seven light emitters are arranged in the layout in *Figure 9.18*, any number in the range 0–9 and any letter from A to F can be displayed. This is known as a seven-segment display. The spectacular increase in calculator sales has made seven-segment display manufacture a major industry, and LED and LCD arrays are available in a vast range of sizes.

Fig. 9.18 The seven-segment display

Decoders are available to decode directly from binary to the seven segments without the need for a driver stage.

With multidigit LED displays, the current requirements can be quite large. To reduce this, it is common to multiplex the display, illuminating each digit in turn. *Figure 9.19* shows a common multiplexer scheme. LCD displays also use multiplexing to reduce the number of connecting wires.

Four binary digits are applied in parallel to the multiplexer (MUX). This selects each display in turn and presents it to the binary to the seven-segment decoder. All the corresponding cathodes in each decade are driven together, but the MUX only applies the positive supply to the common anode on the display, whose data is coming from the MUX.

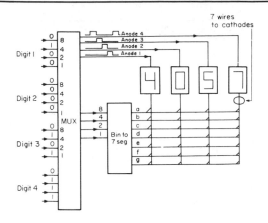

Fig. 9.19 Multiplexed display

Each display is lit in turn, although this is not apparent to the eye because of the high clock frequency (typically 15 kHz). The current consumption is reduced considerably at the expense of only a slight reduction in brilliance.

The seven-segment display only allows numerals to be displayed, along with some letters (A, C, E, F for example). Full alphanumeric displays can be obtained with the 16-segment display of *Figure 9.20(a)* or the dot matrix displays of *Figure 9.20(b),(c)*.

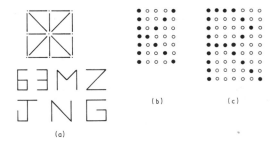

Fig. 9.20 Alphanumeric displays: (a) 16-segment display; (b) 5 × 7 matrix; (c) 7 × 9 matrix

9.4.4 Infra-red remote controllers

Most televisions and video recorders are now equipped with remote controllers that allow the viewer to change channel, adjust the volume and similar functions. These are based around the principle shown in *Figure 9.21(a)*. The keypad input is decoded to give a 5-bit code (allowing 32 options) which is transmitted by several LEDs operating in the infra-red region of the spectrum.

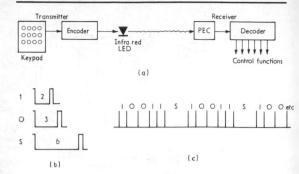

Fig. 9.21 Infra-red remote controller: (a) block diagram; (b) bit pattern for signal 10011. This is sent as long as the corresponding key is depressed

The modulated infra-red signal is received by a photocell at the set and the 5-bit code decoded to produce the desired effect. Receiver ICs can have digital outputs (for channel changing or sound muting) and analog outputs which are ramped up and down remotely (for volume and similar fine adjustments).

The 5-bit code is a form of pulse position modulation (PPM) and is shown in *Figure 9.21(b)*. There are three distinct signals, 1, 0 and S, the last one signifying that all five bits have been sent and serving as a delimiter. These three signals have a fixed interval relationship of 2:3:6 (typically 18, 27 and 54 ms). The coded signal is sent continuously as long as the keypad button is pressed.

The receiver uses a counter running at a fixed high frequency to time the interval between successive pulses, thereby identifying if a pulse is a 1, 0 or S. If it is an S the receiver has the complete 5-bit code. As a precaution this is checked against the previous code received, and only if the two are the same is action taken. In this way a high degree of security is obtained against multi-path reflections and spurious signals.

Although the technique was developed for the control of domestic equipment it is sufficiently reliable for short range remote control in many other applications.

9.5 Fibre optic communication

When a light beam passes from a less dense medium (such as air) to a more dense medium (such as glass) it is bent towards the vertical, as shown in *Figure 9.22(a)*. This effect is known as refraction. Light passing to a less dense medium (e.g. from glass to air) is also bent, as in *Figure 9.22(b)*, but as the angle increases total reflection takes place beyond a certain critical angle. For a glass-to-air transition the critical angle is about 40 degrees.

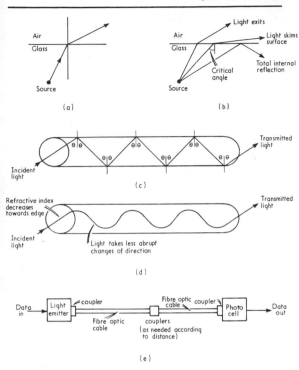

Fig. 9.22 Fibre optic communication: (a) refraction of light; (b) critical angle and total internal reflection; (c) fibre optic rod (step index); (d) graded index fibre optic cable; (e) elements of data transmission system

In *Figure 9.22(c)*, light is entering a glass rod. As the beam passes down the rod it strikes the edges, but because the angle of incidence is larger than the critical angle, internal reflection occurs and the light beam is conveyed without loss (although there will be some attenuation caused by scattering off inevitable flaws in the glass). *Figure 9.22(c)* is the simple basis of data transmission by light signals. All that is required is a modulated light source, a transparent conductor arranged to provide internal reflection and a light-sensitive receiver.

In practice, very small optical fibres (of glass or polymer material) are used in place of the glass rod. This gives a flexible 'cable' and lower losses than the simple arrangement of *Figure 9.22(c)*. The technique is called fibre optic transmission. Two types of fibre are commonly used: Step Index, which operates as in *Figure 9.22(c)* with reflection taking place at a boundary; and Graded Index, where the density varies in a uniform manner across the fibre, giving a gentler reflection, as in *Figure 9.22(d)*. Graded index fibre has a lower transmission loss but is more expensive to manufacture.

Light-emitting diodes (LEDs) are usually employed as transmitters (although low powered lasers are often employed on long distance links). Photo avalanche diodes are commonly used as receivers. Digital encoding and transmission techniques are used. *Figure 9.22(e)* shows the elements of a typical system.

There are a number of advantages in using fibre optic transmission. In theory very large bandwidths are available; up to 10 000 times higher than the highest achievable radio frequency. Fibre optic cables are physically much smaller than conventional low loss coaxial cables. There is no electromagnetic interference from the fibres, and the signal is unaffected by external interference. Finally, if a fibre cable is damaged or broken there is no risk of fire or sparking. This latter characteristic makes fibre optic cable particularly attractive for data transmission through hazardous areas in petrochemical plants and similar sites.

Losses in fibres occur from internal scattering off flaws and at bends where the angle of incidence can decrease. Minimum bending radii are determined by losses rather than physical strength. These losses are length related, and are typically 4 dB/km. Coupling losses, typically 2 dB per connection, also occur at the transmitter and receiver or where cables are jointed. In transmission systems over long distances repeaters are used.

10
Communications

Introduction 10.1

Mankind needs to communicate, and from early history various
means have been used to provide communication at a distance. With
radio, telephones, television and computer links now an integral part
of society, it would seem that our need for information is almost as
great as our need for energy.

This chapter provides a brief introduction to communications. The
subject, however, is a vast one, and any of the topics discussed could
easily be expanded to fill a book.

Line communications 10.2

10.2.1 Transmission lines

The simplest communications systems are those where the sender and
receiver are connected by a cable and a direct electrical circuit exists.
In such a system the properties of the line are very important.
Consider the circuit shown in *Figure 10.1(a)*. We have a voltage
source, a switch, a very long line and a load R_L. We require to know
what happens when we close the switch.

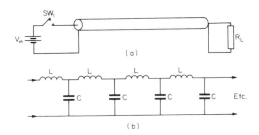

Fig. 10.1 Transmission line: (a) circuit arrangement; (b) equivalent
circuit

The line will have self-inductance and capacitance. These will be
distributed evenly along its length, so the line can be represented by
Figure 10.1(b). Analysis shows that the line will appear as a pure
resistance to the voltage source. This resistance is denoted by Z and is
called the characteristic impedance of the line. It can be shown that

$$Z = \sqrt{\frac{L}{C}} \text{ ohms}$$

where L and C are the inductance and capacitance per unit length.

Typical values for Z are 50–75 Ω for coaxial cables and 600 Ω for a twisted pair.

We can now see what happens in *Figure 10.1(a)*. When SW_1 closes, a current will flow into the line given by

$$I = \frac{E}{Z}$$

This current step passes down the line and appears at the load. If the load and the characteristic impedance are the same, a voltage E will appear across the load. If the load is greater or less than the characteristic impedance, however, the current will cause an initial output voltage larger or smaller than E. This will cause a reflection and a current step will pass back up the line to the source. Multiple reflections will occur which will get smaller until the output voltage is E.

It follows that a long line should be terminated by a load equal to the line characteristic impedance, if reflections are to be avoided. If the signal is a continuous sine wave, similar arguments again show that the line needs to be terminated for efficient transference of power. A reflection coefficient is defined as the ratio of the reflected e.m.f. to forward e.m.f., denoted by ρ. It can be shown that

$$\rho = \frac{(Z - R_L)}{(Z + R_L)}$$

In a perfect transmission line, power is transferred from the source to the load, with no attenuation. In parallel transmission lines, however, losses are caused by radiation from the line, resistance in the line and leakage effects. Loss in a line is quoted in decibels per unit length (usually 10 m) at a specific frequency. Losses increase in proportion to the square root of the frequency. If the line is not correctly terminated, losses will increase.

Transmission line effects become significant when the line length and the signal wavelength become comparable. In audio work, therefore, effects occur only on long lines, but they occur for relatively short lines at radio and video frequencies.

10.2.2 Industrial communications

The simplest communication systems in industrial complexes are those employed for point-to-point communications. These are based on simple send/receive units connected via a ring cable (*Figure 10.2*). Voltage levels on the signal cable are usually set at 0 dBm, defined as 1 mW in 600 Ω (about 0·6 V r.m.s.).

A station comprises a microphone and pre-amplifier for transmission, and a power amplifier and loudspeaker for reception. The press to talk button connects the pre-amplifier to the line and mutes the local loudspeaker to prevent 'howling'. Note that all stations except the transmitter receive the signal.

The signal lines are floating to reduce noise pick-up, and stations are transformer coupled on to the lines. At one point only, on the system, a balance potentiometer RV_1 is provided to null out any induced noise.

Industrial communications systems are very versatile, and the standardisation of a 0 dBm level makes expansion and modification easy.

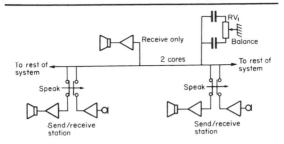

Fig. 10.2 Two-wire industrial communications system

10.2.3 Telephony

A national telephone system is probably more complex than most computer installations, but is conceptually quite simple. In reality, a telephone network is complex because of the sheer volume of equipment rather than its intricacy.

A telephone network starts with the subscriber's telephone. The circuit of a standard GPO telephone is shown in *Figure 10.3*. The unit consists of a carbon microphone, moving coil earphone, bell and dialling contacts. All telephones in an area are connected to an exchange. This allows each telephone in that area to be connected to any other. The exchange can thus be represented by the matrix of *Figure 10.4*. To make a call, one of the matrix switches is closed.

Associated with this selection is the control of bell ringing, engaged tones, and the call charging. In the majority of exchanges in the UK, the selection and control is done by electromechanical means, notably the uniselector-based Strowger system devised by an American undertaker! It would be quite easy to develop an all-electronic system, but progress is hindered by the vast capital tied up in Stowger and crossbar exchanges and any new equipment must be compatible. In addition, it has proved very difficult to provide satisfactory low levels of cross-talk with pure electronic methods, and reed relays are used for selection in most 'electronic' exchanges.

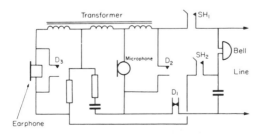

Fig. 10.3 Standard GPO telephone circuit: the transformer controls the level of own speech fed back to the earphone; SH is hook switch; $D_1 - D_3$ are dial contacts, D_1 is pulsing contact; $D_2 D_3$ mute microphone whilst dialling

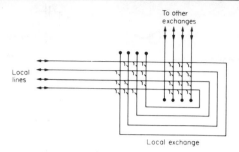

Fig. 10.4 Telephone exchange matrix

Long-distance calls are made via an exchange hierarchy, from local exchange through to main switching centres, which are totally interconnected (*Figure 10.5*). Calls are made by the shortest available routes. On local and short links the cables carry audio. On trunk lines the audio is modulated on to RF and one cable is used to carry many telephone calls. Microwave links are becoming very common for linking between main switching centres.

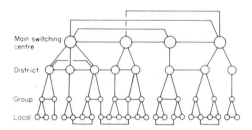

Fig. 10.5 The exchange hierarchy

10.3 Radio communication

10.3.1 Basic principles

Radio signals are an electromagnetic wave of fundamentally the same nature as light and X-rays. An electromagnetic wave is produced by a disturbance in an electrical system. The small, but rapid, motion of electrons at an atomic level produces light, whereas the large and more leisurely motion of electrons in an electric circuit produces radio waves.

Basic electrostatics shows that an electron is surrounded by an electric field which is usually represented by radiating lines of force, as in *Figure 10.6(a)*. If the electron is oscillating vertically, the electric field cannot follow instantly, and distortion in the field will radiate out from the electron, as shown in *Figure 10.6(b)*. These distortions constitute an electric wave which radiates out at the speed of light, namely 3×10^{10} cm/s.

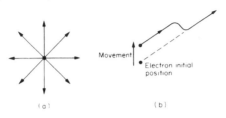

Fig. 10.6 Formation of an electric wave: (a) field surrounding an electron; (b) field distortion due to movement

Analysis of the effect mathematically is beyond the scope of this book, but it can be shown that the wave field strength is inversely proportional to the distance from the origin (unlike the static field strength, which is inversely proportional to the square of the distance). Reception of an electric wave is therefore possible over long distances.

Since the velocity of propagation is constant, it follows that the higher the frequency, the shorter the wavelength, and the relationship is given by

$$c = \lambda f$$

where c is the velocity of propagation (3×10^{10} cm/s), λ the wavelength (cm), and f the frequency (Hz).

To generate a radio wave, therefore, it is necessary to feed a high frequency alternating current into a practical radiator called an aerial.

Consider the circuit of *Figure 10.7(a)*. We have an RF generator feeding into an open-circuit transmission line. Because we have a mismatch, reflection will occur at the end of the line. If, however, the line length is exactly one-quarter of the wavelength of the generator, the reflections will arrive exactly in phase and cause resonance, as shown in *Figure 10.7(b)*. For all practical purposes the line behaves as the series LC circuit of *Figure 10.7(c)*, with the impedance at resonance being determined solely by the resistive elements of the circuit.

If we now open up the line to form a straight rod of length $\lambda/2$, as shown in *Figure 10.7(d)*, the circuit is basically unchanged, and the rod will resonate at a frequency of wavelength λ. In practice, the actual length at which resonance occurs is about 80% of the theoretical $\lambda/2$ because the rod is no longer a perfect transmission line.

The circuit of *Figure 10.7(d)* is a practical aerial, known as a dipole.

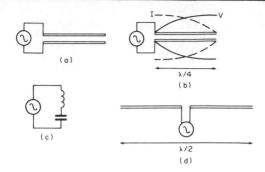

Fig. 10.7 Aerial theory: (a) transmission line; (b) resonant line; (c) equivalent circuit; (d) the half-wave dipole

Radio waves are received by an aerial similar to that used for transmission. As the electric wave passes the aerial, an e.m.f. is produced, dependent on the field strength and the aerial length. This in turn produces a current which will be a maximum when the aerial is resonant at the received frequency. The induced e.m.f. is very small (typically a few microvolts), so considerable amplification is required.

The analysis above assumes that the waves pass uninterrupted from transmitter to receiver, and by implication a line of sight path must exist between them. In practice, radio communication is possible between places on the surface of a curved earth, and reception normally occurs by a combination of three types of propagation: (1) line of sight; (2) ground waves; (3) reflections from the upper atmosphere.

Line of sight is important at higher frequencies, where other types of propagation do not occur. The range is determined mainly by the height of the transmitter and receiver, *Figure 10.8(a)*. Local dead spots are formed by buildings and hills which block high frequency radio signals, and by multiple reflections from the ground and local objects arriving in antiphase to the line of sight signal. The characteristics of high frequency line-of-sight propagation makes it very suitable for short-range mobile radios (e.g. in taxis), where it is useful to predict coverage and avoid interference with other users.

At low frequencies, propagation is mainly by the ground wave effect. The velocity of a wave close to the surface of the earth is reduced by a phenomenon known as wave drag. The effect is small, but the slight reduction in velocity causes the wavefront to bend in a similar manner to a light ray entering a block of glass, *Figure 10.8(c)*. The ground wave effect extends the range of low frequency transmitters beyond that obtainable from their theoretical line of sight.

Most long-distance communications, however, utilise reflection from layers in the upper atmosphere. At a height of around 50–100 km the gases of the atmosphere are at such a low pressure that they are permanently ionised by ultraviolet radiation from the sun causing a layer of ionised gas, called the ionosphere, to surround the earth.

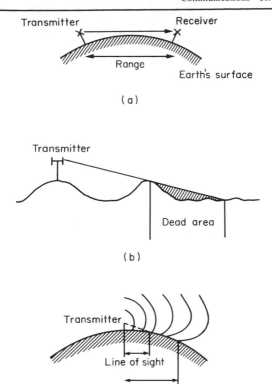

Fig. 10.8 Direct propagation of radio waves: (a) line of sight; (b) shading at VHF and UHF; (c) ground wave

The mechanism of reflection is somewhat complex, but depends largely on the angle of incidence and the operating frequency. If the operating frequency is too high (typically around 30 MHz) or the angle of incidence is too steep, the ionosphere is transparent and the signal is lost or absorbed. At shallow angles, and frequencies below 30 MHz, reflection will occur as shown in *Figure 10.9*, extending the range of the transmitter. Multiple reflections can occur between the ionosphere and the surface of the earth to give global communication.

The ionosphere is greatly affected by occurrences such as sun-spots and temperature variations, and its characteristics vary from minute to minute. The use of reflections for reliable long-distance communications is therefore somewhat of an art rather than an exact science.

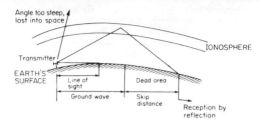

Fig. 10.9 Long-distance communication

10.3.2 Aerials

A radio wave can be polarised by adjusting the attitude of the
transmitting aerial. A signal is said to be horizontally polarised if the
lines of the electric field are horizontal and vertically polarised if they
are vertical. Polarisation is used by television stations, for example, to
improve discrimination between different transmitters.

The simple dipole described earlier will respond equally to
vertically polarised signals from all directions when mounted
vertically. This can be represented by the so-called polar diagram of
Figure 10.10(a). If the dipole is mounted horizontally, however, as in
Figure 10.10(b), for the reception of horizontally polarised signals its
response will become directional. The direction of maximum
sensitivity is at right angles to the aerial.

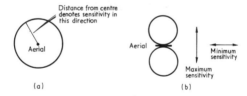

Fig. 10.10 Polar diagrams for simple dipole. Both diagrams are
viewed from above: (a) vertical dipole, equal sensitivity in all
directions; (b) horizontal dipole, directional sensitivity

A simple dipole gives a certain directionality, but for VHF and
UHF signals a very directional aerial is needed to reject spurious
signals arising from multi-path reflections. This can be provided by
the multi-element aerials of *Figure 10.11*. The addition of a reflector
gives a heart-shaped polar diagram (called a cardoid response).
Increased directionality and increased sensitivity can be obtained by
adding one or more director elements as shown. Multi-element
aerials are often called Yagi aerials, and need to be aligned according
to the polarisation of the received signal.

At the microwave frequencies used by satellites and telephone
links, the use of a parabolic dish to focus the signal onto a small
dipole becomes feasible. These give very high gain and directionality,
and will become a common back-garden sight as satellite
communications develop.

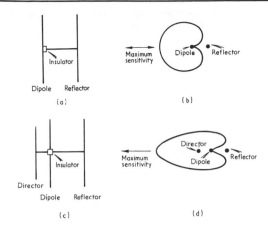

Fig. 10.11 Improving the sensitivity and directionality of a dipole:
(a) dipole plus reflector; (b) polar diagram for dipole plus reflector;
(c) addition of director element; (d) polar diagram with added director
element

Modulation 10.4

10.4.1 Introduction

A simple radio wave carries no information except its own presence.
To convey information the wave has to be modulated in some
manner. Early telegraphy carried messages by coding dots and
dashes, called Morse code after its inventor. When Morse code was
first conveyed by radio waves, two techniques were used to modulate
a carrier wave. The first method, illustrated in *Figure 10.12(a)*, used
the dots and dashes to alter the amplitude of the carrier. These
amplitude changes could be detected at the receiver and used to
reproduce the original signal. The second method, illustrated in
Figure 10.12(b), changed the frequency of the carrier, and this again
allowed reproduction of the original signal at the receiver.

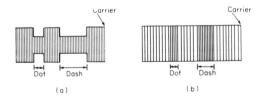

Fig. 10.12 Modulation of a carrier wave: (a) amplitude modulation;
(b) frequency modulation

The first technique is a simple form of amplitude modulation, and the second a form of frequency modulation. These two techniques can also be used to convey speech, music and other information.

10.4.2 Amplitude modulation

In amplitude modulation (AM), the information to be transmitted is used to vary the amplitude of the carrier wave. *Figure 10.13* shows a typical complex signal and the resulting modulated carrier. The amplitude of the carrier varies from almost zero to nearly twice its unmodulated level. The ratio of the change in amplitude to the unmodulated level is called the depth of modulation. Normally the modulating circuit is designed to limit the modulation depth to 80% on peaks, giving an average level of around 30%.

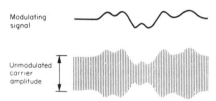

Fig. 10.13 Amplitude modulation

An amplitude-modulated wave can be represented by

$$e = (E_0 + E_1 \sin \rho t) \sin \omega t$$

where ω is 2π times the carrier frequency, ρ is 2π times the modulation frequency, E_0 is the amplitude of the carrier, and E_1 is the amplitude of the modulating signal. The ratio E_1/E_0 is the modulation depth, represented by m.

If the above equation is expanded we get

$$e = E_0 \sin \omega t + \frac{E_1}{2} \cos (\omega - \rho)t - \frac{E_1}{2} \cos (\omega + \rho)t$$

An amplitude-modulated wave thus consists of the original carrier $E_0 \sin \omega t$ and two side frequencies: one above and one below the carrier.

If the modulating frequency is a complex waveform such as speech or music, it will contain a range of frequencies, and the resulting modulated waveform will consist of the carrier plus bands of side frequencies above and below the carrier frequency. These are known as sidebands and their width depends on the components of the modulating waveform.

Speech to telephone standards, for example, covers a frequency range from 300 Hz to 3 kHz. A 200 kHz carrier modulated with speech will occupy a band of frequencies from 197 kHz to 203 kHz. The presence of the sidebands in an amplitude-modulated waveform makes it necessary to separate frequencies on different transmitters to avoid interference. A minimum spacing of 6 kHz is necessary for speech, and a channel spacing of 12·5 kHz is normally used.

The power in a sine wave is proportional to the square of the amplitude. For an amplitude-modulated waveform, therefore,

$$P \propto E_0^2 + \frac{E_1^2}{4} + \frac{E_1^2}{4}$$

or

$$P \propto E_0^2 + \frac{E_1^2}{2}$$

Since $m = E_1/E_0$, we can write

$$P \propto E_0^2 \left(1 + \frac{m^2}{2}\right)$$

We saw above that a typical value for m is $0\cdot3$. The value of $m^2/2$ is $0\cdot045$, so less than 5% of the transmitted power is being used to convey information. AM is not an efficient way to use a carrier wave, and improved techniques such as single sideband will be discussed later.

10.4.3 Frequency modulation

In frequency modulation (FM), the amplitude of the carrier is kept constant, but the frequency is varied by the modulating signal (*Figure 10.14*). The frequency shift is proportional to the instantaneous amplitude of the modulating signal. If, for example, we modulate a 100 MHz carrier by a 1 V 1 kHz sine wave, the carrier frequency will swing 25 kHz, say, either side of 100 MHz 1000 times per second. If the amplitude of the signal is increased to 2 V, the carrier will swing 50 kHz, but still at the same rate.

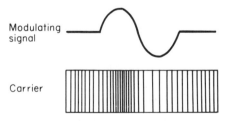

Fig. 10.14 Frequency modulation

The shift in frequency caused by the modulating signal is known as the deviation. In most FM applications a peak deviation of 75 kHz is used (corresponding to peak amplitude).

A frequency-modulated signal can be represented by

$$e = E_0 \sin(\omega t + m \sin \rho t)$$

where ω is 2π times the carrier frequency, ρ is 2π times the modulating frequency, and m is the modulation index, defined as the ratio of the deviation to the modulation frequency ($\Delta f/f$).

Analysis of a frequency-modulated waveform is somewhat complex, requiring the use of Bessel functions and other higher mathematical techniques. For most practical purposes, however, the sidebands can be taken as $\pm(\Delta f + f_m)$, where Δf is the deviation and f_m the maximum modulating frequency.

The information in an FM signal is carried in the frequency of the carrier. Interference from external noise and other transmitters generally causes amplitude variations in the carrier. If the signal is passed through a limiting stage in the receiver, these variations will be removed, but the frequency variations will be retained. FM thus has excellent noise rejection, provided the signal strength is sufficient to operate the limiter in the receiver.

10.4.4 Phase modulation
In phase modulation the phase of the carrier is varied by the modulating signal. Since phase modulation implies instantaneous FM, and vice versa, these two forms of modulation are interchangeable. In practice, phase modulation is easier to achieve than true frequency modulation.

10.4.5 Single sideband
In Subsection 10.4.2 we saw that less than 5% of the power of an amplitude-modulated carrier is used to convey information. Most commercial communication transmitters (other than those for broadcasting) suppress one of the sidebands and the actual carrier. This gives improved utilisation of the transmitted power and reduced bandwidth. This mode of operation is known as single sideband (SSB).

The carrier has to be reinserted at the receiver, and it must match the transmitter in both frequency and phase. Reinsertion of the carrier is simplified if the carrier is not totally suppressed at the transmitter.

SSB is an efficient method of implementing AM, at the expense of receiver complexity. It is therefore used for commercial communications, but it is not generally suitable for domestic broadcasting.

10.5 Transmitters

A radio transmitter can be represented by the block diagram of *Figure 10.15*. The carrier frequency is generated by an oscillator. In most communication applications, frequency stability is very important, and crystal oscillators are widely used.

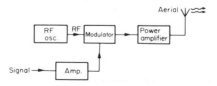

Fig. 10.15 Block diagram of radio transmitter

The modulation signal is amplified, then applied to a modulating stage. AM is usually obtained by varying the collector voltage of an RF stage; a typical circuit is shown in *Figure 10.16*. In simple transmitters the modulator and oscillator are sometimes combined as one stage, but this does lead to poor frequency stability.

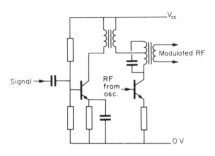

Fig. 10.16 Amplitude modulator

The modulation signal is amplified, then applied to a modulating stage. AM is usually obtained by varying the collector voltage of an RF stage: a typical circuit is shown in *Figure 10.16*. In simple transmitters the modulator and oscillator are sometimes combined as one stage, but this does lead to poor frequency stability.

FM is more difficult to achieve. The simplest way is to utilise a voltage-controlled oscillator. The frequency can then be varied by the use of a varicap diode in a tuned LC circuit. This technique is not suitable, however, for applications where the stability of a crystal-controlled oscillator is needed.

It was mentioned in Subsection 10.4.4 that for most practical purposes phase modulation and FM can be considered interchangeable. Phase modulation is relatively easy to achieve, and a typical circuit is shown diagrammatically in *Figure 10.17(a)*. A crystal

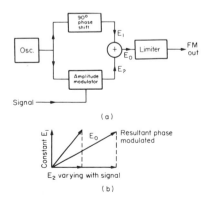

Fig. 10.17 Phase modulation: (a) block diagram; (b) circuit operation

oscillator goes to a 90° phase shift circuit to produce E_1, and through a conventional amplitude modulator to produce E_2 in phase with the original oscillator output. There is thus a 90° phase shift between E_1 and E_2. These voltages are added, the resulting voltage E_0 being produced as shown on the vector diagram, *Figure 10.17(b)*. As E_2 is modulated, the phase of E_0 with respect to E_2 will vary. E_0 is thus phase modulated by the modulating signal. AM is introduced as well, but this is removed by succeeding stages.

It is often convenient to operate the oscillator and modulator at relatively low frequencies, then utilise frequency multiplier stages to obtain the correct carrier frequency. In FM transmitters, the deviation will be increased by the same factor as the frequency. A class C amplifier introduces severe distortion, and the output is hence rich in harmonics. If a tuned circuit, resonant at the required harmonic, is used as the collector load, the class C amplifier can be used as a frequency multiplier.

Finally we have a power amplifier stage, which drives into the low impedance of the aerial. Current flowing in the aerial then produces electromagnetic waves which are radiated as described in earlier sections.

10.6 Receivers

The essential portions of a radio receiver are shown in *Figure 10.18*. The incoming RF induces a small voltage in the aerial, typically a few microvolts, and this must be amplified considerably. The signal is then obtained from the carrier by a demodulator stage, and then amplified to the required level.

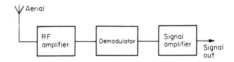

Fig. 10.18 Receiver block diagram

RF amplifiers are described in Subsection 4.6.4. They are required to amplify only a narrow band of frequencies and reject all others. The band of frequencies must, however, be sufficiently wide to pass the sidebands described in Section 10.4. A simple fixed frequency RF amplifier will thus consist of several successive RF stages.

Problems occur, however, if the receiver has to tune over several frequencies. With a simple multistage RF amplifier, each stage will have to be tuned, and it is both difficult and expensive to achieve accurate matching between the stages. Most radio receivers overcome these problems by the use of the superheterodyne techniques shown in *Figure 10.19*.

The received signal at frequency f_1 is amplified by a broadband amplifier and mixed with a frequency f_2 from an oscillator. The

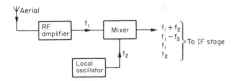

Fig. 10.19 The superheterodyne receiver

output from the mixer contains component frequencies of $(f_1 + f_2)$ and $(f_1 - f_2)$, with the original modulation (be it FM or AM) preserved. The mixer stage is followed by a multistage RF amplifier tuned to one particular frequency. This is known as the intermediate frequency amplifier (IF amp.), and is commonly tuned to 465 kHz for receivers up to HF and 10·7 MHz for VHF and higher frequencies.

The IF amplifier will amplify all aerial signals which combine with the local oscillator to produce the IF frequency. There will be two frequencies which meet this criteria; $(f_2 + \text{IF})$ and $(f_2 - \text{IF})$. These will be separated by $2 \times \text{IF}$, and the first-stage RF amplifier is designed to pass one frequency only. Tuning of the receiver is thus obtained by varying the frequency of the local oscillator f_2, and by coarse tuning of the first-stage RF amplifier. There is no tracking problem, as the RF amplifier stage can be designed to pass quite a wide band of frequencies.

The oscillator and mixer are shown separately in *Figure 10.19* for simplicity, although they are often combined in one stage. *Figure 10.20* shows a typical self-oscillating mixer. Tuning is done by capacitor C_1 which is ganged to the capacitor C_2 in the preceding RF stage. The performance of a self-oscillating mixer is not as good, however, as the separate circuits of *Figure 10.19*.

The output from the IF amplifier is still a modulated carrier, and a demodulator stage is necessary to extract the signal. The demodulation of an AM signal is quite straightforward, and can be

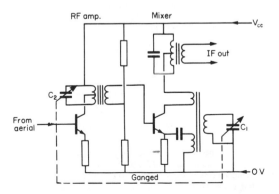

Fig. 10.20 Self-oscillating mixer

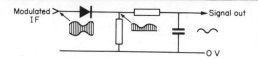

Fig. 10.21 AM demodulator

achieved with the simple diode circuit of *Figure 10.21*. The signal is
obtained by filtering of the half-wave rectified carrier. This circuit is
sometimes referred to as a detector stage.

The demodulation of an FM signal is somewhat more complex,
and there are several circuits in common use. The simplest circuit (but
not the most common) is the double-tuned discriminator shown in
Figure 10.22(a). The two secondary circuits are tuned above and
below the IF, and are connected in opposition, as shown in *Figure
10.22(b)*. These combine to produce an output which has a linear
response to frequency either side of the IF. The circuit will, however,
respond to AM, and it must be preceded by a limiter stage if the full
advantage of FM is to be realised.

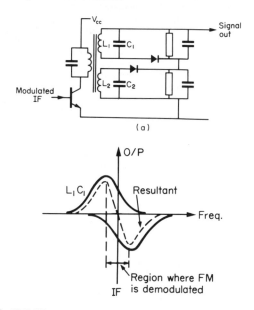

Fig. 10.22 FM demodulator: (a) circuit diagram; (b) circuit response

The commonest FM demodulator is the ratio detector, one version
of which is shown in *Figure 10.23(a)*. The circuit utilises a transformer
with a tuned primary and secondary, and an untuned tertiary
winding L_3. When a tuned transformer is at resonance, it can be
shown that there is a 90° phase shift between primary and secondary
voltages. As the frequency moves away from resonance, this phase

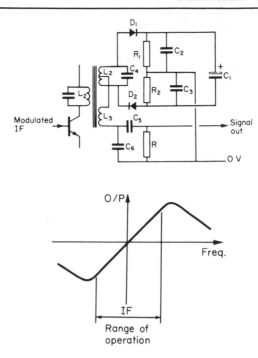

Fig. 10.23 The ratio detector: (a) circuit diagram; (b) circuit response

shift increases or decreases dependent on the direction the frequency moves.

The voltage across L_3 is in phase with the primary voltage across L_2, and L_3 is connected to the centre top of L_1. When the carrier is unmodulated, the centre tap of L_1 and the junction of R_1 and R_2 will be at the same potential. If the carrier moves away from the centre frequency, the phase on L_1 will alter, and the voltage on L_3 will add to the voltage on one-half of L_1 and subtract from the voltage on the other half. The circuit is no longer balanced, and the modulating signal is produced across R_3. Full analysis of the circuit requires quite complex mathematics, and as such is beyond the scope of this book. The response of the circuit is shown in *Figure 10.23(b)*.

The RF carrier is rectified by D_1 and D_2 to produce a d.c. voltage across C_1 proportional to the carrier amplitude. C_1 and R_1, R_2 are chosen to have a long time constant, so the circuit is fairly insensitive to sudden amplitude changes caused by noise. The ratio detector thus acts as a limiter circuit as well as a demodulator.

The RF signal at an aerial can vary from a few microvolts to several millivolts according to the distance from the transmitter and local obstructions. In a simple radio receiver this will be reflected in the signal strength from the demodulator, particularly so for AM. It is essential therefore, that some form of automatic gain control (AGC) is incorporated in a practical receiver.

The gain of a transistor amplifier can be controlled by altering the base potential. A typical IF stage with AGC is shown in *Figure 10.24*. Diode D_1 produces a d.c. voltage on C_1 proportional to the RF level at the output of the IF stage. As the voltage increases due to an increase in the signal at the aerial, the voltage on C_1 becomes more negative, reducing the gain of TR_1 to compensate.

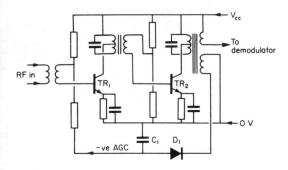

Fig. 10.24 AGC circuit

An alternative method which is sometimes used is shown in *Figure 10.25*. Diode D_1 produces a positive voltage proportional to the IF output. As the IF output increases, the base potential rises, and TR_1 passes more current. The d.c. voltage across R_2 increases, and the collector emitter voltage across TR_1 falls. The fall in collector emitter voltage reduces the gain of TR_1, again compensating for the change.

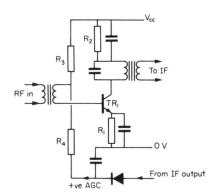

Fig. 10.25 Alternative AGC circuit

Television 10.7

10.7.1 Scanning

Before a picture can be transmitted over a cable or radio link, the
picture must be converted into an electrical form. Conceptually the
simplest way to do this would be to have an array of photocells,
amplifiers, cables and lamps connected together as shown in *Figure
10.26*. Obviously, however, such a scheme although simple to
understand would be prohibitively expensive to install and almost
impossible to maintain.

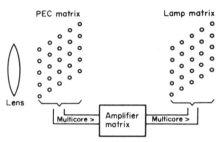

Fig. 10.26 Crude TV system

The picture in a television or facsimile system is therefore scanned
in a manner similar to the one in *Figure 10.27*, to turn it into a serial
electrical signal. It will be seen that the picture is effectively turned
into lines, and the scanning is achieved by the application of
horizontal and vertical movements to a scanning spot. In facsimile
systems the scanning can be quite slow, but in a TV system the scan
must be sufficiently fast to avoid flicker. In the British TV system, 625
lines are used, and one complete field is drawn 50 times a second (this
is modified somewhat by interlacing, which is described in Subsection
10.7.4).

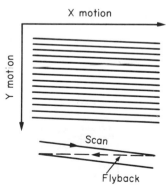

Fig. 10.27 Scanning

10.7.2 Camera tubes

There are many camera tubes in use, but the simplest to understand is the vidicon, which is shown in *Figure 10.28*. The tube consists of an electron gun and a photosensitive target covered in a thin, optically transparent coating of aluminium. The operation of the target is actually quite complex, but for a simple analysis it can be considered as being a photoresistive material. The resistance from the target connection to any point on the rear of the target depends on the illumination falling on the front of that point.

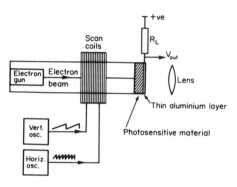

Fig. 10.28 The vidicon tube

The electron gun emits a narrow beam of electrons, and sawtooth voltages are applied to vertical and horizontal scan coils, causing the beam to scan across the target in a manner similar to that in *Figure 10.27*.

As the beam passes across the target, the beam current will vary with the instantaneous resistance of the target, and will follow the illumination on the target face, as shown in *Figure 10.29*. The load resistor R_L in *Figure 10.28* turns these current variations into voltage variations which can be amplified to a reasonable level for transmission.

The beam moves across the screen at a steady speed, followed by a quick flyback to start the next line. Simultaneously, the beam is moving down the screen at a steady speed, followed by a quick flyback to the top to start the next field. Magnetic deflection coils are used to deflect the beam; hence sawtooth-shaped currents are required from the vertical and horizontal oscillators in *Figure 10.28*.

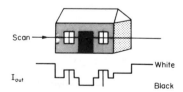

Fig. 10.29 Operation of camera tube

10.7.3 Synchronisation

The receiver can be many miles away from the camera, and in addition to the serial picture information it must also be told when to start a new line and when to start a new field. This process is known as synchronisation.

This could be done by utilising three separate signals, as shown in *Figure 10.30(a)*, one for the video and one each to convey a pulse each time we start a new line or field. These pulses are called sync pulses.

This can be simplified slightly by remembering that line sync pulses occur much faster than field pulses. If the field sync pulse is made much broader than the line sync pulse, they can be combined in one signal and separated again at the receiver. The resulting signal is known as mixed syncs, and is shown in *Figure 10.30(b)*.

From this it is easy to add the sync pulses to the video below the level defined as black, as shown in *Figure 10.30(c)*. The combined video/sync signal is known as composite video, and is the signal usually transmitted in domestic and closed-circuit TV. At the receiver a simple level splitter circuit will separate the video and sync signals.

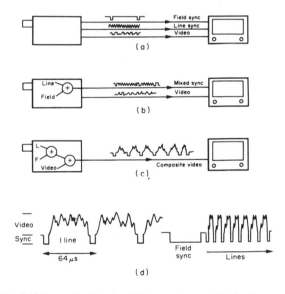

Fig. 10.30 Composite video signal: (a) separate syncs; (b) mixed syncs; (c) composite video; (d) video signal

10.7.4 Interlacing

A TV signal consists of a rapidly changing voltage, and consequently contains frequencies from d.c. to several megahertz. It can be shown that to transmit a 625-line picture at 50 frames per second, a bandwidth in excess of 10 MHz would be required.

The bandwidth can be reduced to around 5 MHz if a compromise called interlacing is used. In a 625-line interlaced picture, 312·5 lines are transmitted every field, two complete fields being needed to transmit a complete picture. The two half-fields slot together, as shown in *Figure 10.31*, and persistence of vision eliminates any flicker.

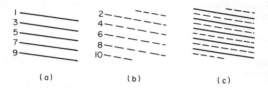

Fig. 10.31 Interlaced TV picture

10.8 Television receiver

A TV signal can be conveyed by cable or modulated on to a carrier for transmission. We saw above that a TV signal has a bandwidth of around 5 MHz, so if normal double-sideband AM was used an allocation of about 11 MHz would be needed.

Broadcast 625-line TV is transmitted in the UHF band (420MHz to 480 MHz) on an 8 MHz channel. The video signal is amplitude modulated with suppressed carrier and one vestigial sideband (*Figure 10.32*). The sound is frequency modulated on a carrier 6 MHz away from the main video carrier.

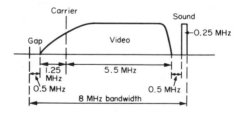

Fig. 10.32 UK broadcast TV standard

A block diagram of a 625-line receiver is shown in *Figure 10.33*. The picture is produced on a CRT which is scanned in the same way and at the same frequency as the camera tube. The video signal is used to vary the intensity of the electron beam in the tube, and hence the instantaneous brightness on the tube face.

The early stages of the receiver follow the basic ideas outlined in Section 10.6. Because of the large bandwidth of the TV signal, an IF of around 30 MHz is used. The signal from the video detector

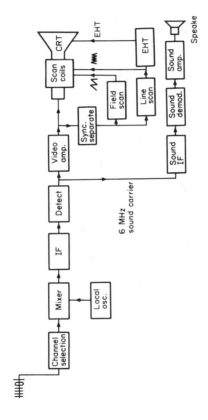

Fig. 10.33 625-line TV block diagram

contains both the unmodulated video and the 6 MHz modulated sound carrier. The sound carrier has its own IF, demodulator and amplifier. The video is further amplified and applied to the cathode of the CRT to control the electron gun.

A simple level splitter extracts the sync signals from the video, and the line and field sync pulses are separated by the circuit of *Figure 10.34*. The line and field oscillators are free-running and are controlled by the sync pulses. This technique avoids problems with synchronisation if the occasional pulse is missed due to noise.

The tube final anode needs an EHT of around 15 kV. In early receivers this was derived via a transformer direct from the mains supply. In modern receivers, it is derived from an overwind on the line output transformer which produces the EHT more efficiently and with greater safety.

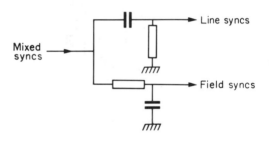

Fig. 10.34 Sync separation

10.9 Colour television

The subject of colour television is rather complex, and even an introduction would fill a book. The treatment given here can only outline the most basic philosophy, and the reader is referred to the many books on the subject for more details.

Colour TV is based on the principle of colour addition. Any colour can be obtained by the addition of the three primary colours, red, green and blue, in the correct proportions. Yellow, for example, is obtained by the addition of red and green. This mixing should not be confused with the mixing of paint colours, which works on colour subtraction.

Phosphors are available for use in CRTs which will emit red, green and blue light, allowing a three-gun colour tube to be made. The commonest colour tube is the shadow-mask type, which was designed in the USA. Red, green and blue phosphor spots are arranged in triads, and a metal shadow mask is placed behind the tube face such that the beam from the red gun only strikes red dots, and so on.

The colour camera must have three tubes, sensitive to red, green and blue. In practice, four tubes are used, the fourth producing a normal monochrome signal to assist with compatibility discussed below. In a closed circuit colour TV there is little problem; the red camera tube goes through an amplifier in the camera, down its own cable, through an amplifier in the monitor to the red gun. In all, three signal cables (RGB) and one sync cable are needed, and this arrangement is sometimes used. This approach is, however, totally unsuited to domestic colour TV.

A domestic colour TV system has to meet some very difficult criteria:

(1) It must not increase the 8 MHz bandwidth allocated for monochrome transmissions.

(2) It must be compatible, i.e. a colour broadcast must produce a satisfactory monochrome picture on a monochrome set.

(3) There must be reverse compatibility, i.e. a monochrome broadcast must produce a satisfactory monochrome picture on a colour set.

These requirements seem to be impossible, but a reasonable compromise can be achieved. The eye is not as sensitive to colour variation as it is to luminance variation, and as a result the colour information can be transmitted in far less detail. Colour TV schemes, in general, use the normal 5·5 MHz bandwidth for the luminance and a 1 MHz bandwidth for the colour information. This approximates to the process of painting colour on to a black and white photograph.

There are many schemes that have been proposed for the transmission of colour TV, e.g. NTSC, PAL and SECAM. These differ in detail, but all utilise the basic philosophy outlined below.

The luminance signal is, in effect, the normal monochrome signal and this is modulated on the video carrier in the normal manner. The colour information is modulated on to a subcarrier of 4·43 MHz and this modulated carrier is transmitted along with the video. The modulated carrier would appear as fine patterning on a monochrome picture, but the effect is reduced by a careful choice of the colour subcarrier. Analysis of a normal monochrome picture shows that the component frequencies are grouped around multiples of the line frequency. The colour subcarrier is chosen such that the colour component frequencies interleave the luminance component frequencies with little or no interaction. The frequency allocations of a colour TV signal are shown in *Figure 10.35(a)* and *10.35(b)*.

We have not described how the colour information is modulated on to the colour subcarrier. At first sight it might be thought that we need to encode all three colours – red, green and blue. In fact we only need two, since the luminance is the sum of all three, and with any two transmitted the third can be derived by subtraction from the luminance signal.

In practice, red and blue are chosen and colour difference signals $(R - Y)$ and $(B - Y)$ are modulated on to the carrier, where Y is the luminance signal. These colour difference signals are sometimes called V and U, respectively. The V and U signals are amplitude modulated on to the colour carrier, and to allow separation at the receiver a technique called quadrature modulation is used. The V and U signals are modulated on to two carriers which are identical in frequency but shifted in phase by 90°. The two carriers are summed to produce the modulated subcarrier. This process suppresses the carrier, so the modulation consists purely of sidebands and will be completely absent in a monochrome picture.

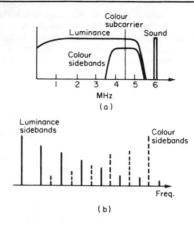

Fig. 10.35 Broadcast colour TV: (a) frequency allocation of colour carrier; (b) interlacing of luminance and colour sidebands

Obviously this leads to considerable complexity in the receiver, as a local oscillator is needed to demodulate the colour signals, and this oscillator must match the transmitter subcarrier in both frequency and phase. Phase variations can occur from multi-path reflections, and in the original NTSC system used in the USA these variations appeared as changes in hue. The UK system, PAL, includes modifications to overcome phase errors.

PAL stands for Phase Alternate Line, which describes, to some extent, the operation. The phase of the $R-Y$ subcarrier and the colour burst is shifted by 180 degrees on alternate lines, and the information on successive line pairs averaged out. This averaging (which involves a 64 μs delay line store) causes phase errors to cancel. The PAL system thus does not suffer from phase-induced colour changes.

The French SECAM system uses a totally different principle from NTSC and PAL. Colour information is not transmitted simultaneously but sequentially, as two colour difference signals $(R-Y)(B-Y)$ which are modulated onto a subcarrier on alternate lines. These are stored in delay lines then algebraically manipulated to give the RGB signals as before. SECAM stands for *Séquential Couleur à Mémoire*, and like PAL is not affected by phase shift errors.

10.10 **Stereo radio**

Compatibility is an important in stereo radio as it is in colour TV. A stereo broadcast must be received normally on a monophonic receiver, and a stereo receiver must be able to receive a monophonic broadcast.

Stereo broadcasting is normally limited to FM transmissions on

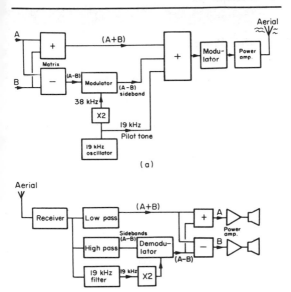

Fig. 10.36 Principles of stereo broadcasting: (a) stereo transmitter; (b) stereo receiver

the VHF bands, and is based on the system devised by the Zenith and General Electric Corporation. The basic system for transmission is shown in *Figure 10.36(a)* and that for reception in *Figure 10.36(b)*.

The two stereo signals are denoted by A and B, and sum and difference signals (A + B) and (A − B) are produced by the matrix circuit. The sum signal (A + B) is the normal monophonic signal. The difference signal (A − B) is amplitude modulated on to a 38 kHz carrier by a modulator which suppresses the carrier leaving the sidebands. The 38 kHz is derived from a 19 kHz oscillator which is combined with the (A + B) signal and the sidebands of the 38 kHz carrier modulated with the (A − B) signal.

At the receiver, the (A + B) signal and the (A − B) sidebands are separated by low pass/high pass filters and the 19 kHz pilot tone is used to generate the original 39 kHz subcarrier. The (A − B) signal is demodulated by a synchronous detector, and then the original A and B signals are obtained by addition and subtraction of the (A + B) and (A − B) signals.

Compatibility is obtained, since monophonic receivers will reject the 19 kHz pilot tone and the (A − B) sidebands which are outside the audio bandwidth. Reverse compatibility exists, since the (A − B) signal will be zero in a monophonic broadcast, and the 19 kHz pilot tone will be absent. Both speakers will then correctly reproduce the monophonic signal.

10.11 **Satellite communications**

The advent of satellite communications will probably have as large an impact on society as the arrival of cheap computing. Communications no longer rely on physical cable, and as a result there is not a single place on the globe that is out of reach. News can be instantly reported from anywhere, by news reporters with satellite transceivers that can be carried in the boot of an estate car. International telephone, telex and television links no longer rely on vulnerable and channel-restricted undersea cables. Great benefit to mankind has come from satellite applications in meteorology and agriculture. More sinister military applications have inevitably arisen, from overt spying to satellite-borne weapons and 'Star Wars'.

Any object in orbit around the earth has two forces acting on it, as shown in *Figure 10.37*. Gravity tries to return the object to earth, and centrifugal force tries to keep the object travelling in a straight line away from earth. When an object is in orbit these two forces balance. There is an obvious relationship between the speed of the object and the distance from the earth at which it will attain a stable orbit; the faster the speed, the further out it will travel. Also related to the speed and radius of the orbit is the period of the orbit. An object just grazing the atmosphere, for example, has a speed of around 30 000 km/hr and a period of about 80 minutes.

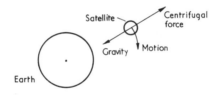

Fig. 10.37 Forces on the satellite, and the geostationary orbit

If the speed of an object is chosen to give an orbit of radius 35 880 km, the period of the orbit increases to 24 hours. As the satellite is now circling the earth at the same speed as the earth itself is rotating, it will remain over the same spot on the surface of the globe. Such a satellite is said to be in a geostationary orbit. A geostationary satellite views about 40% of the surface of the globe, and is therefore an ideal platform for a communications relay station. In theory the entire globe can be covered by three satellites.

Communication between ground and a satellite is essentially line of sight, and is largely unaffected by distance if tight-beamed signals are used. There is therefore little difference in cost between low orbit (non-synchronous) satellites and those in geostationary orbits. Low orbit satellites need lower launch velocities, however, and are cheaper to place in orbit. Satellite communications are consequently split between multiple satellite low orbit systems (with a satellite rising above the horizon to take over from its predecessor, which is just setting) and pure geostationary systems. As launching costs decrease, geostationary systems are predominating.

Three frequency bands are currently used for satellite communications: 6/4 GHz (0·5 GHz bandwidth) for commercial telecommunications; 14/11 GHz (again 0·5 GHz bandwidth) for television and telecommunications); and 30/20 GHz (with 2·5 GHz bandwidth) for telecommunications. In each case the higher frequency is used for the ground to satellite link, and the lower for the return signals. Interference between satellites is avoided by allocation of position in the 'sky'.

Intelsat V (launched in 1979) is a typical communications satellite. It operates in the 14/11 GHz and 6/4 GHz bands and can handle 12 000 telephone circuits as well as two colour TV channels. 1·2 kW of power is provided by solar panels.

Military and meteorological satellites are usually in non-synchronous orbits. Of particular interest are polar orbits, which allow coverage of the whole globe as the earth progressively rotates below the satellite. Weather satellites produce TV pictures of the earth in the visible and infra-red regions of the spectrum which are transmitted back to earth for analysis.

The TV pictures are usually produced by a mechanical scanning mirror system rather than a conventional TV tube. The mirror scans a strip across the earth's surface, and the picture is built up by the slow forward movement of the satellite with respect to the earth. A line scan rate of 120 lines per minute is common. Typical resolution is about 1 km, which is adequate for tracking weather detail. Pictures are continuously transmitted to earth, usually in the 136–138 MHz band. Some weather satellites are also equipped for a Search and Rescue (SAR) role, to monitor distress frequencies and assist rescue services.

Cellular radio 10.12

Two-way radio communication with motor vehicles has been possible for many years, but its use has been rather limited. There are many reasons for this. Mobile communications, usually in the 90 MHz and 168 MHz regions of the VHF band, and the 460 MHz region of the UHF band, have been tied to a single fixed base station. The driver can only communicate with one place, although the base station can connect him into the telephone network. True person-to-person communication is not possible, and the involvement of the manned base station at all times is inconvenient.

Base stations and mobiles also have to be relatively high powered to give reasonable coverage, and as a result there is a shortage of frequencies. Shared frequencies are not unknown, and in many areas it is not possible to obtain a mobile licence, purely on the grounds that the authorities are unable to allocate a frequency.

The final problem is ease of use. Mobile radios with a base station operate as a simplex unit; only one end can speak at once (a press-to-talk button is needed). While this might not seem a great restriction, in practice it imposes a need for discipline on the users that can be frustrating. With more than one mobile under the control of a base station, the need for disciplined procedures becomes even more critical to avoid clashes between users (and the banshee wail that occurs when two transmitters operate at the same time).

As a result of the above restrictions, mobile car transceivers, with a few exceptions, have been limited to public authorities (ambulance and fire services), taxi firms and organisations such as steel works or petrochemical plants which need to communicate with vehicles over a large site.

A new technology (or rather an updating of an old idea) called cellular radio promises to bring true mobile communication that is as easy to use as a telephone. Person-to-person calls are possible, with direct dialling into and from the telephone network and no need for a manned base station.

Cellular radio is built around the idea of frequency sharing. If transmitter power is limited, it is possible for transmitters in quite close proximity to share a common frequency. The idea is used, for example, in the allocation of TV channels. Cellular radio uses a network of very low powered stations, as in *Figure 10.38*, to cover a given area. Each transmitter covers a cell (hence the name). Depending on the type of area, cells can be from 1 to 12 miles in diameter.

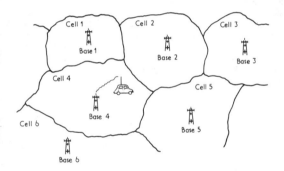

Fig. 10.38 Cellular radio. The car is moving from Base 4. It is monitored by Bases 1, 2 and 5. When the quality of signal at one of these is better than that at Base 1 a handoff to a new base (probably 2) occurs automatically

A user is not allocated a specific frequency, but has access to all the available frequencies in his area. A control channel is used to initiate and control calls via digitally coded messages. Comprehensive error-checking codes are used to prevent maloperation. The user simply dials the number required and an automatic sequence between the mobile and the base selects the best available frequency. This control sequence and selection are totally invisible to the user. Communication can then take place on a pair of frequencies to allow full duplex operation, as with a normal telephone.

As the call progresses, the signal is automatically monitored by the mobile and the base. If the quality starts to fall off, adjacent cells are requested to monitor the call and, if an improvement is possible, control is passed to the next cell (an operation called a 'handoff'). It is not necessary for the new cell to use the same frequency pair as the old cell, and the mobile can be instructed (via the control channel) to change channel. The handoff and the frequency skipping are again invisible to the user.

Calls to a mobile can be initiated from a normal telephone or another mobile. When not in use the mobile scans the control channel at regular intervals. A request for a call to a mobile is sent to all cells and transmitted on the control channels. When the mobile acknowledges (automatically, of course), a cell is chosen and a frequency pair allocated for the conversation. Thereafter the call quality is monitored and handoffs implemented as before.

Cellular radio is not limited to vehicles. Hand portables are also available, which can be used by farmers, surveyors, engineers and other people who spend a lot of time away from the office. They can even be taken by people on fishing trips or out for a round of golf.

Obviously, a great financial investment is needed to set up a cellular radio network, particularly in the computer equipment for the call handling, monitoring and billing. This will be reflected in the cost of the service. While cellular radio, and the cost of the calls, are expensive by domestic standards, many commercial organisations will think the cost of instant communications with their out-of-office staff worthwhile. An explosive growth in mobile communication is confidently predicted, with a cellular radio becoming a new status symbol!

Citizens' band radio 10.13

Until recently, people wanting mobile radio communications had two options: they could become licensed radio amateurs (which required time, effort and examinations to test their technical knowledge); or they could utilise commercial mobiles licensed for use on one specific frequency. These latter (usually operating around 90 or 168 MHz in the VHF band or 460 MHz in the UHF band) were not true mobiles as they operated to a central base station.

A true restriction-free citizens' band has operated in the USA for many years, but its utilisation jumped in the 1970s as the result of petrol shortages and a few notable films (Convoy) and TV series in which the CB was almost the star.

Not surprisingly, there was considerable pressure for a similar CB system in the UK, and for several years there was a flourishing, but illegal, use of imported American and Japanese CB equipment. This all used the American standard of 27 MHz bands, AM. These bands overlapped with existing users, notably radio control frequencies, and for some time a mild state of chaos existed as 'pirates' increased the power of their transmitters with linear amplifiers and poorly aligned sets splattered their way across other legitimate users. The author feels that many of the pirates at this time had more fun from the illegality of their actions than from the technical interest.

In due course the Government bowed to the inevitable and legitimised CB. Two bands were allocated: 40 channels at 10 kHz spacing between 27·601 25 MHz and 27·991 25 MHz; and 20 channels with 50 kHz spacing between 934·0125 MHz and 934·9625 MHz. Interestingly, the 27 MHz band uses FM and a slightly different band allocation from the American CB network, which precludes the use of imported sets designed for the USA. Almost all available CB sets use the 27 MHz band and the UHF band is almost empty.

The licence requirements are simple: RF output must not exceed 4 watts on the 27 MHz band and 8 watts on the UHF band. The 27 MHz aerial must not exceed 1·5 m in length (which is less than a true half-wave dipole) and must be bottom-loaded with an inductor. UHF elements can be made directional by the use of up to four elements. All transmissions must be in plain speech (music and data transmission are specifically forbidden).

These requirements, and the low price of legal CB, has almost totally ended the maverick AM CB user. The initial laxity of operating procedures, bad language, bad manners and use of high powered linear amplifiers has ceased, allowing CB to become a valuable service. It is invaluable for long distance driving, where road reports are available from other drivers; and CB clubs deserve great credit for public service, not only at spectacular disasters but for more mundane assistance to local charities organising events such as marathons and yacht races, which require widespread radio communication.

10.14 **Reproduction**

10.14.1 Disc recording
Despite the upsurge in popularity of tape recording in recent years, most hi-fi enthusiasts still prefer to use records for high quality systems. The record disc has a long history, from the early cylinder days to the modern microgroove stereo record, and shows little sign of being replaced by tapes.

Stereo recording is now universal, and the basic principle is shown in *Figure 10.39*. The two channels, denoted by A and B, are recorded on the two walls of the record groove which are set at 90°. The stylus is mechanically connected to two transducers which produce the two stereo signals with the minimum of interaction. The stylus movement is a combination of both horizontal and vertical movements, and older monophonic styli which could only move horizontally will severely damage the record.

Two types of transducer are commonly used in pick-up heads. The first, and cheapest, type is based on piezoelectric elements similar to those described in Subsection 12.6.1. These produce a large signal at a high impedance, but their performance is not good enough for true high fidelity applications.

The second type of pick-up transducer uses electromagnetic techniques similar to the moving coil microphone, which is described in Subsection 12.6.1. Dependent upon the design of transducer, either the magnet or the coils can be moved. Magnetic cartridges give a low output (typically a few millivolts) of very high quality.

The mechanical design of the pick-up is very important. Although

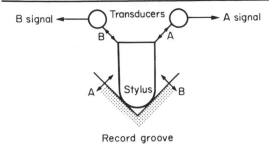

B signal ◀── ○ Transducers ○ ──▶ A signal

B A

A Stylus B

Record groove

Fig. 10.39 Stereo recording

the movement of the stylus is small, very high rates of acceleration are encountered. If the mechanics are poorly thought out, the stylus will be unable to follow the grooves and rapid record wear will result.

The recording characteristic of a disc is not linear with frequency. To avoid excessive groove width on loud low frequency, notes and excessive acceleration on high frequency notes, the recording follows a curve defined by the Record Industries Association of America (RIAA) and subsequently adopted as a British Standard. Magnetic pick-ups have an output dependent on stylus velocity, and piezoelectric pick-ups are dependent on displacement. Both types need some form of equalisation in the pre-amplifier to give the correct response at the loudspeakers.

The laser disc is an interesting alternative to the conventional LP. This uses the same technology as the laser video disc, described below. Because there is no contact with the surface of the recording, there is no degradation of quality with age. The system is also very tolerant of surface contamination from fingerprints etc.

10.14.2 Tape recording

Tape recording is done on a plastic tape coated with iron oxide. The tape passes in front of an electromagnet fed with the signal to be recorded (*Figure 10.40*). As the tape passes the gap in the magnet, the particles of iron oxide becomes magnetised by the variations in flux.

The recording on the tape is in the form of variations in the magnetisations of the oxide layer. At a fixed frequency, the spacing of these variations will depend directly on the tape speed, so it follows that a higher tape speed should be used for best results. Other factors affecting the performance are the tape grain size and the head gap.

The magnetisation of the tape is very nonlinear, and the marked kink in *Figure 10.41(a)* is caused principally by magnetic hysteresis. If a simple audio waveform was applied to the head, a very distorted output would occur. If, however, the signal is added to the large amplitude high frequency bias shown in *Figure 10.41(b)*, the audio signal is reproduced with little distortion. A bias frequency of around 50 kHz is normally used.

In playback, the tape is run at constant speed past a head similar to the recording head (often in cheaper units the recording and playback heads are the same unit). The magnetic variations on the tape produce voltages in the head windings which are amplified by a conventional audio amplifier.

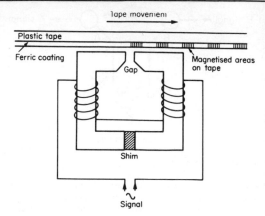

Fig. 10.40 Principles of tape recording

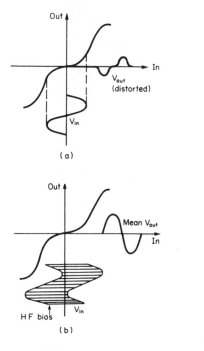

Fig. 10.41 Tape recording waveforms: (a) distortion due to hysteresis; (b) recording with bias signal

Tape recording was once done on reel-to-reel machines, and it was widely thought that a minimum speed of 7·5 in/s was necessary for good quality. The cassette recorder was originally introduced for convenience recording, and with its narrow tape and a speed of only $1\frac{7}{8}$ in/s it was considered totally unsuitable for hi-fi applications. Recent improvements in head design, tape oxide and techniques such as the Dolby noise reduction circuit, have completely transformed the cassette recorder into a worthy part of a hi-fi system.

10.14.3 Video recording

In Section 10.7 it was shown that a TV signal has component frequencies in excess of 5 MHz. If a video signal is to be recorded, the recording process must be capable of reproducing frequencies up to several megahertz.

An audio tape recorder handling frequencies up to, say, 15 kHz runs at a few centimetres per second. The response of a tape recorder is directly dependent on tape speed (other factors being constant); hence a tape speed in excess of 1 m/s would be needed to record a video signal. Although high tape speeds are used on some broadcast recorders, the large spools of tape that are necessary are both too inconvenient and too expensive for domestic use.

There are several different standards that have evolved for domestic video recording, but all are based on a rotating recording head. Simple economics make it impossible to utilise a high tape speed, but the same effect is obtained by utilising a slow tape speed and moving the head at high speed. This is achieved by the use of the so-called helical scan.

The tape is passed round a drum which contains two heads on a rotating arm, *Figure 10.42(a)*. The heads rotate at 25 rev/s, so each head records one complete TV field in the 180° it is in contact with the tape. The tape mechanics are arranged such that the head moves at an angle to the tape, and the tape movement causes each field to be recorded as a diagonal stripe across the tape, *Figure 10.42(b)*.

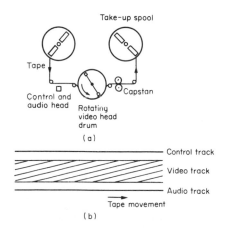

Fig. 10.42 Video tape recording: (a) tape mechanics; (b) tape format

On replay, it is essential that the rotation of the tape heads is matched to the field rate of the recorded video. This is achieved by means of a control track on which synchronising pulses are recorded. These pulses are used by a servoamplifier controlling the head rotation motor to lock the head rotation to the video on the tape. An additional track is used to record sound in a conventional manner. The sound and control tracks use conventional stationary heads.

Video recorders are available as reel-to-reel machines, or self-threading cassette recorders. Very ingenious mechanisms are needed to thread the cassette tape round the drums, and cassette machines are more expensive than their reel-to-reel counterparts. At the time of writing there is no standard for video cassettes, and there is considerable competition to capture the market. It seems at present that the market is influenced by the video hire firms, and VHS has become the market leader with Betamax in second place.

10.14.4 Future developments in video recording

The history of video recording has been plagued by the lack of common standards, and there are many incompatible video tape systems, and many incompatible video cassette systems. The whole topic is highly confusing to the consumer. *Figure 10.43* shows some of the systems currently available. Unfortunately, future developments will add to this confusion.

The first development is the linear video recorder, or LVR. In principle, this is similar to a conventional tape recorder with a stationary head. To obtain a satisfactory response, high quality CrO_2 tape and exceptionally good tape heads are used, together with a tape speed in excess of 3 m/s. To allow reasonable play times, the tape has around 30 tracks which are scanned in turn, either by reversing the tape at each end and stepping the head down a track, or by utilising an endless spool system. Several manufacturers have announced (incompatible) LVR systems, and some have promised plug-in LVR cassettes for CCTV cameras, to rival the familiar 8 mm home movie camera.

The second development is the video disc, and here again we encounter problems with incompatibility. The video disc actually has a longer history than the VTR, and a low resolution system was available in 1930. Since then, many video disc systems have been announced, subsequently to vanish. At the time of writing, two systems appear likely to succeed.

The first system, known as Laserdisc and marketed by Philips, uses a 300 mm disc scanned optically with three low powered helium/neon laser beams. Two beams are used to provide signals for the tracking servos, and the third actually reads the data encoded on the disc. The data is recorded as a series of regular pits which vary in length, and is hence a form of pulse modulation (see Section 10.15). The information is encoded below a protective transparent plastic coating, and the laser beams are precisely focused to the correct depth. As a result, the system is very tolerant of surface contamination from grease, dirt, fingerprints etc.

To get a single still frame, one rotation of the disc must contain one complete frame. This occurs at a rotational speed of 1500 rev/min. Unfortunately, this means that the packing density will vary from outer to inner tracks and the play time will be correspondingly reduced. Optimum packing is obtained by keeping the record density

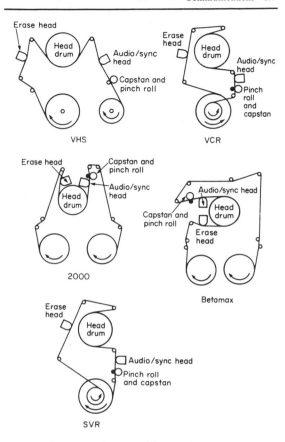

Fig. 10.43 Comparison of common video recorder systems

constant and increasing the disc speed as the head tracks toward the centre. Disc players for the educational market use the smaller capacity principle with single frame/slow play facilities, whereas the domestic players give 60 minutes' play time without freeze frame. More expensive players accept both types of disc. In theory it is possible to hold a single frame in some form of store, but this is prohibitively expensive at present.

The second video disc system stores the data as capacitance variations in transverse slots of varying width. A metal electrode serves as a probe to recover these variations and tracks across the disc in a spiral groove similar to conventional audio discs. A rotational speed of 450 rev/min is used giving, again, 60 min play per side. As before, single-frame hold is not possible without a separate store. Two (inevitably incompatible) systems have been announced by RCA and JVC, but these have yet to appear in the market.

It will be noted that both these systems are replay only, and the user can only purchase prerecorded discs. In theory, the laser scan system can have a user record facility, but details are not obtainable. A magnetic recording system was announced in the mid-1970s which used 300 mm discs rotating at 150 rev/min. A play time of 30 min per side was anticipated. Unfortunately, it seems to have vanished without trace. Professional magnetic disc recorders with a play time of 60 s are used for action replays on sports events.

The manufacturers of video discs seem to be aiming at a slightly different market from the VCR. Advance advertising suggests that initially, at least, production will be devoted to feature movies. At present, however, it would seem the domestic market prefers the record/playback facilities of the VCR, and sales of video discs have been sluggish. Educational sales, however, have been encouraging, particularly to industry. Linking of a video disc player and a computer to select tracks allows programmed-learning teaching packages to be developed. Similar techniques have appeared (more trivially) in arcade games.

10.15 Digital techniques

10.15.1 Introduction
The basic theory behind logic and digital systems is given in Chapter 7. Digital techniques are becoming widely used in communications, both for data transmissions between computers and peripherals and as a method of encoding analogue information. In recent years, cheap LSI chips have made information systems such as Teletext and Prestel available to the domestic market.

10.15.2 Pulse modulation
Pulse modulation is a sampling technique where an analogue signal is represented by a pulse train. There are three forms of pulse modulation, and these are summarised in *Figure 10.44*.

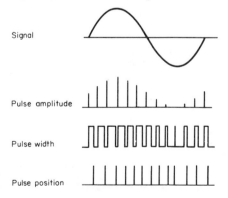

Fig. 10.44 Forms of pulse modulation

In pulse amplitude modulation, the waveform is sampled at regular intervals to produce variable height pulses. This is not a common form of pulse modulation.

The commonest form of pulse modulation is probably pulse width modulation. The pulse train occurs at a fixed rate, but the width of the pulses is controlled by the analogue signal.

Pulse position modulation is a variation on pulse width modulation. A constant frequency clock is used to produce a pulse whose position is controlled by the analogue signal.

Pulse width and pulse position modulation have excellent noise rejection characteristics, as the signal can only be in one of two states. In telephony applications, the gaps between pulses are sufficiently wide to allow other signals to be transmitted on the same line if their clock pulses are shifted in time. This technique is known as multiplexing, and gives optimum use of telephone lines.

Pulse modulation (with multiplexing) can be modulated on to a carrier, and is particularly well suited to FM. A pulse modulated FM carrier is a very secure and very elegant method of transmitting analogue signals.

The frequency response of a pulse modulation system is determined by the clock rate, and it can be shown that the signal must be sampled at twice the highest frequency component in the signal.

10.15.3 Pulse code modulation (PCM)

An analogue to digital converter (or ADC) is a device that is used to convert an analogue voltage to a binary number. If the binary number has 4 bits (called a nibble) it can represent 16 levels from 0 to 15. If the binary number has 8 bits (called a byte) it can represent 256 levels from 0 to 255.

In PCM the analogue signal is measured by an ADC at regular intervals and turned into a binary number, which can be transmitted by line or modulated on to a carrier (*Figure 10.45*). At the receiver, a device called a digital to analogue converter (or DAC) turns the digital signal back into a copy of the original signal. A small amount of noise is introduced into the signal in the form of steps of the smallest level the ADC can resolve. This is known as the quantization error.

PCM is widely used for telemetry, where data is transmitted from remote sites such as reservoirs and electricity substations. It is also used to encode telephony signals on some landlines. Like pulse modulation, PCM has excellent noise rejection characteristics.

10.15.4 Data transmission

Computer systems transmit data from processor to peripherals and from computer to computer in commercial data processing applications such as banks and payroll. The data takes the form of binary words (usually 8 or 16 bits long) and special techniques have been developed for their transmission.

There are two basic methods used to transmit data, and these are summarised in *Figure 10.46*. Parallel transmission uses one line for each bit, and one word is sent for one clock pulse. Serial transmission uses an 8-bit pulse train on one line, and eight clock pulses are needed to transmit an 8-bit word. Parallel transmission is thus faster than serial transmission, but considerably more expensive in cables and electronics.

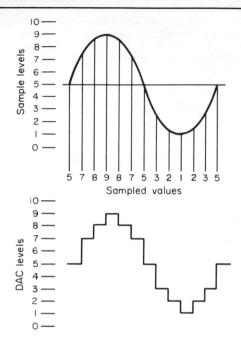

Fig. 10.45 Pulse code modulation: (a) signal sampled by ADC; (b) signal rebuilt by DAC

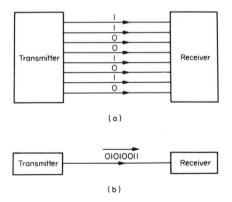

Fig. 10.46 Data transmission: (a) parallel transmission; (b) serial transmission

Noise is far more important in data transmissions, as a single error could garble a complete transmission. Error checking is thus an integral part of any data transmission system, and two common techniques are parity and block sum checks.

It was stated above that data is sent in the form of an 8-bit word. There are two common codes (ASCII and ISO) and these utilise seven bits for information and the eighth bit as an error check. The parity bit is used to make the total number of bits in the word 'odd' (for odd parity) or 'even' (for even parity). An error in transmission will lead to a change in parity which will be detected at the receiver. For example, suppose we are using odd parity:

Data	Parity	Data	Parity	
1011011	0	1011011	0	OK
1101100	1	1101100	1	OK
1000001	1	1001001	1	Error!

Alternatively, the data is transmitted in blocks (often with parity checks on each word). At the end of the block the transmitter sends a binary word which contains the total number of bits in the block. The receiver checks the total number of bits received, and any errors will be apparent (*Figure 10.47*).

When the receiver detects an error, either by parity or sum-check, it can either alert an operator or automatically request a re-transmission.

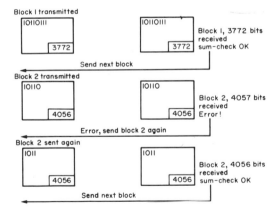

Fig. 10.47 Data transmission with sum-check

Serial transmission is used in most applications. For short distances where telephone lines are not used, simple techniques are used to transmit the data. There are three common standards in use: 20 mA loop, V24 and RS232.

The 20 mA loop utilises a current generator, a switch at the transmitter and a current sensor at the receiver. The current source can be at the transmitter end (as in *Figure 10.48(a)*, called active transmit/passive receive), or at the receiver (as in *Figure 10.48(b)*,

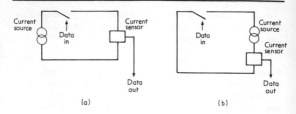

Fig. 10.48 Data transmission by 20 mA current loop: (a) active transmit/passive receive; (b) passive transmit/active receive

called passive transmit/active receive). It is obviously important to establish which standard is being used!

V24 and RS232 are almost identical, V24 being a European standard and RS232 the equivalent American standard. These originated as standards for connecting devices via modems (described below) but have become, somewhat by default, a standard for connecting computers and peripherals when serial transmission is being used. Their origin as a modem standard does bring confusion, however, with references to DTEs and DCEs.

Both standards utilise voltage signals, with '1' being a negative voltage and '0' a positive voltage. A nominal voltage of ± 12 volts is used. Transmission distance is limited to a few metres (dependent on transmission speed).

The speed at which data is sent is measured in baud, where a baud is defined as one bit per second. ASCII coding, described below, uses 10 or 11 bits to represent a single character, so the character rate is approximately the baud rate divided by 10. Common baud rates are 110 (corresponding to about 10 characters per second), 300, 1200, 4800 and 9600 baud.

If text (in upper and lower case) is to be transmitted along with numerals, punctuation and control signals (e.g. 'start a new page') some form of coding is needed. Approximately 120 different codings are needed to represent alphanumerical characters. This needs a minimum of seven binary bits, and various 7- and 8-bit codes have evolved over the years. The commonest, however, is the American Standard Code for Information Interchange, known more commonly and conveniently as ASCII.

This is a 7-bit code plus parity; A is represented by 1000001 for example, which is 41 in hex or 65 in decimal. The complete ASCII coding is given in *Table 10.1*.

The signal format is shown in *Figure 10.49*. The data is preceded by a start bit (which tells the receiving device to get ready) and succeeded by the parity bit and (according to the particular system being used) one or two stop bits (which tell the receiver that the character is complete). A single character therefore requires 10 or 11 bits. Note that *Figure 10.49* is drawn with '1' signals positive although RS232 uses a negative voltage to represent a binary '1'.

10.15.6 Modems

A digital signal cannot be passed over a standard telephone line without unacceptable distortion and attenuation. Where data transmission is needed over a long distance the digital signals are

Table 10.1 ASC11 characters

32		56	8	80	P	104	h
33	!	57	9	81	Q	105	i
34	"	58	:	82	R	106	j
35	#	59	;	83	S	107	k
36	$	60	<	84	T	108	l
37	%	61	=	85	U	109	m
38	&	62	>	86	V	110	n
39	'	63	?	87	W	111	o
40	(	64	@	88	X	112	p
41	)	65	A	89	Y	113	q
42	*	66	B	90	Z	114	r
43	+	67	C	91	↑	115	s
44	,	68	D	92	↓	116	t
45	-	69	E	93	←	117	u
46	.	70	F	94	→	118	v
47	/	71	G	95	–	119	w
48	0	72	H	96		120	x
49	1	73	I	97	a	121	y
50	2	74	J	98	b	122	z
51	3	75	K	99	c	123	(
52	4	76	L	100	d	124		
53	5	77	M	101	e	125	)
54	6	78	N	102	f	126	~
55	7	79	O	103	g	127	

Codes less than 32 are control codes

7 Bell	8 Backspace
10 Line Feed	13 Carriage Return

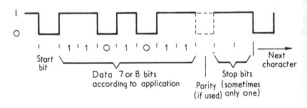

Fig. 10.49 Serial data format. Note that RS232 uses a negative voltage to represent a '1' and a positive voltage to represent a '0'

converted into audio tones, which can then be passed over the normal telephone network. This is known as frequency shift keying (FSK). A device which converts between digital signals and audio tones is called a modem (for MODulator/DEModulator).

The audio frequencies are defined by standards laid down by the CCITT (International Telegraph and Telephone Consultative Committee) in Europe and the Bell standards in the USA. For example the CCITT standard for a 1200/75 baud system (as used by Prestel) is:

| 1200 baud | '0' 2100 Hz | '1' 1300 Hz |
| 75 baud | '0' 450 Hz | '1' 390 Hz |

The different frequencies allow full duplex operation over a telephone line.

There are two types of modem, shown in *Figure 10.50*. A direct connect modem, as its name implies, connects directly to a telephone line. Acoustic modems use a standard telephone whose handset is placed into a rubber holder equipped with a microphone and loudspeaker. Direct connect modems are more reliable and can operate at higher baud rates. Direct connect modems have to be approved by the Board of Approval for British Telecommunications (BABT). Acoustic modems are exempt.

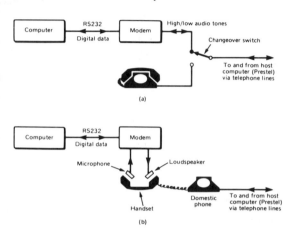

Fig. 10.50 Connecting a computer to telephone lines: (a) direct-coupled modem; (b) acoustically coupled modem

Standard modem operating speeds are 75, 300 and 1200 baud. Faster rates, up to 9600 baud, are achievable on private dedicated lines.

Some form of operating protocol is necessary to avoid clashes. There are essentially three types of system:

1. *Simplex*. This is essentially a two-wire system in which data can only be sent in one direction.
2. *Half duplex*. This is a system in which bidirectional data transfer can take place, but only in one direction at any given time.
3. *Full duplex*. True simultaneous bidirectional data transfer can take place. Signal separation can be achieved by separate circuits (four-wire operation) or by different modulation tones.

One such protocol is RS232, described below.

10.15.7 RS232
The RS232 standard was set up by the Electronic Industries Association (EIA) as a standard for data transmission via modems. It defines the signal levels, pin connections on a 25-pin D-type

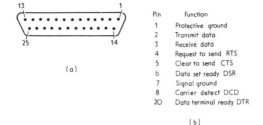

Pin	Function
1	Protective ground
2	Transmit data
3	Receive data
4	Request to send RTS
5	Clear to send CTS
6	Data set ready DSR
7	Signal ground
8	Carrier detect DCD
20	Data terminal ready DTR

(b)

Fig. 10.51 RS232 connections: (a) 25-way D-type connector; (b) pin allocation

connector (*Figure 10.51*) and protocols. Most of the signals defined in *Figure 10.51* are not used in simple applications.

RS232, being defined for modems, defines two types of equipment. DTE stands for Data Terminal Equipment and is the device (peripheral *or* computer) connected to the modem. DCE (for Data Circuit termination Equipment) is the communication device, i.e. the modem itself. This distinction is necessary to establish the meaning of some of the signals.

Pin 2, transmitted data, for example, is defined as data from DTE to DCE. Similarly, received data, pin 3, is from DCE to DTE.

The common control signals (or handshaking) are Request to Send (from DTE to DCE, telling the modem that the DTE wants to send), Clear to Send (from DCE to DTE, telling the DTE that the modem can accept data), Data Set Ready (from DCE to DTE, saying the DCE is alive and well) and Data Terminal Ready (from DTE to DCE, saying the DTE is alive and well). Other functions are for specialist applications.

Although RS232 is well defined it was designed to connect a DTE and a modem. The problems come when a computer is linked directly to a peripheral such as a printer without a modem. This is a similar problem to constructing a lead to record from one tape recorder to another. Somewhere a cross needs to be made in the leads (between transmit and receive data for example).

Similarly, the handshaking signals (RTS, CTS, DSR and DTR) can take on totally new meanings at the whim of the computer and peripheral suppliers. If the computer and peripheral are both to *true* RS232 standards a back-to-back plug with crossovers (called a null modem) will suffice.

10.15.8 Teletext and Prestel

The first 25 lines in each TV field are not used for video information, since they are blanked for the insertion of the field sync pulse and to allow the electron beam to return to the top left-hand side of the screen. The 25-line field blanking period was specified some time ago, and is longer than is strictly necessary for modern TVs.

Lines 19 and 20 (and 332 and 333) are already used for test signals, and lines 17 and 18 (and 330 and 331) are available for other purposes. Teletext uses these lines to transmit digit signals in place of video signals, which are used to present pages of text at the receiving set. The TV set can then be used as a newspaper, with information displayed on the screen in a similar manner to a computer VDU.

A Teletext page consists of 24 rows of 40 characters per row. Characters consist of the normal alphanumeric symbols, together with a comprehensive range of graphic symbols for the construction of diagrams. Characters can be displayed in any of seven colours.

Each TV line used for teletext carries the data for one row of characters. Four rows are transmitted for each TV field, and it takes approximately 0·15 s to transmit a page.

The user selects Teletext mode on his set and dials the page number he requires. When this page number is transmitted, the Teletext logic accepts the data and displays it. A typical Teletext magazine contains around 100 pages, so the user can wait up to 12 s for his page to be transmitted. In practice, common pages such as the Index or News Headlines are transmitted more frequently and are available every few seconds.

Teletext is now transmitted regularly by the BBC and ITV companies under the names Ceefax and Oracle. The standards adopted by both organisations are fortunately identical, and most set makers are producing Teletext sets. Special ICs and modules are produced for Teletext, but the semiconductor manufacturers and set makers have a problem, because public demand is not as high as expected and this is preventing the price of Teletext sets being lowered by mass production.

Prestel is a service offered by the GPO that is similar in many respects to Teletext. It is an information service operated via a normal telephone. Unlike Teletext, data is transmitted from a computer database, and the response is instantaneous. The size of a Teletext magazine is limited by the access time, but since this time on Prestel is independent of magazine size, there is virtually no limit to the number of pages on offer. However, these advantages literally have to be paid for. Prestel is accessed with a modem via a telephone call which is charged in the normal way, usually at local rate for 95% of users, with additional charges being made for each page viewed. Many pages are, however, free. Teletext is, of course, free once a Teletext set has been purchased. At the time of writing, Prestel seems best suited to the business user, and this is reflected in the pages available in the service, although a section called Micronet 800 is available for the home computer user.

11

Servo-mechanisms and process control

Introduction 11.1

The topic of process control is often thought to be a modern one, but in fact the ideas go back to the eighteenth century when the governor was introduced to control the speed of steam engines.

Most industrial processes cannot be left to run themselves, but need some form of regulation to counteract outside influences and changes. In *Figure 11.1*, for example, the tank is required to be kept at a constant level despite changes in outflow rate (caused by variable demand from processes P1, P2 etc.) and changes in inflow rate (caused by supply pressure changes). Control is established by observing the tank level and adjusting the inflow control valve, either manually or automatically.

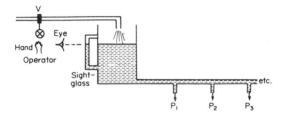

Fig. 11.1 A typical process control problem

Control strategies 11.2

To control a process it is necessary to establish a control strategy. There are various possible control techniques, illustrated in *Figure 11.2*.

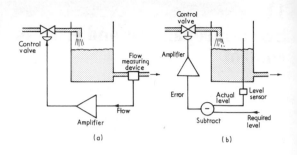

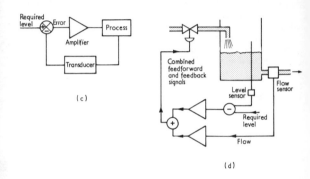

Fig. 11.2 Control strategies: (a) feedforward control; (b) feedback control; (c) schematic representation of feedback control; (d) combined feedforward and feedback control

11.2.1 Open-loop control
In open-loop control there is no attempt to control the process; it is left to run itself. This approach is equivalent to setting the inflow valve and letting the level vary. This approach can only be used on the most tolerant of processes.

11.2.2 Feedforward control
This approach attempts to measure the disturbances to the plant and to predict their effect. Suitable compensation can then be applied. In *Figure 11.2(a)*, for example, the outgoing flow is measured and used to set the ingoing flow valve. In a perfect world, ingoing flow and outgoing flow would match, and the tank level remain constant. In practice, of course, slight mismatches will lead to a gradual increase or decrease in level.

11.2.3 Feedback control

In *Figure 11.2(b)* the tank level is measured by some suitable sensor to give a voltage representing the level. This is compared with the desired level to give a voltage representing the error between the actual and set level. This voltage is used to open or close the inflow valve until the actual level and set level are the same. This can be represented schematically by *Figure 11.2(c)*.

Because the output is fed back to the input this technique is known as feedback or closed-loop control. This strategy will automatically compensate for disturbances in outflow or inflow, and allow an operator to change the set level.

Feedback can only compensate for disturbances after they have affected the plant. The combination of feedback and feedforward, *Figure 11.2(d)*, gives a degree of anticipation to the control, thereby reducing the transient effect of a disturbance.

Types of closed-loop control 11.3

11.3.1 The bang-bang servo

In *Figure 11.3* the error signal is used to turn the controlling element full on or full off (with suitable hysteresis to prevent chatter). A common example of this type of control is found in central heating room temperature thermostats.

Although this technique is simple and cheap, inherently it causes the controlled variable to oscillate as shown. The magnitude and period of the oscillations depend on the size of the hysteresis (dead band) and the properties of the process being controlled. With domestic room thermostats, oscillations of 1 or 2 degrees Centigrade are usually encountered.

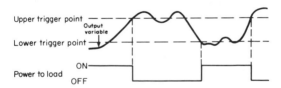

Fig. 11.3 The bang-bang servo

11.3.2 Proportional control

In *Figure 11.4* the inflow valve is made fully adjustable and the error signal amplified to drive the valve directly. If the level is too low the valve will open to admit more liquid and gradually shut as the level rises. This is intuitively correct, a large error being counteracted by a large correction. There will, however, always be some error in the system.

The valve requires a signal to operate it, and, as the valve signal is an amplified version of the error, there will always need to be some

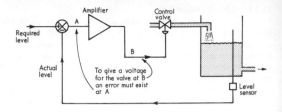

Fig. 11.4 Proportional control and steady state error

error voltage to open the valve at all. This is known as the steady state error, and its magnitude depends on the characteristics of the system.

Obviously, the larger the amplifier gain the smaller the steady state error; but too high a gain will cause the system to become unstable, a topic discussed below.

11.3.3 Three-term (PID) control

In *Figure 11.5* the error signal is passed through a control block which sums three signals:

1. An amplified error signal
2. A signal proportional to the time integral of the error
3. A signal proportional to the time derivative of the error.

A mathematical analysis is beyond the scope of this book, but it is possible to see the effect of each component intuitively. The proportional term acts as in Subsection 11.3.2 above.

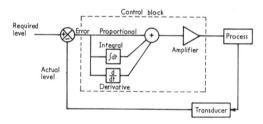

Fig. 11.5 Three-term (PID) control

The integral term will keep the valve ramping open or closed as long as there is any error, and therefore will eventually remove the steady state error completely.

The derivative term serves to stabilise the system (in the same way as shock absorbers on a car damps out the spring oscillations) and gives a faster response to rapid changes in error.

Controllers performing the above function are widely used in process control, and are known as three-term or PID controllers. Adjustment of the relative effect of the three terms is made by the process control engineer to give the fastest response in a particular application.

Plant modelling 11.4

Before a plant can be controlled the engineer needs to know how the plant behaves. To this end it is usual to construct a mathematical model of the plant. As we have seen above, the controller is usually of the form:

$$V_0 = K\left(e + \frac{1}{T_i}\int e\,dt + T_d\frac{de}{dt}\right)$$

where K is the gain, e the error, and T_i and T_d adjust the effects of the integral and derivative terms.

As far as possible, similar expressions must be obtained for the rest of the plant.

Many sub-systems can be considered to follow an exponential response, as in *Figure 11.6(a)*. A typical example is the heater of *Figure 11.6(b)*, whose temperature is related to heat input by the expression

$$\theta = \frac{H}{A}(1 - e^{-t/T})$$

where H is the heat input, A is a constant and T is known as the time constant.

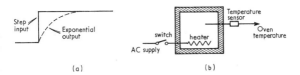

Fig. 11.6 First-order systems: (a) exponential response; (b) typical first-order system. Temperature changes exponentially for step change in power to heater

These are known as first-order systems (or lags) and are characterised by a time constant. The output reaches approximately 63% of its final value in one time constant period, and 99% of the final value in five time constants. Many systems exhibit lags; inertia and thermal heat transfer are common examples.

If a system includes any springy characteristics (due to mechanical or gaseous vibration) it is said to be a second-order system. Such systems, as in *Figure 11.7*, have the response:

$$\frac{d^2x}{dt^2} + 2b\omega_n\frac{dx}{dt} + \omega_n^2 x = a$$

where a is the step size.

This is characterised by the damping factor b and the natural frequency ω_n. Together these determine the size and frequency of the natural vibrations. If b is greater than 1 the system does not vibrate and is said to be overdamped. If b is less than 1 damped oscillations

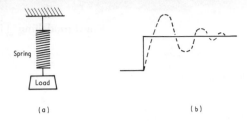

Fig. 11.7 Second-order systems: (a) typical systems; (b) step response of underdamped second-order system

occur, dying out more slowly as b gets smaller. If $b = 0$ the vibrations do not die out.

Many systems with pipework have a constant time between a control action and its effect on the plant. This is called a transit delay, and is usually a difficult problem to deal with.

The tank in *Figure 11.1* integrates the difference between inflow and outflow. Similarly, a position control system driven by a motor/gearbox integrates the motor speed to give position. Such systems are said to have integral action.

The above are the common characteristics encountered in constructing mathematical models. A typical model of a real plant is shown in *Figure 11.8*.

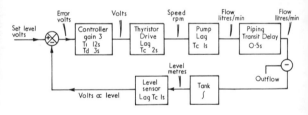

Fig. 11.8 Typical plant model. Note variety of units

11.4.1 Analysis and stability

From the previous discussions it might be thought that all that is necessary to achieve acceptable control is to use very high gain in the proportional control part of the PID controller. Unfortunately, this will lead to instability.

A servosystem can be represented by *Figure 11.9*, where G represents the block transfer function of the plant and controller and H the transfer function of the transducer and feedback components, as given by the model. By simple analysis it can be seen that:

$$\frac{\theta_{out}}{\theta_{in}} = \frac{G}{1 + GH}$$

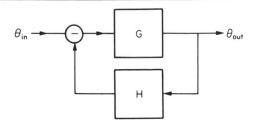

Fig. 11.9 General servo block diagram

The system will be unstable if the bottom term goes to zero or reverses in sign, i.e. GH = –1. This is not as simple a relationship as might at first be thought, as we are dealing with dynamics of a process. In general we must consider the frequency response of the system (i.e. the gain *and* phase shift at all frequencies) as predicted by the mathematical model derived above. If the phase shift is 180 degrees *and* the gain is greater than unity at some frequency, the system is unstable.

This is best seen graphically by plotting the gain/phase shift relationships for different frequencies. There are three common ways of doing this, shown on *Figures 11.10(a)–(c)*.

Figure 11.10(a) is called a Bode diagram and plots gain (in dB) and phase shift on separate graphs. For stability, the gain must cross the 0 dB axis before the phase shift crosses the 180 degree axis.

Figure 11.10(b) is called a Nyquist diagram and plots gain against phase shift on a polar diagram (gain represented as the distance from the origin). For stability, the – 1/180 degree point must be to the left of the graph for increasing frequency.

The final plot, *Figure 11.10(c)*, is called a Nicholls chart, and plots gain (in dB) against phase shift on rectangular coordinates. For stability, the 0 dB/180 degree point must be to the right of the graph

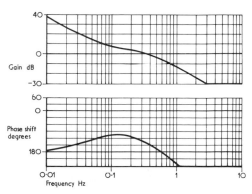

(a)

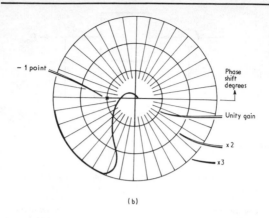

(b)

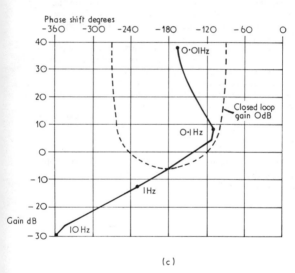

(c)

Fig. 11.10 Various methods for predicting stability. All are drawn for the same system: (a) Bode diagram; (b) Nyquist diagram; (c) Nicholls chart

for increasing frequency. The Nicholls chart also allows prediction of the closed-loop response. If, for example, the graph crosses the dotted line, damped oscillations will result.

The above techniques allow the system to be analysed and tuned for best control. The techniques are also applicable to the analysis of amplifiers employing negative feedback (which can also oscillate if the feedback is wrongly chosen).

High power electronics 11.5

The load in a servosystem is controlled by some form of power
amplifier and actuator. This may, for example, be a hydraulic valve
and ram, but some form of electronic power amplifier is common.

11.5.1 Basic thyristor circuits
The principles of the thyristor were described in Chapter 2. The
device blocks conduction in the reverse direction, and will conduct in
the forward direction when a positive pulse is applied to the gate.

The simplest way of using a thyristor to control a load is shown in
Figure 11.11. The control circuit is synchronised to the incoming
supply, and applies a pulse to the gate. This turns the thyristor on,
and it remains on for the rest of the half-cycle.

By varying the timing of the pulse, the point in the cycle at which
the thyristor fires can be controlled. The circuit thus provides a
variable d.c. voltage to the load. This is known as phase shift control.
A practical circuit (commonly used as a light dimmer or drill
controller) is shown in *Figure 11.12*. VR_1 and C_1 give a delayed
supply voltage to the thyristor gate, the delay being determined by
the setting of VR_1.

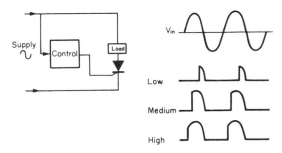

Fig. 11.11 Basic phase shift control

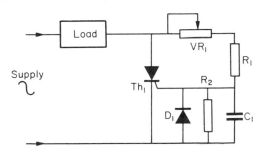

Fig. 11.12 Practical phase shift circuit

The circuits of *Figures 11.11* and *11.12* give control over one half-cycle, the other cycle being blocked. If the thyristor is replaced by a triac or two thyristors back to back (known as inverse parallel connection), control can be given over both cycles, and a controlled a.c. output is given as shown in *Figure 11.13*. The thyristor can thus be used to control a.c. or d.c. loads, and various connections are shown in *Figure 11.14*.

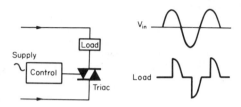

Fig. 11.13 A.C. phase shift control

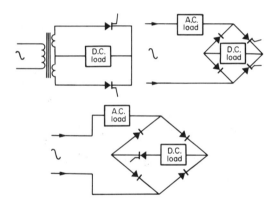

Fig. 11.14 Various thyristor circuits

11.5.2 Burst control

Phase-shift control causes severe problems with mains-borne interference. Where the load time constants are relatively long, as in an electrically heated furnace for example, operation of the load for several mains cycles is preferred. If the turn on is made to coincide with the zero crossing point of the mains, interference will be kept to a minimum. This technique is known as burst control, and is summarised in *Figure 11.15(a)*.

The control calls for the load to be turned on at point A, but the zero crossing circuit delays the turn on until point B. The control calls for the load to turn off at point C, normal thyristor action continues until point D. Both turn on and off thus occur at zero crossing points.

The zero crossing control is usually performed by ICs specially designed for burst control applications.

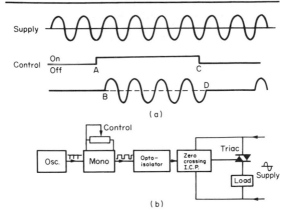

Fig. 11.15 Burst control: (a) principle of burst control; (b) block diagram of burst control circuit

A proportional form of burst control is shown in *Figure 11.15(b)*. The control voltage is a free-running oscillator (typically 0·1 Hz) and the mark/space ratio is adjusted to control the load.

11.5.3 Motor control

D.C. machines are widely used in servosystems because of their excellent control characteristics. Thyristor phase control is a very convenient method to control a d.c. motor, and a single-phase motor control scheme is shown in *Figure 11.16*.

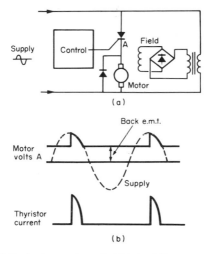

Fig. 11.16 Single-phase motor control: (a) circuit diagram; (b) waveforms

A d.c. motor can be controlled either by its armature volts or by the field current, as described in Chapter 13. In *Figure 11.16* the field current is constant and the speed is controlled by the armature volts. The waveforms occurring in the circuit are shown in *Figure 11.16(b)*.

This circuit will compensate for changes in load to a small extent. If the load increases, the motor speed will drop. This reduces the back e.m.f., causing the thyristor to conduct for a longer period. This will tend to maintain the motor speed. For accurate speed control, however, the motor and thyristor are made part of a closed loop.

In closed-loop control, the motor speed is measured, and fed back to control the phasing of the gate pulses. The actual control of the gate pulses is described in Subsection 11.5.5.

The motor speed can be measured accurately by a tacho, but for less critical applications we can return to the motor equation:

$$V = IR + E$$

where E is the back e.m.f., I the current, R the internal armature resistance, V the applied volts, and

$$E = K\omega$$

where ω is the rotational speed and K a constant.

If we can measure the current, we can deduce IR and hence extract E. Knowing E we can infer ω, and feed this back to form a speed control loop. This technique can be implemented with a few operational amplifiers and is known as I–R compensation.

11.5.4 Inversion

In *Figure 11.17(a)*, a controlled bridge rectifier is supplying current to a load. Assume that the nature of the load is such that the current drawn is continuous (i.e. does not fall to zero with the voltage); this

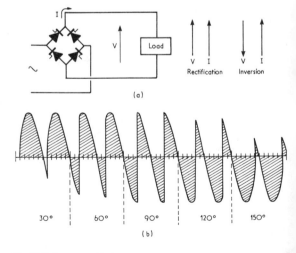

Fig. 11.17 Inversion: (a) circuit diagram; (b) waveforms for various firing angles

can arise if the load has high inductance or is, itself, some form of generator.

Figure 11.17(b) shows the effect of changing the firing angle. With small values of firing angle, power is transferred from the supply to the load. As the firing angle increases, the continuous current causes the load voltage to go negative for part of the cycle.

Eventually, when the firing angle reaches 90 degrees, the positive and negative half-cycles are equal and there is no net transfer of power from the supply to the load.

If the firing angle is increased beyond 90 degrees, the area below the curve increases. As the mean voltage and current are now of opposite sign, power is being returned from the load to the supply. This is known as inversion.

For inversion to occur, the load must have some capability to supply current. It cannot occur with a purely resistive load. A common example is the controlled dynamic braking of a large motor, which acts as a generator and returns the stored kinetic energy to the supply. This requires a cross-connected bridge, as in *Figure 11.20* (below). Highly inductive loads such as electromagnets can also return their stored electromagnetic energy by inversion.

11.5.5 Gate control

The control for the thyristor gates needs to follow the principle shown in *Figure 11.18(a)*. An error signal (say 0–10 V) is applied to the control input, and this controls the gate pulses from off to full conduction (180° back to 0° in the supply cycle).

A common way of achieving this is shown in *Figure 11.18(b)*. A sawtooth waveform is synchronised with the supply, and compared with the voltage input. When the sawtooth and the input are the same, the gate is triggered. This produces a pulse early in the cycle for a high V_{in}, and late in the cycle for a low V_{in}, as required.

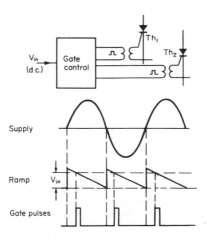

Fig. 11.18 Gate control: (a) schematic; (b) operating principles

11.5.6 Three-phase circuits

A simple three-phase circuit is shown in *Figure 11.19*. Speed is controlled by phase control of the thyristors, and direction by field polarity. Inversion is used to give regenerative braking, as described earlier. The control of the gate pulses is somewhat more complex in three-phase circuits, but generally follows the principles outlined in the preceding subsection.

Figure 11.20 shows a circuit known as the cross-connected bridge arrangement. Two bridges are used to give high speed reversals with a constant field. Although it is expensive, this circuit is widely used in applications where a controlled reversal of direction is required.

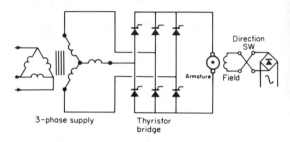

Fig. 11.19 Three-phase motor control with field reversal

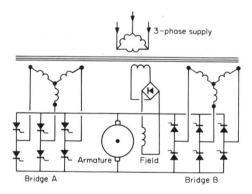

Fig. 11.20 Three-phase motor control with armature reversal

A typical large drive is shown in *Figure 11.21*. This gives regeneration and full speed control in both directions. The motor speed is measured by a tacho and compared with the set speed. The rate of change of the set speed is limited by a ramp circuit to reduce mechanical stress on gearboxes and couplings.

The speed error is passed through a PI controller to become a demanded current signal. A high rate of change of current (di/dt) implies high voltages, which could cause a flashover at the motor armature. The demanded current is therefore passed through a second ramp circuit to limit the rate of change of current.

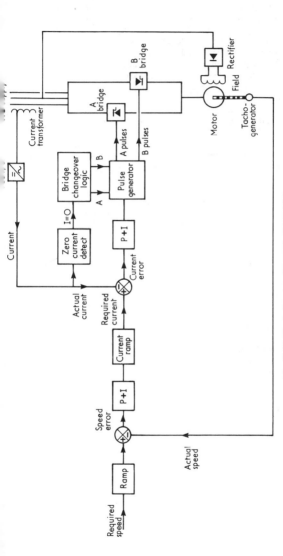

Fig. 11.21 Block diagram of large thyristor drive

The motor current is measured on the a.c. side of the thyristor bridges by a current transformer, and rectified to give a d.c. signal. This inevitably introduces a lag into the current measuring circuit, but it is difficult to measure large d.c. in the armature circuit.

The current error is passed through another PI controller and used to set the firing angle for the bridges. Changeover between bridges can only take place when there is no motor current, so a zero-current detection circuit controls the bridge changeover logic.

Field current is provided by a separate rectifier. In some drives the motor speed range is increased by reducing the field current when the motor armature reaches its maximum voltage. This is known as field weakening.

Thyristor drives and microprocessor technology are starting to come together. In modern drives, most of the analog circuitry and logic of *Figure 11.21* is implemented by a program in a microcomputer. The current measuring lag is removed by using a voltage-controlled oscillator and counter, with the VCO frequency controlled by the a.c. from the current transformer. This allows the current pulse for each thyristor to be measured.

Voltage tachos are being replaced by pulse tachos, with a phase-locked loop being used to give the speed error. With these techniques, the cupboard full of electronics that is currently necessary for the control of a drive can be reduced to one small PCB. Speed accuracies of 0·01 % are readily achievable with a micro/PLL drive.

11.5.7 Variable speed a.c. drives

The induction motor is the cheapest and most robust rotating machine. Having no brushes or commutator it requires little or no maintenance, and is usually the first choice for a prime mover. Unfortunately, the speed of an induction motor is tied to a multiple of the frequency of the a.c. supply. Common speeds with a 50 Hz supply are 3000 and 1500 rpm. In some motors it is possible to change speed by altering the winding connection, but the change is very coarse (2:1 for example).

To vary the speed of an a.c. machine, it is necessary to alter the frequency of the supply. This is commonly done with the circuit of *Figure 11.22*, which is called a d.c. link inverter.

The principle is very simple. The a.c. supply is rectified to give a d.c. supply, which is then chopped by thyristors acting as switches to give a pseudo-a.c. supply at a different frequency.

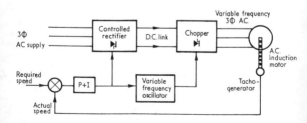

Fig. 11.22 Speed control of an a.c. induction motor

The motor volts need to be controlled along with the frequency, being reduced at low frequencies to prevent the motor from overheating. The rectifier section therefore needs to be controlled, and is usually a simple thyristor rectifier similar to those described earlier.

Figure 11.22 is arranged to give closed-loop speed control. With care a speed adjustment range of 6:1 is attainable. This is not as good as a d.c. motor, but is adequate for many applications.

11.5.8 Protection of thyristors

Thyristors can be damaged by overcurrent or overvoltage. Providing adequate voltage ratings for the thyristors is a question of correct design, and consideration of factors such as mains-borne spikes.

Most thyristor circuits have some form of overcurrent protection, operated off a current sensing device. This will cause the control to delay the gate pulses as the current limit is reached.

Thyristors are usually connected in series with high speed fuses to protect the thyristors in the failure of the gate control circuit. These are fast-acting fuses and in theory (but not always in practice!) will rupture before damage can occur.

A thyristor can be triggered into conduction by a rapid change of anode voltage. Gate current is provided by the anode to gate capacitance, *Figure 11.23(a)*, and the thyristor turns on. This is known as dV/dt triggering and is not, in itself, a device failure. It is fairly certain, however, that a thyristor being turned on at the wrong time will suffer some damage.

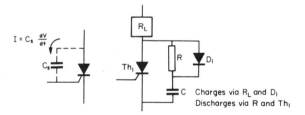

Fig. 11.23 Thyristor failure and protection: (a) mechanism of failure; (b) snubber circuit

Protection against dV/dt triggering is obtained by the simple RC snubber circuit shown in *Figure 11.23(b)*. This limits the anode voltage to a time constant of $R_L C$. Resistor R is provided to limit the current when C is discharged by the thyristor.

Computers and industrial control 11.6

To most people, conditioned by television, the role of the computer in industry is seen as the robot. In reality the robot is still relatively rare, being best suited for mundane and repetitive assembly, welding and painting jobs. Computers are, however, widely used in controlling industrial processes.

Any process can be represented as shown in *Figure 11.24*. The plant is interfaced to the operator by some form of control system. This can be conventionally constructed from discrete controllers, meters and relays, but is increasingly becoming some form of computer.

It is possible to identify three types of control operation. Most processes will require all of these in some form:

1. *Monitoring and display of plant status*. This ranges from a simple light to indicate that a pump is on, to analog displays of, say, temperature and pressure. Here the computer allows very clear and concise displays with colour graphics on VDUs.
2. *Sequencing*. This covers the control of on/off items of plant, such as motors, valves, pumps etc. Sequencing is probably the largest area of industrial control, and specialised computers called programmable controllers (PCs) or programmable logic controllers (PLCs) have evolved for this task, along with very simple programming languages described later.
3. *Closed-loop control*. The closed-loop algorithms described earlier in this chapter can easily be implemented by computer programs. The operator can enter a setpoint at a VDU keyboard and the computer can be left to control the plant. This is known as direct digital control (DDC). More sophisticated PLCs include PID and other closed-loop functions.

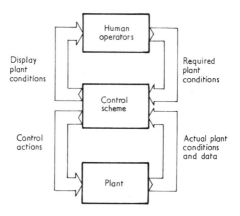

Fig. 11.24 Symbolic representation of industrial control

The computer can therefore be used easily as the central block of *Figure 11.24*, but it is reasonable to ask what advantages it brings.

Any largish control system goes through several distinct stages from conception to completion. First, there is a design period when the plant is studied and the control designed. With conventional equipment every i must be dotted before equipment can be ordered. With a computer all that is needed is a conservative estimate of the size of machine and the amount of input/output (I/O) necessary.

Next, the system is built. With conventional equipment each job is a time-consuming one-off. With computers, standard items are used. The only one-off item is the computer program itself and this can easily be written in the comfort of an office.

The installation comes next. Industrial control computers make wide use of serial communications to link items of plant. A control desk, for example, can connect to the computer via a telephone cable. This gives simple installation and allows large items to be pretested before delivery.

Finally comes commissioning. No plant works correctly first time; there is always some human error. With a computer system these can usually be corrected simply and quickly by program changes. With conventional equipment, time-consuming wiring changes are often needed. Very few plants stay the same for their whole life; there are always changes and modifications to be made. With a computer these can often be made quickly and easily without the need to take the plant off line.

A typical scheme is shown in *Figure 11.25*. Analog inputs are scanned by a multiplexer for conversion by a single ADC. The scan rate is important if meaningful information is to be obtained. Shannon's Sampling Theorem states that the minimum sample rate is twice the highest frequency component of interest. Typically, inputs are scanned 2–5 times per second. A sample-and-hold circuit is used to freeze each value during conversion.

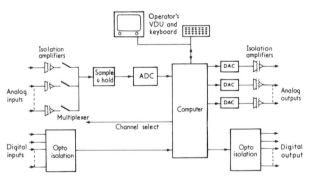

Fig. 11.25 Industrial control computer

Optical isolation is used on all inputs and outputs to give high noise immunity and to prevent damage to the computer from inter-cable short-circuits, which frequently arise from cable damage.

Many specialised computer languages have evolved for process control. A typical example is the ladder diagram of *Figure 11.26*. This is built around the relay symbols familiar to electricians and technicians. No special skills are necessary to use this language. The example shown is a starter for a hydraulic pump, with protection against the pump not attaining pressure. TON represents a timer, A a plant input, B a plant output and G internal storage.

Computers are also being used to assist plant maintenance. So-called expert systems have diagnostic routines built in to advise the maintenance staff on the fastest and cheapest way to find a fault.

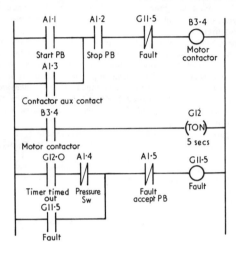

Fig. 11.26 Ladder diagram program

12

Transducers

A transducer is a device for converting energy from one form to another. The term is generally applied, however, to devices which convert mechanical and other forms of energy to electrical energy for measurement purposes. The description of servosystems in Chapter 11 shows the sensing of the output to be a critical part of the system. This chapter describes the basic principles of some common transducers.

Position measurement 12.2

12.2.1 General position measurement
Many electronic systems require accurate measurements of position; examples are automatic lathes, rolling mills and gunnery control. In addition, many other variables are converted to a movement for measurement purposes. Liquid level, for example, can be measured by use of a float, or pressure by utilising a piston pushing against a spring.

12.2.2 Resistance measurement
The simplest measurement of position is obtained by using a potentiometer, as shown in *Figure 12.1*. This can be a conventional rotational potentiometer (multiturn for resolution) or a linear displacement potentiometer.

The output voltage is given by

$$E_{out} = \frac{r}{R} \times E_{in}$$

If r is proportional to the distance or angle moved by the slider, E_{out} will be proportional to the distance. Obviously E_{in} must be a stable reference voltage.

Resistance measurement of position is used where high accuracy is not required, a typical application being the float used on a car fuel gauge. A more sophisticated system is the aerial rotator shown in *Figure 12.1(c)*.

Carbon track potentiometers tend to become 'bitty' with age, and wire-wound types are used exclusively for position measurements. Fine gauge wire is used to give adequate resolution, and this means that low currents have to be used to avoid heating effects. The electrical measuring circuit must have a high input impedance to avoid loading the output voltage. Loading errors appear as a marked nonlinearity in the measurement.

The resistance of the load must be large compared with the resistance of the potentiometer itself. *Figure 12.1(d)* shows the effect of loading a potentiometer. The maximum error occurs at two-thirds

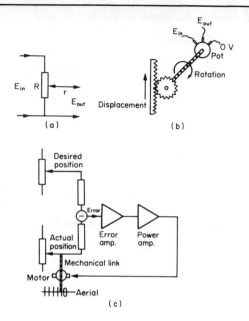

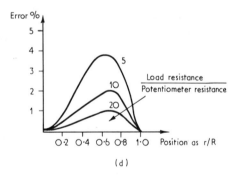

Fig. 12.1 Measurement of position by a potentiometer: (a) basic equations; (b) linear to rotary conversion; (c) simple servo; (d) error induced by loading a potentiometer

travel, and is approximately $25\, r/R$ per cent where r is the potentiometer resistance and R the load resistance. The error can be reduced by lowering the potentiometer resistance, but this in turn increases the potentiometer dissipation (V_s^2/r).

Care needs to be taken with the design of the mechanical linkages in a potentiometric measurement system. The friction in the system is inherently high, and can easily cause errors.

12.2.3 Linear variable differential transformer

The LVDT is a device used for measuring small displacements, and as such is often used for measurements of variables other than position (e.g. weighbridges and accelerometers). A typical arrangement is shown in *Figure 12.2(a)*. The device consists of three transformer windings (one primary and two secondaries in anti-phase) and a movable core.

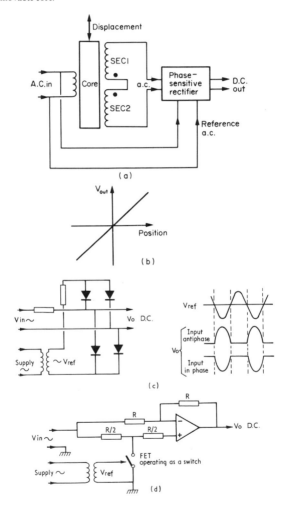

Fig. 12.2 The LVDT: (a) electrical circuit; (b) output voltage versus core position; (c) Cowan phase sensitive rectifier; (d) full-wave phase sensitive rectifier

When the core is at the centre position, the voltages in the two secondary windings will be equal and opposite, giving zero a.c. volts and zero d.c. volts. As the core moves, the voltage in one coil will decrease and the voltage in the other increase. The two a.c. voltages no longer cancel, and there is a net a.c. voltage in the secondary which is in phase with the input voltage. The amplitude of this voltage depends on the displacement.

If the core moves in the opposite direction there is again an imbalance and a voltage, dependent on the displacement, is induced in the coil. This voltage is, however, anti-phase with the input voltage. The output is therefore an a.c. voltage whose amplitude indicates the magnitude of the displacement, and whose phase indicates the direction. This is converted to a positive or negative d.c. voltage (sign dependent on phase) by a phase sensitive rectifier (PSR).

There are several phase sensitive rectifier circuits, two of which are shown in *Figure 12.2*. The circuit of *Figure 12.2(c)* is a half-wave rectifier called a Cowan circuit. When V_{ref} is negative, the diodes are back-biased and V_o follows V_{in}. When V_{ref} is positive the diodes conduct and short out the input signal. The output consists of positive half-cycles if V_{in} is in phase with V_{ref} and negative half-cycles if it is anti-phase. The resistors limit the current through the diodes.

The circuit of *Figure 12.2(d)* is a variation of the inverting/non-inverting amplifier of Subsection 5.4.10. V_{ref} drives the CMOS switch to change the sign of the amplifier gain; positive when V_{ref} is positive, negative when V_{ref} is negative. The amplifier output is full-wave rectified d.c. whose sign depends on the phase relationship between V_{in} and V_{ref}.

LVDTs have many advantages. They are simple, robust and accurate devices. Compared with potentiometers the actuating force is very small. They are accurate and theoretically have infinite resolution. Since they are a low impedance device they do not suffer from loading errors.

12.2.4 Linear variable reluctance transducer

The LVRT is a close relative of the LVDT. It consists of the two coils and movable core shown in *Figure 12.3(a)*. With the core in the null position the inductance of the two coils is equal. As the core moves the inductance of one coil is increased, and the inductance of the other decreased.

The LVRT is usually connected with a transformer to form a bridge circuit, as shown in *Figure 12.3(b)*. Changes in the inductance unbalance the bridge, and with suitable design a linear relationship between output voltage and position is obtained.

12.2.5 Synchros and selsyns

The synchro is the classic position-measuring device (also known as a selsyn, from 'self-synchronous'). It is actually an angular measuring device, but angular and linear movements can easily be translated by simple rack-and-pinion mechanisms.

The term 'synchro' covers a wide family of devices, the simplest of which is the synchro transmitter (CX). This consists of a movable rotor winding and three symmetrical fixed stator windings (*Figure 12.4*).

The rotor is energised with a.c. (usually at 400 Hz), and the voltages induced in the three stator windings uniquely define the

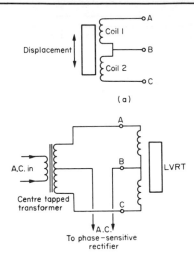

Fig. 12.3 The LVRT: (a) circuit of LVRT; (b) LVRT bridge circuit

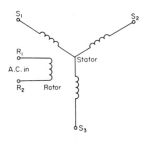

Fig. 12.4 The synchro transmitter

angle of the rotor. The three stator voltages are often referred to as 'three phase', although this is not true in the strict electrical sense. The voltages in the stator windings can only be in phase or antiphase with the rotor signal.

A synchro receiver (CR) has the same electrical construction as the transmitter. The stator leads S_1, S_2, S_3 are connected back to back and the rotor leads in parallel, as shown in *Figure 12.5*. If the rotors of the two synchros are not at the same position, current will flow in the stator leads, producing a torque on the receiver shaft. This torque will rotate the shaft until the two rotors are at the same angle. The receiver thus follows the transmitter position.

The final synchro device to be described is the control transformer (CT). This again has the same electrical construction as the transmitter. A transmitter and control transformer are connected as shown in *Figure 12.6*.

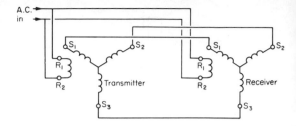

A.C. in

Transmitter

Receiver

Fig. 12.5 A simple synchro link

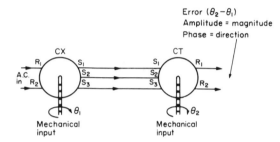

Error $(\theta_2 - \theta_1)$
Amplitude = magnitude
Phase = direction

A.C. in

Mechanical input

Mechanical input

Fig. 12.6 The control transformer

A voltage will be induced in the rotor of the control transformer, dependent on the angle between the two rotors. If they are at the same angle the voltage will be a maximum, if they are at 90°, the voltage will be zero. In practice, the output shaft and input shaft are deemed to be aligned when the output voltage is zero, as this makes the design of a servosystem easier.

The control transformer thus produces an error voltage between the electrical signal on the stator lines and the mechanical signal on the shaft. The magnitude of the voltage indicates the size of the error and the phase, the direction.

The resolver, shown on *Figure 12.7(a)*, is a close relative of the synchro family. As can be seen it has a single wound rotor and two stator windings at 90 degrees. The resolver can be used in two modes.

In the first, *Figure 12.7(b)*, an a.c. voltage is applied to the rotor. A.C. voltages are induced into the stators with amplitudes:

$$E_1 = K\,V\cos\theta$$
$$E_2 = K\,V\sin\theta$$

where V is applied a.c. voltage and K a coupling constant.

In the second arrangement, *Figure 12.7(c)*, the stators are fed with a.c. voltages of equal amplitude but phase shifted by 90 degrees. This gives a constant amplitude output voltage from the rotor with phase shift directly equal to the rotor angle (this follows from trigonometrical manipulations which are beyond the scope of this book).

The first circuit is commonly used for coordinate conversion, and the second circuit for position measurement.

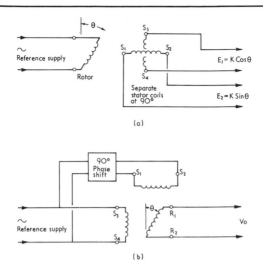

Fig. 12.7 The resolver: (a) drive signal applied to rotor coil, outputs from stator coil; (b) drive applied to rotor with phase shift

A recent addition to the synchro family is the synchro to digital converter (SDC); this converts the three stator voltages to a digital binary number (*Figure 12.8*). The binary number can then be converted to an analogue voltage by a DAC or read directly by a computer.

Synchros are high precision, low torque devices. A typical resolution is ± 3 min of arc in $360°$, or 1 part in 7200. This can be improved further by the use of coarse/fine synchros.

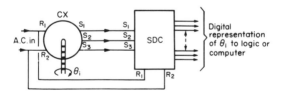

Fig. 12.8 The synchro to digital converter

12.2.6 Shaft encoders

Shaft encoders are again angular measurement devices which use optical techniques to convert a shaft angle to a digital number. Shaft encoders can be either incremental or absolute.

An incremental encoder simply gives a pulse every time the shaft moves through a certain angle. Depending on the resolution required, this can be a toothed wheel moving in front of a probe or a fine optical grating moving in front of a PEC. By the use of two offset pulse trains, the direction of rotation can be inferred. Incremental encoders require external logic to count the pulses, and hence suffer from the disadvantage that the position is lost in the event of a power failure.

Absolute encoders are based on an optical disc and multitrack PECs, as shown in *Figure 12.9*. By their nature, absolute encoders keep their position during a power failure.

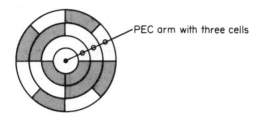

Fig. 12.9 3-bit absolute encoder disc (outer track is least significant)

A simple device such as *Figure 12.9*, however, has some inherent problems. Consider what happens as it goes from position 3 (011) to 4 (100). It is unlikely that all PECs will change at the same time, so transitions 011–000–100 or 011–111–111 or any other combination of three bits are possible. To overcome this undesirable characteristic, a so-called unit distance code is commonly used. This changes by only one bit between successive steps. A three-bit code (called a Gray code) is:

Decimal	Gray
0	000
1	001
2	011
3	010
4	110
5	111
6	101
7	100

Sometimes these codes are called reflective codes because it will be seen that they have a symmetry about the centre point. 'Binary' Gray codes can be constructed to any desired length and non-binary unit distance codes can also be obtained by using subsets of a full code. A six-step code, for example, can be obtained by using steps 1–6 of the three-bit Gray code above. Note that the reflective property gives no invalid state between steps 6 and 1.

Conversion between Gray code and binary is obtained with simple circuits based on XOR gates. A four-bit circuit is shown in *Figure 12.10(a)*.

An alternative approach is to add anti-ambiguity tracks, as in *Figure 12.10(b)*. These are used with hold/follow latches, as shown, to inhibit changes around the transition points. Anti-ambiguity tracks are used with pure BCD or angular BCD (degrees, minutes, seconds) encoders which are difficult to obtain with unit distance codes.

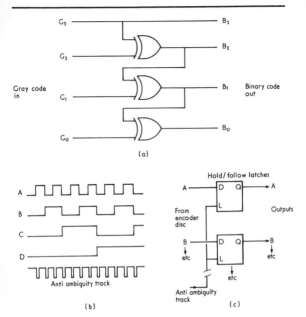

Fig. 12.10 Avoiding false outputs from shaft encoders: (a) Gray to binary conversion; (b) adding anti-ambiguity track to encoder disc; (c) using anti-ambiguity track

Commercial encoders are available to 12-bit resolution (one part in 4000) and usually have the Gray–binary or anti-ambiguity logic in the body of the encoder. All the user has to provide is a power supply, and the outputs can be read directly.

Shaft encoders do not quite have the resolution of synchros, but are preferred where a synchro 400 Hz supply is not available. The resolution can again be improved by the use of a coarse/fine system.

Velocity measurement 12.3

12.3.1 Tachogenerator
The most accurate method of measuring velocity is by tachogenerator. This basically consists of a permanent magnet generator (see Section 13.5) giving a d.c. output voltage directly proportional to shaft speed and polarity, dependent on the direction. Most tachogenerators operate above 100 rev/min.

12.3.2 Contactless tachometers
The incremental shaft encoders of Subsection 12.2.6 can be used to measure velocity. In *Figure 12.11* the pulses are used to trigger a

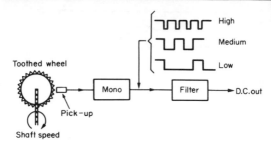

Fig. 12.11 Contactless tachometer

monostable which gives a constant width pulse. The pulses are smoothed to give a mean d.c. level which is proportional to speed.

The pick-up and wheel are usually fairly coarse, making the cost of this device cheaper than a tachogenerator. Contactless tachometers can be used at very low speed.

12.4 Temperature measurement

12.4.1 Introduction
Accurate knowledge of temperature is an important part of many process control schemes. Temperature measurement is thus a well-established subject, with the two basic techniques described below being used in the majority of instruments.

12.4.2 Resistance thermometers
If a wire has a resistance R_o at temperature T_o then its resistance R_T at temperature T will be

$$R_T = R_o(1 + a T + b T^2)$$

where a, b are constants. If $0 < T < 150°C$ the b term can be ignored. Typical values of a per degree C are:

Metal	$a/°C$
Platinum	0·0039
Copper	0·0043
Nickel	0·0068

This change in resistance can be used as the basis of a thermometer. Such devices are known as resistance temperature detectors or RTDs.

Platinum is widely used because it is most linear (but lowest in sensitivity). A common standard uses platinum wire wound for 100 ohms at 0°C. Such devices are called PT100 sensors or PTRs, for platinum resistance thermometer. These can be used over a range from −200°C to 800°C with an accuracy of about 2%. Care is taken in the construction of the sensor to avoid resistance changes from thermal- or shock-induced strain in the wire.

A resistance thermometer is often defined by its change in

resistance between 0°C and 100°C (called the fundamental interval). A PT100 sensor has a resistance of 138·5 ohms at 100°C and hence a fundamental interval of 38·5 ohms.

The change in resistance can be converted to a useful signal by two methods. The first, shown in *Figure 12.12(a)*, uses a constant current source to convert the resistance change to a voltage change. The offset V_r corresponds to IR_o, giving an output voltage proportional to temperature.

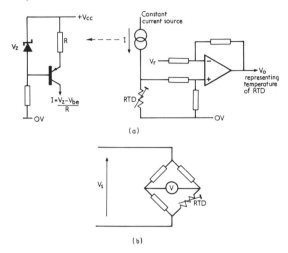

Fig. 12.12 Measuring temperature with an RTD: (a) constant current source; (b) Wheatstone bridge

The second circuit, *Figure 12.12(b)*, uses a Wheatstone bridge circuit with automatic null balancing (unlike the strain gauge bridge circuits described later, the relatively large resistance change gives a non-linear bridge output voltage). The control circuit measures the bridge voltage and injects a current into the other leg to rebalance the bridge. The balancing current is a measure of the resistance change and hence the temperature.

Whichever circuit is used the current through the PTR must be limited to avoid errors from I^2R heating. Typically, dissipation must be kept below 10 mW. Connecting cable resistance can also cause errors, particularly if the cabling itself is subject to temperature changes. These errors can be overcome by using either the three- or four-wire connection circuits of *Figure 12.13*, which ensure that lead resistance errors cancel.

A more sensitive device whose resistance is temperature sensitive is the thermistor. This is a semiconductor crystal whose resistance decreases with temperature. Unfortunately, the change is very non-linear, as shown in *Figure 12.14*. The relationship is given by:

$$R_t = R_o \exp \left[B \left(\frac{1}{T} - \frac{1}{T_o} \right) \right]$$

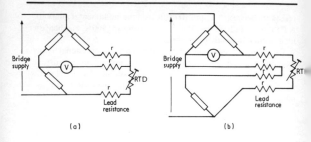

Fig. 12.13 Overcoming the effects of lead resistance on RTDs:
(a) three-wire circuit; (b) four-wire circuit

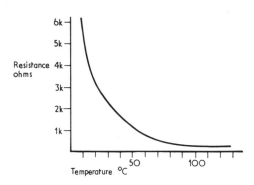

Fig. 12.14 The response of a thermistor

where R_o is the defined resistance at temperature T_o, R_t resistance at
temperature T, and B is a constant (called the characteristic
temperature). A typical device will go from a resistance of 300 KΩ at
0°C to 5 KΩ at 100°C.

Although the response is non-linear, thermistors can be used for
temperature measurement over a restricted range. Their high
sensitivity, however, makes them ideally suited for temperature
switching circuits where a signal is required if a temperature goes
above or below a preset level.

12.4.3 Thermocouples

If two dissimilar metals are joined as shown in *Figure 12.15*, and one
junction is maintained at a high temperature, T_2, while the other is
kept at a lower temperature, T_1, a current will flow which is
dependent on the difference ($T_2 - T_1$). This current, known as the
Peltier effect, is the basis of the temperature sensor called a
thermocouple.

The simplest thermocouple consists of a pair of dissimilar wires
joined to form a hot junction and insulated by materials such as high
temperature plastic, asbestos or glass fibre. The simplest circuit is
shown in *Figure 12.16(a)*, although in practice this is rarely used. A

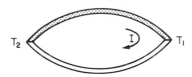

Fig. 12.15 The Peltier effect

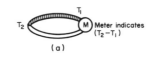

(a)

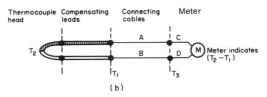

(b)

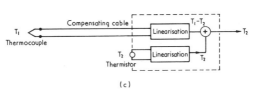

(c)

Fig. 12.16 The thermocouple: (a) simple circuit; (b) practical circuit; (c) cold junction compensation

cold junction is kept at some known temperature T_1 (e.g. melting ice) and the meter will indicate the temperature $(T_2 - T_1)$.

In practice, the meter is remote from the thermocouple, and it would be prohibitively expensive to run thermocouple wires for long distances. A practical circuit is shown in *Figure 12.16(b)*. The thermocouple head is at temperature T_2, and compensating leads made of the same material as the head are used to run to some convenient place at temperature T_1. Normal connecting leads A, B are then run to the meter whose connecting leads are C, D. Providing A and B are the same material and C and D are the same material (not necessarily the same as A and B), then the temperature of the meter connections T_3 has no effect. The meter will indicate $T_2 - T_1$.

In most applications the junction between the compensating leads and the connecting cables will be made in the cubicle containing the indicating meter so T_1 and T_3 will be the same. Usually the meter will be required to indicate T_2 directly, and ignore T_1 and T_3. If the cubicle temperature is constant this can be done with an offset zero, otherwise some form of automatic correction is needed.

The technique in *Figure 12.16(c)* is called cold junction compensation. The cubicle temperature T_3 is measured (by a resistance thermometer or a thermistor) and a correction added to the thermocouple indicated temperature ($T_2 - T_1$). An alternative, but not very practical, technique immerses the junction between compensating and connecting leads in an ice/water bath, giving T_1 a temperature of 0°C. The indicator now reads T_2 directly in degrees C.

Common thermocouple combinations with well-documented characteristics have evolved. These have been given code letters. Some of the more usual are given below, along with their ranges and sensitivities.

+ Material	− Material	Code	Range °C	μV/°C
Nickel/chromium	Nickel/aluminium	K	0 to 1100	42
Copper	Copper/nickel	T	− 185 to 300	45
Iron	Copper/nickel	J	20 to 700	50
Platinum/rhodium	Platinum	R	0 to 1600	10

Type R alloy is made from platinum/13% rhodium, and is commonly used in the UK. Elsewhere 10% rhodium is more commonly used and this thermocouple is designated type S. This is similar in range and sensitivity to type R.

Over limited ranges a thermocouple output is linear, but it is more usual to represent the response by:

$$V = a + bT + cT^2 + dT^3$$

where T is the temperature, V the thermocouple voltage and a, b, c, d are constants (not necessarily positive). Linearising circuits are provided as part of the cold junction compensation on most indicators.

The above table shows that thermocouple voltages are very small, usually a few millivolts at most. High gain, high stability d.c. amplifiers are therefore needed, and extreme care must be taken to avoid noise effects in the plant-to-cubicle cabling. Input amplifiers must be designed for high CMMR. In critical applications, a high impedance voltage source is connected across the thermocouple cables so that, in the event of an open circuit failure, the indicator goes to full-scale high and alarms the operators to the fault.

D.C. amplifiers are described in Chapter 5.

12.4.4 Other techniques

There are many other physical quantities which vary with temperature, and all can be used as the basis of thermometers. The leakage current of a back-biased diode is very temperature-dependent, for example, and transducers have been built utilising this change. The response is, however, extremely nonlinear and varies greatly from device to device.

The V_{be} drop of a conducting transistor is also temperature-dependent, varying predictably by 2 mV per °C. A thermometer based on this principle is shown in *Figure 12.17*. An accuracy of 1 °C is achievable over the range 0–100 °C.

The bending of a bimetallic strip due to differential expansion has been used in some devices. The bending is measured by a position-measuring device to indicate the temperature. At its simplest, this type of circuit is used as an on/off room thermostat in domestic central heating.

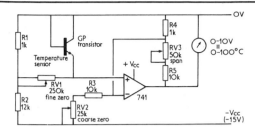

Fig. 12.17 Thermometer based on Vbe of a transistor

Despite all these ingenious methods, however, the resistance thermometer and the thermocouple are used in over 90% of temperature measurement circuits.

Weighing and load measurements 12.5

Accurate measurement of weight is required in many applications, from packaging to process control. There are two basic techniques in use. The first is shown in *Figure 12.18(a)*, where the weight to be measured is balanced against the force *F*. In its simplest form this principle is used in old-fashioned grocery scales, while complex schemes using pneumatic or hydraulic pressure to balance the weight are used in industrial weighers.

The second technique loads part of the weigher, to cause a change in dimensions. The simplest form of this technique is a spring balance, as shown in *Figure 12.18(b)*, where the deflection is a measure of the weight.

Devices using the second technique are known as strain weighers, where we define

$$\text{Strain } E = \frac{\Delta L}{L}$$

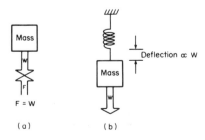

Fig. 12.18 Basic weighing techniques: (a) balance weigher; (b) strain weigher

where L is the unloaded dimension and ΔL the change in length. To a very good approximation, the strain is proportional to the applied load.

Because the weight is converted to a change in position, many weighers use the position-measuring devices described in Section 12.2 to give an electrical signal. Circuits based on LVDTs are particularly popular.

Most weighers, however, utilise circuits based on strain gauges. A strain gauge consists of a very thin resistive film, with a layout similar to that in *Figure 12.19(a)*, which is bonded to some stressed part of the weigher. The bonding is done using normal epoxy resin adhesives. As the load is applied to the weigher, the stressed members undergo strain and change dimension. Similar changes in dimension occur in the attached strain gauge, causing the gauge resistance to alter.

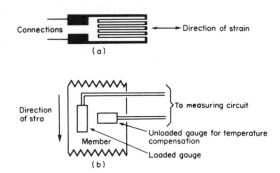

Fig. 12.19 Strain gauges: (a) typical strain gauge; (b) temperature compensation

The sensitivity of a strain gauge is defined by the 'gauge factor', denoted by K, where

$$K = \frac{\Delta R/R}{\Delta L/L} = \frac{\Delta R/R}{E}$$

A typical gauge will have a resistance R of 100 Ω and a gauge factor of 2.

Strain gauges and resistance thermometers have similar constructions, so it is not surprising that the resistance of a strain gauge varies with temperature. To overcome this, two gauges are often used, as shown in *Figure 12.19(b)*. The unloaded gauge provides temperature compensation when both gauges are connected in a bridge circuit.

Improved sensitivity and temperature compensation can be obtained by the use of four strain gauges in a bridge, with two gauges undergoing tensile forces and two undergoing compressive forces. Many weighers use the O-ring arrangement of *Figure 12.20(a)*. Under tension, gauges A and D suffer compressive forces and gauges B and C suffer tensile forces. A similar result is obtained from the four gauges mounted on the hollow cylinder of *Figure 12.20(b)*.

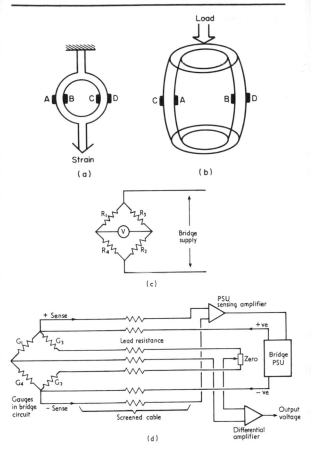

Fig. 12.20 Load cells: (a) 'O'-ring cell; (b) cylinder cell; (c) four-gauge bridge circuit; (d) bridge cabling and zeroing

A typical bridge circuit is shown in *Figure 12.20(c)*. If the circuit is arranged such that R_1 and R_2 increase in resistance with load, and R_3 and R_4 decrease with load, voltage V_x will increase and V_y decrease when load is applied. Temperature will affect all gauges equally and hence have no effect. If E is the applied strain and V the applied bridge voltage, the output voltage V_o is given by:

$$V_o = 2 E K V$$

where K is the gauge factor. The above equation implies that the bridge voltage should be large to increase the sensitivity. The bridge currents must not cause heating, however, and 24 V is a practical limit.

Cabling of strain gauge bridges must be done with care to avoid interference and errors induced by the resistance of the connecting leads. *Figure 12.20(d)* shows a typical scheme, which also incorporates zeroing for the bridge. The lead resistances, r, cancel and do not affect the indicated voltage. High gain, high stability d.c. amplifiers with good CMMR are required to bring the bridge voltage to useful levels.

The use of strain gauges is rather a 'black art', and great care is needed to obtain satisfactory results. In particular, the manufacturer's mounting instructions must be followed implicitly regarding mounting and connections.

12.6 **Sound**

12.6.1 **Microphones**
A microphone is an essential part of any recording or sound measurement system, and is, of course, a transducer converting sound into electrical energy.

The commonest form of microphone is the moving coil, illustrated in *Figure 12.21(a)*. A coil of wire is suspended between the poles of a permanent magnet, and the coil is connected to a movable diaphragm. Sound waves cause the diaphragm to move, and this movement causes the coil to move in the magnetic field. A varying voltage is thus induced in the coil, dependent on the velocity of the coil which in turn depends on the sound impinging on the diaphragm. Moving coil microphones are low output (typically a few millivolts), low impedance (typically a few hundred ohms), high quality devices.

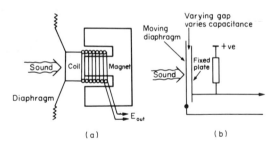

Fig. 12.21 Microphones: (a) moving coil; (b) capacitor

A second type of microphone is based on the piezoelectric effect. Several materials, notably Rochelle salt, develop an electrical potential across their surfaces when subjected to stress. The voltage is proportional to the stress, and voltages sufficiently high to jump a spark gap can be obtained if the crystal is struck sharply. The piezoelectric effect is used in the so-called 'crystal' microphones. A piezoelectric crystal is coupled mechanically to a microphone diaphragm. Sound impinging on the diaphragm induces stress in the crystal, which causes a voltage to appear on the output leads. Crystal microphones are high impedance (megohm), high output (about 0·5 V) devices. The quality is not as good as the other types of microphone described in this subsection.

The piezoelectric effect is also used in a wide range of transducers, common applications being accelerometers and gas igniters. Subsection 12.6.2 expands further on the use of ultrasonic transducers.

The final type of microphone (known as a condenser microphone) utilises the sound to vary the capacitance of an electrical circuit. In *Figure 12.21(b)*, the diaphragm is shown mounted parallel and close to a second plate. These two plates form a capacitor, whose value depends on the area of the plate and their separation (see Section 2.2).

Sound waves cause the diaphragm to vibrate, varying the separation between the plate, and hence the capacitance. The capacitor is connected to a fixed voltage through a resistor R. Changes in capacitance cause the voltages across it to vary, and the output voltage will be a representation of the sound impinging on the diaphragm.

Condenser microphones are generally of high quality, and give a fairly high output at a reasonable impedance level. The major disadvantage is the need to apply the fixed d.c. voltage.

12.6.2 Ultrasonics

The piezoelectric effect described above can be used to make a microphone that can operate above audio frequencies. Frequencies above 20 kHz are known as ultrasonics. The piezoelectric effect can also be used to produce sound. If a large amplitude a.c. signal is applied to a piezoelectric crystal, the crystal will vibrate producing sound at the applied frequency.

Ultrasonic transmitters and receivers are constructed such that mechanical resonance occurs at the operating frequency. This gives receivers of high sensitivity and transmitters of high intensity output.

A typical receiver and transmitter circuit is shown in *Figure 12.22*. The transmitter has a simple IC oscillator, driving the transmitter directly. The receiver is a simple a.c. amplifier, with a bandpass filter to increase the sensitivity at the operating frequency. The amplifier output is rectified to drive a relay.

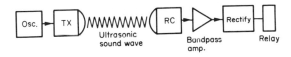

Fig. 12.22 Ultrasonic replacement for PEC system

Ultrasonics has a wide range of uses – in remote control, burglar alarms and level detection, for example. A particularly important use is crack detection, illustrated in *Figure 12.23*. A sharp ultrasonic pulse is applied to the surface under test. The ultrasonic beam is reflected off any cracks in the material, allowing them to be observed. Ultrasonic scanning is widely used in the construction and aircraft industries.

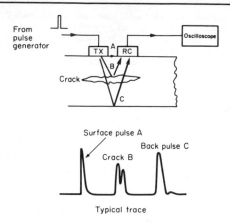

Fig. 12.23 Ultrasonic scanning

Similar techniques are used in medicine for body scans where X-rays cannot be used (e.g. during pregnancy).

12.7 The Hall effect

In *Figure 12.24(a)* a crystal is carrying current in a transverse magnetic field. In this arrangement certain crystals develop a potential across the faces that are normal to both the electric current and the magnetic field. The potential developed is proportional to the magnitude of the current and the strength of the magnetic field.

This phenomenon is called the Hall effect (after its discoverer E. H. Hall) and arises because the magnetic field deflects a proportion of the electrons moving in the electric current.

Hall effect transducers are used in some magnetic and electric transducers. *Figure 12.24(b)*, for example, shows a Hall effect wattmeter. The magnetic field is produced by the line current, and the driving current derived from the line voltage. The output voltage from the Hall crystal will be $K I E \cos \phi$, where ϕ is the phase angle and K a constant. The output voltage is thus proportional to true watts.

The Hall effect is also used for oscilloscope current probes and as a linear multiplier.

12.8 General observations

All signals from transducers are small and need amplification before they can be of use. Particular care needs to be taken at the low level

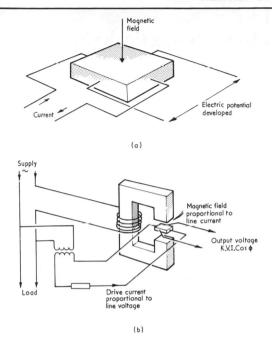

Fig. 12.24 The Hall effect transducer: (a) the Hall effect; (b) Hall effect wattmeter

signal side where unwanted effects like noise, thermoelectric voltages, ground loops, etc., can introduce errors greater than the voltage from the transducer. Amplifiers must therefore have differential inputs and high CMRR.

Current outputs from the amplifier are often used in preference to voltage outputs to provide increased noise immunity. A common standard utilises a current range of 4–20 mA, where 4 mA represents zero and 20 mA full scale. The offset means that an open circuit or shorted cable will cause the indicator to read offscale negative. This safety feature is very important in, say, nuclear reactor or chemical plant instrumentation.

The subject of transducers and instrumentation is very wide, and this chapter has only dealt with it superficially. There are transducers available to measure any obscure variable, and for further details the reader is referred to any of the standard texts on instrumentation.

13
Electromagnetic devices

13.1 Introduction

It can easily be demonstrated, by experiments similar to those in
Figure 13.1, that a coil of wire carrying an electric current produces a
magnetic field. In general, the field strength is directly proportional to
the product of the current and the number of turns in the coil, i.e.

$$\phi = K \cdot I \cdot N$$

where K is the constant of proportionality.

The electrical properties of a coil are discussed in Section 2.3.

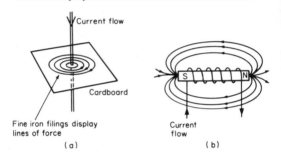

Fig. 13.1 Electromagnetic effects: (a) magnetic field around single
wire; (b) magnetic field around a coil

13.2 Relays

A relay is a device which uses a small control current to switch a
considerably larger load current. A conventional relay is shown in
Figure 13.2. The control current passes through the coil attracting the
armature against the force of the return spring, completing the load
circuit.

There are many variations on relay design. The coil voltage can be
d.c., with the coil current defined by the coil resistance, or a.c., with
the coil current defined by the inductance. Relays can be obtained
with coil voltages from a few volts to several hundred volts.

Relay contacts are defined as 'normally open' or 'normally closed'.
Movement of the armature can be 'slugged' for a few milliseconds by
short-circuit rings around the poles or for periods of up to several
minutes by pneumatic bellows.

The common arrangements are summarised in *Figure 13.3*.

Relays are slow devices. A small low voltage relay will energise in
around 15 ms and de-energise in around 30 ms. Times of over 100 ms
are typical for large relays used in motor circuits.

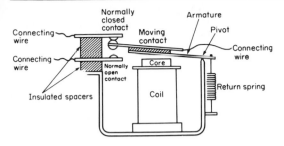

Fig. 13.2 Mechanical parts of typical changeover relay

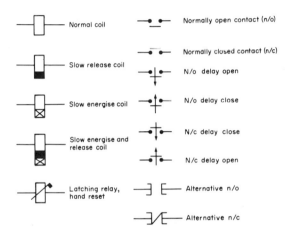

Fig. 13.3 Relay symbols

13.2.1 Reed relays

Reed relays are popular in mixed electronic/electromagnetic circuits. These consist of two flat magnetic reeds, hermetically sealed in a glass tube. The tube is enclosed in an operating coil (*Figure 13.4*).

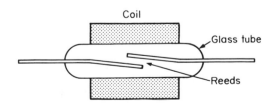

Fig. 13.4 The reed relay

The magnetic field in the coil causes the reeds to attract each other, completing the load circuit. The required field is small, hence the coil power is low. A typical reed relay will require 10 mA at 10 V to switch. The small dimensions of the contacts limit the load current to around 200 mA and the load voltage to around 100 V.

Reed relays can also be switched by small permanent magnets. Typical applications are counting circuits and safety interlocks.

13.3 Applications of relays

In many relay applications a solid-state logic scheme could often have been used, taking up less space and using less power at lower cost. It is worth while considering the peculiar advantage of relays that have kept them popular in the age of the microprocessor.

Relays give far greater isolation between input and output than is possible with simple electronic circuits, and the 'power gain' from coil to load is considerable.

In many industrial applications the technical expertise of maintenance staff is low, and a relay is a readily understandable device. An electrician can easily follow a complex relay scheme incorporating slugged and latching relays, but could not follow the same scheme translated into AND gates and monostables. Relays are thus both robust and simple to maintain.

Electrical noise is a common problem with logic schemes, although it is almost impossible for a relay scheme to have noise problems (internally, anyway; they are prone to cause noise problems elsewhere).

Finally, relays can be designed to be fail-safe. In the traffic light scheme in *Figure 13.5* we can say the relays might fail to either road, or fail with two reds or no lights; but we can guarantee it will *not* fail with two greens. This is an assurance we are unable to give with any purely electronic scheme.

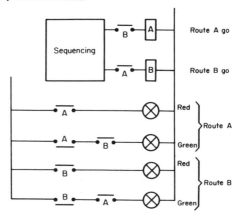

Fig. 13.5 Fail-safe relay scheme

Relays can easily be driven from electronic circuits, with transistors being used to switch d.c. coils and triacs for a.c. coils. The inductance of the coil can cause large voltage spikes at turn-off, and in d.c. circuits a spike suppression diode, similar to that in *Figure 13.6(a)*, should be used. In a.c. circuits, such as that in *Figure 13.6(b)*, the triac will automatically turn off a zero current, thereby minimising the problem.

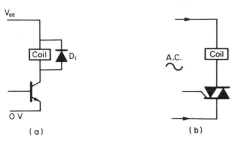

Fig. 13.6 Inductive loads: (a) d.c. circuit (spike-suppression diode); (b) a.c. circuit

Solenoids 13.4

A solenoid is simply a coil of wire wound around a cylindrical former. Inside the former an iron plunger is free to move. When current passes through the coil it behaves like a magnet pulling the plunger. The solenoid is thus an actuator, converting electrical energy into linear mechanical motion.

Solenoids can be designed to work on a.c. or d.c. In general, d.c. operation is preferred as the pull on an a.c. solenoid is not constant. The coil of a solenoid is highly inductive, and the precautions outlined in Section 13.3 should be followed.

Solenoids are frequently pulsed to step a ratchet or drive a model railway point, for example. Capacitance discharge circuits are popular for driving pulsed solenoids. A typical circuit is shown in *Figure 13.7*.

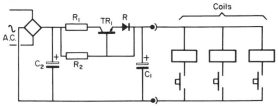

Fig. 13.7 Capacitor discharge circuit for driving solenoids: C discharges into selected coil, recharges via R and Tr when all PBs are released

13.5 Generators and motors

13.5.1 Introduction
Although they are not electronic devices, generators and motors are often controlled by electronic circuits, so it is useful to have some knowledge of their operation. This section outlines the basic principles.

13.5.2 Generators
If a coil is moved through a magnetic field, an e.m.f. is produced which is given by

$$E = BlNv$$

where B is the field strength, l the length of the coil, N the number of turns in the coil, and v the velocity.

It follows that if the coil in *Figure 13.8(a)* is rotated, an alternating voltage will be produced at the slip rings. The frequency will depend on the speed of rotation, and the amplitude on the factors in the equation above. This is the basis of an alternator.

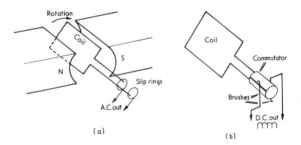

Fig. 13.8 A.C. and d.c. generators: (a) a.c. generator (alternator); (b) d.c. generator

If the slip rings are replaced by a commutator as shown in *Figure 13.8(b)*, pulsating d.c. is produced. In practice, multisegment commutators are used to reduce the ripple to acceptable levels.

In *Figure 13.8*, the field is provided by a permanent magnet. In practice, field coils are usually used, common arrangements of which are shown in *Figure 13.9(a)–(d)*. The arrangement of *Figure 13.9(d)* is particularly useful, as it allows easy control of the output voltage.

13.5.3 Motors
An electric motor is identical in construction to a generator. If current is passed through a wire in a magnetic field, the wire will experience a force proportional to the field strength and the current. It follows that the motor coil in *Figure 13.10* will rotate. As before, multisegment commutators are used in practice to provide smooth torque.

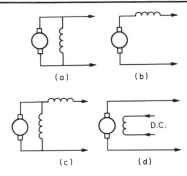

Fig. 13.9 Field excitation: (a) shunt field; (b) series field; (c) split field; (d) separate field

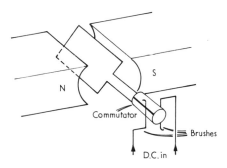

Fig. 13.10 D.C. motor

As the coil starts to rotate, the coil will generate a voltage opposing the applied volts, as explained in the previous section. At any given speed, therefore, the motor equation is

$$V = E + iR$$

where V is the applied volts, E the generated back-e.m.f., i the armature current, and R the armature resistance.

Since $E \propto wB$, where w is the rotational speed and B is the field strength, it follows that i is maximum at zero speed and decreases as the speed increases. The torque, T, is proportional to the current and the field strength; thus

$$T \propto iB$$

so the speed will rise until the torque balances the applied load.

The speed of a d.c. motor can therefore be controlled by varying the field strength or the armature voltage. The field can be provided by a permanent magnet, or by arrangements similar to the generator fields in *Figure 13.9*.

13.5.4 The stepper motor

Normal d.c. or a.c. motors can assume any angular position. If they are used for position control, some form of separate position transducer and control system must be used. The stepper motor can only assume fixed angular positions, and is moved from one to the next by a series of pulses. It is therefore possible to drive a stepper motor from, say, a computer and know where the load is at all times without a position transducer. The torque available from stepping motors is, however, small, and they can only be used in applications such as small robots or head positioners for disc drives.

One form of stepper motor, called the variable reluctance motor, is shown in *Figure 13.11(a)*. The rotor is made of soft iron, and has a number of teeth which are unequal to the number of stator teeth. The stator has series of coils which are driven as three (or more) separate groups from the controlling logic. This is sometimes (incorrectly) called a three-phase supply.

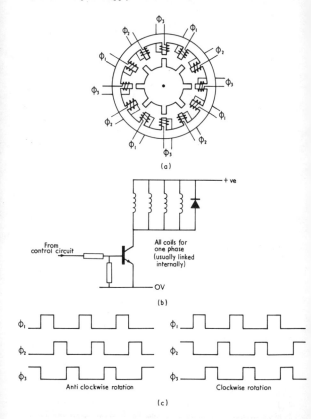

Fig. 13.11 The stepper motor: (a) stepper motor construction; (b) drive circuit (one phase shown, three identical); (c) driving waveforms

When a group is energised (phase 3 in the diagram) the rotor will align itself with the energised coils to give least magnetic reluctance. To move the rotor, the current group is de-energised, and a new group energised. The rotor rotates to a new position of minimum reluctance. If phase 1 was energised after phase 3, the rotor would rotate one step to the left for example. Phase 2 after phase 3 would cause it to rotate one step to the right.

The number of steps per revolution is given by:

$$N = \frac{S \cdot R}{S - R}$$

where S is the number of stator slots and R the number of rotor slots. Common step sizes are 7·5 degrees and 1·8 degrees.

The stepper motor of *Figure 13.11* needs to have one phase energised to hold the rotor in position. A variation, called a hybrid stepper motor, has a magnetically energised rotor with offset slots. This allows the rotor to hold its position without any power being applied.

Stepper motors are driven by quite simple circuits such as *Figure 13.11(b)*. Pulsing the outputs as in *Figure 13.11(c)* will cause the motor to rotate a known angular distance for each pulse.

13.5.5 The loudspeaker

The loudspeaker is a device for converting electrical energy into sound energy, and is, in fact, a close relative of the electric motor. A moving coil loudspeaker is shown in *Figure 13.12*.

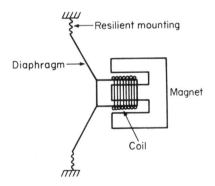

Fig. 13.12 Moving coil loudspeaker

The electrical signal is applied to a coil suspended between the poles of a strong permanent magnet. The current produces forces on the coil as explained above, deflecting the diaphragm. The deflection of the diaphragm causes sound waves to radiate from the loudspeaker. In a correctly designed loudspeaker, the sound waves will be a copy of the applied voltage.

14
Electronic instruments

14.1 Introduction

Any engineer involved with electronics, whether for design or
maintenance, requires instruments. Depending on both finance and
the complexity of the equipment, the needs can vary from a simple
cheap multimeter to a full electronics laboratory.

In this chapter, several useful instruments are described.

14.2 Multimeters and bridge instruments

14.2.1 Multimeters

It is no exaggeration to say that a multimeter is an essential part of
any electronics engineers tool kit. All meters are based on the moving
coil meter shown in *Figure 14.1*.

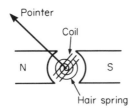

Fig. 14.1 Moving coil meter

A lightweight coil is pivoted between the poles of a permanent
magnet, and is restrained by a hairspring. When direct current passes
through the coil, it is deflected by the magnetic field, causing the
pointer to move. The pointer movement is proportional to the coil
current.

The meter is basically a current measuring device, and is usually
designed to have a full-scale current of around 100 μA. Voltages are
measured by means of a series resistor and current by means of a
shunt resistor, as in *Figure 14.2(a)* and *14.2(b)*.

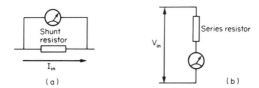

Fig. 14.2 Basic circuits of multimeters: (a) current measurement;
(b) voltage measurement

The moving coil meter only operates on d.c. For use with alternating current measurements the meter is connected via an internal bridge rectifier. The meter is then calibrated for r.m.s. readings on a true sine wave. It will not read correctly on other a.c. waveforms.

Multimeters are simply a moving coil meter with suitable shunt and series resistors selected by the mode/range switches. They can vary in price from a few pounds to around £100.

The basic difference between these meters is their sensitivity. Any meter will affect the circuit to which it is connected. On the current range the meter will have a voltage drop across it; on the voltage range the meter will draw significant current from the circuit. Both of these measurements will affect the validity of the reading to some extent.

The better the meter, the less will be the loading. The sensitivity of a voltmeter is determined by the current drawn for full-scale deflection (FSD). A cheap meter will have 1 mA for FSD (sometimes represented as 1000 Ω/V). A good meter will need 50 μA for FSD (represented as 20 000 Ω/V).

Equipment circuit diagrams often give test voltages at various places in the circuit, and these are usually specified at a particular instrument sensitivity. Meters with other sensitivities will give different readings because the loading will not be the same.

Most multimeters measure resistance by variations on the circuit shown in *Figure 14.3*. The terminals are shorted and RV₁ is adjusted for FSD on the meter, then the measurement is made. Note that the scale reads the opposite way to the voltage and current ranges, and is nonlinear.

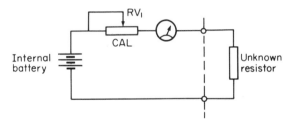

Fig. 14.3 Measurement of resistance

Multimeters have hazardous lives and most get connected across a high voltage while on a current range at some times in their life. With a cheap meter that is the end of the meter, but more expensive versions incorporate some protection. The commonest protection is a current trip in series with the meter, and diodes across the meter to shunt the excess current. The voltage across the meter movement will not rise above a few tenths of a volt in ordinary use, so the diodes will normally have no effect.

If finances permit, the ideal arrangement is to have two multimeters – a cheap one to carry round and generally 'misuse', and a good one as a standard back at the workshop.

14.2.2 Electronic multimeters

There are many circuits where even the loading of a 20 kΩ/V meter is intolerable. The use of a high impedance electronic amplifier before a conventional meter gives sensitivities of several megohms per volt. Electronic multimeters, once known as valve voltmeters (VVMs), now use transistors, FETs or integrated circuits.

The basis of an electronic multimeter is shown in *Figure 14.4*. This is basically a long-tail pair amplifier (see Chapter 5) and could be made equally well with FETs or valves. The normal multimeter switching to give different ranges for current, voltage or resistance precedes point A.

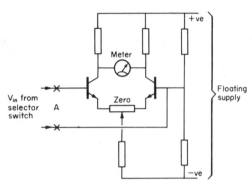

Fig. 14.4 Electronic multimeter

Electronic multimeters are usually more versatile than simple ones, and have voltage ranges from a few millivolts to several kilovolts, and a similar wide range on current and resistance. They do, however, have some peculiar quirks. Unlike a conventional meter they do not have a 'true' zero, and most have adjustments for zero and FSD. Often these interact. On several multimeters the zero and FSD drift noticeably as the meter warms up, and even more significantly as the battery runs down.

An electronic multimeter is an instrument that is indispensable in several applications, but its use should be tempered with care.

14.2.3 Digital multimeters (DMMs)

The DMM is a variation on the electronic multimeter. It is a conventional multimeter, but displays the value as a digital number on LED or LCD displays (see Chapter 9). There are several ICs designed for DMMs which accept a voltage input in the range 0–200 mV and drive displays directly.

The IC is preceded by the usual shunts and potential dividers to allow the DMM to measure any voltage, current or resistance range required. The stability of these ICs is very good and DMMs do not usually exhibit the quirks of electronic multimeters. Their sensitivity is, however, as good as most electronic multimeters.

The displays can show a reading in the range 0–1999 with decimal point (known as $3\frac{1}{2}$ digit) or 0–19999 (known as $4\frac{1}{2}$ digit). In both cases the top digit can only display 0 or 1.

Most DMMs have auto-polarity selection in the IC, and a plus or a minus sign is displayed accordingly. This is useful for the observation of a slowly varying voltage which changes polarity.

DMMs are very useful where extreme precision is required (e.g. zeroing d.c. amplifiers), but they are not suited for some applications. If the voltage being measured is varying quickly, it is not possible to interpret the blur of fast-varying digits. A DMM is thus useless for applications such as measuring the volts across a d.c. drive motor.

Many expensive DMMs have auto-ranging. This is a mixed blessing, as it can be infuriating when you are observing a voltage that is varying around a range change trigger point. The annoyance is increased if you are observing a voltage varying from 1 V to 200 V, say, which requires two range changes. On some meters, range changes take about 1s, and these instruments are totally useless for following even a slowly varying voltage. If an auto-ranging DMM is being purchased, it should have at least a 'hold high range' switch, and preferably manual range selection as well as auto-range.

The DMM is thus best suited as a laboratory bench instrument where it can be invaluable. Its purchase should be considered in addition to, not in place of, a conventional multimeter.

14.2.4 Bridge instruments

The instruments described in the preceding section can measure resistance, but cannot measure capacitance or inductance. These quantities can be measured by bridge circuits.

There are many variations on the basic principle, but all bridge circuits are based on the Wheatstone bridge, shown in *Figure 14.5*. The meter G is a sensitive galvanometer.

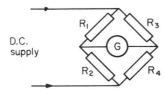

Fig. 14.5 Wheatstone bridge

Simple analysis will show that the current through G will be zero when

$$\frac{R_1}{R_2} = \frac{R_3}{R_4}$$

In practice, R_3 and R_4 are equal precision resistors, and R_1 is unknown. R_2 is a precision resistance box which is varied until the galvanometer reads zero. R_2 is then equal to R_1.

The relationship of the Wheatstone bridge applies equally well to a.c. circuits, and can be used to measure capacitance and inductance. There are many a.c. bridges, a typical example being the Maxwell bridge shown in *Figure 14.6*, where an unknown inductance is balanced against a standard capacitor.

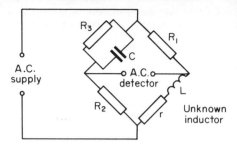

Fig. 14.6 Maxwell bridge

Analysis will show that

$$L = CR_1R_2$$

and

$$r = \frac{R_1R_2}{R_3}$$

where r is the internal resistance of the inductor.

The balance condition is independent of the supply frequency.

Bridge meters are readily available for measurement of L, C and R. Usually these consist of a balance meter or a 'magic eye', a mode switch to select L, C or R, a coarse range switch and a fine variable dial. These are laboratory instruments, and are not really part of the first-line technician's tool kit.

14.3 Oscilloscopes

The cathode ray oscilloscope is an essential part of any electronic workshop or laboratory. The oscilloscope is a device which permits the visual examination of high frequency waveforms which would be totally impossible to observe by other means.

The basis of the oscilloscope is shown in *Figure 14.7*. The heart of the instrument is a cathode ray tube (CRT). An electron gun emits a narrow beam of electrons which strike a fluorescent screen at the front of the CRT. In the absence of any deflection this would produce a small spot on the screen face.

The electron beam, however, passes between two plate sets, called the X plates and the Y plates. Application of a voltage to these plates will cause the beam to deflect because of the electrostatic effects described in Chapter 1. The X plates deflect the beam horizontally, whereas the Y plates deflect the beam vertically.

In most applications, the X plates are driven from a time-base. This produces a sawtooth voltage comprising a linear rise and a sharp return to zero. This deflects the spot of the electron beam across the tube face at a constant speed, followed by a fast return for the next scan.

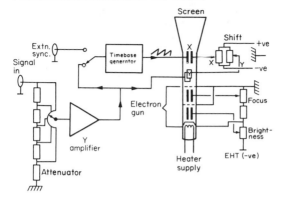

Fig. 14.7 Oscilloscope

The voltage to be measured is amplified by a high input impedance amplifier and is applied to the Y plates. This will deflect the beam vertically, and the resulting electron beam path will trace out a path on the screen, visually representing the variation of the input voltage with time. The phenomenon of vision persistence will make the electron path appear as a continuous trace.

The input waveform is often quite small, but superimposed on a large d.c. voltage (e.g. a 100 mV audio signal at a transistor collector could be at several volts d.c. with respect to earth). A useful facility is an a.c./d.c. coupling switch to allow the d.c. component to be removed if required. Often a ground position is provided to allow the beam to be positioned accurately.

If the waveform is to appear in the same position on the screen each time, the timebase and the input must be synchronised. It is impractical to control the timebase frequency accurately enough, so a trigger circuit is used. The timebase is triggered each time the input waveform crosses an adjustable trigger voltage. This is summarised in *Figure 14.8*. Triggering can also be controlled to occur on an edge, and most oscilloscopes have five trigger modes: d.c. positive level; d.c. negative level; positive edge; negative edge; trigger to supply (50 or 60 Hz). Some oscilloscopes have an 'auto' trigger facility which detects the mean d.c. level of the input and starts the timebase when the mean level is crossed. The front panel controls of a typical single-beam oscilloscope are shown in *Figure 14.9*.

An oscilloscope is mostly used to observe high frequency waveforms (i.e. audio and above). The performance of an oscilloscope is limited by the response of the Y amplifier and the probes. The amplifier must have a flat response from d.c. to several megahertz (around 5 MHz is adequate for most applications). The probes must have high input impedance and very little capacitance to avoid loading the circuit. A typical probe will have figures of 10 MΩ and 5 pF. These can be improved if the probe attenuates the signal before the Y amplifier, and high quality probes are often 10 to 1 attenuators (known as × 10 probes).

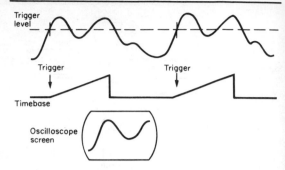

Fig. 14.8 Synchronising of the timebase

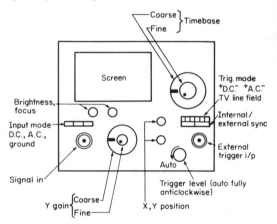

Fig. 14.9 Oscilloscope controls

In pulse circuits, the probes themselves can produce ringing or poor edges if the probe frequency response is not flat (see *Figure 14.10*). High quality probes are provided with adjustments to level out the response. These usually consist of some form of trimming capacitor.

The oscilloscope shown in *Figure 14.9* is a fairly basic model, and there are many additional features on more expensive scopes. The most useful facility is the addition of a second Y amplifier to allow two waveforms to be displayed.

The cheapest way to display two waveforms is to use an electronic switch to 'chop' between the two amplifiers. If the chopping frequency is sufficiently fast it will not be apparent to the eye, and the two traces will appear to be separate. It is possible to turn an ordinary single trace scope into a two-scope by purchase of a so-called 'beam splitter' box.

A more elegant way of obtaining two traces is by displaying each trace alternately. If the repetition frequency of the timebase is above about 20 Hz, the two traces will appear steady.

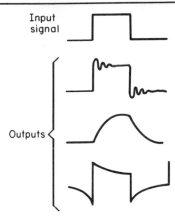

Fig. 14.10 Possible displays from poor probes

Care must be taken with the triggering of two-trace scopes if true time relationships are to be observed. Consider the simple amplifier shown in *Figure 14.11(a)*. The waveform at the collector is an amplified and inverted version of the waveform at the base. If the scope is connected as shown, and triggered normally, we will obtain the trace of *Figure 14.11(b)*, which shows the amplification but not the inversion since the timebase triggers both times on a positive edge. If, however, we connect the scope as shown in *Figure 14.11(c)*, the external trigger input will trigger the timebase at the same time on each trace, giving the correct waveform of *Figure 14.11(d)*.

A useful feature found on some scopes is a delay trigger feature. This allows a small part of a long waveform to be displayed in detail. In *Figure 14.12*, the timebase is triggered by the negative pulse A, but the delay is set such that the positive pulse B is displayed. Since the delay time T is much greater than the timebase period t, the pulse B is displayed in greater detail than would be possible with simple triggering.

In many oscilloscopes the X plates can be driven off an external input instead of the timebase. This allows the scope to be used with a wobbulator (see Section 14.8) or as a curve tracer. Frequency comparisons can be made by means of Lissajous figures, obtained with the arrangement shown in *Figure 14.13*.

The most expensive scopes have a storage facility. This allows one single sweep of the trace to be stored and viewed. The trace storage is achieved by the use of a special storage CRT. A storage mesh is provided adjacent to the screen and this mesh is scanned by the beam in the normal manner. The activated elements of the mesh hold their charge for a long period. The tube is then irradiated with electrons from an auxiliary 'flood gun' and the mesh acts as a grid, allowing electrons on to the tube where the scan passed previously.

Storage scopes are more expensive than conventional scopes, and somewhat less robust. Their use is, however, invaluable for the investigation of transient events.

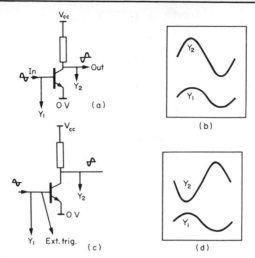

Fig. 14.11 Use of external trigger: (a) incorrect connections;
(b) misleading display; (c) correct connections using external trigger;
(d) correct display

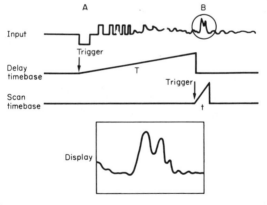

Fig. 14.12 Use of delay feature

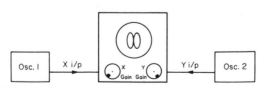

Fig. 14.13 Frequency comparison with Lissajous figures

Power supplies 14.4

A versatile power supply is an essential part of any electronic workshop or laboratory, both for prototype work and the repair of boards and battery-powered equipment. The principles of power supply design is outlined in Chapter 15, and this section will be restricted to a description of commercial units.

Three voltages are commonly used in equipment; 5 V for TTL logic, and ± 15 V for operational amplifiers. Fixed voltage supplies should be used for these voltages, and many firms manufacture a combined 5 V/± 15 V power supply. The use of a fixed voltage supply precludes the possibility of damage from using an incorrectly set variable supply. All commercial supplies are fitted with overvoltage protection.

TTL draws quite a large current from a 5 V rail, and sense inputs are often provided to allow compensation for voltage drops in cables (see *Figure 14.14*). If the sense outputs are disconnected, the 5 V output will rise until damage to TTL may occur. The links to the sense inputs must always be made.

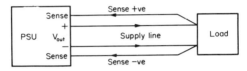

Fig. 14.14 Power supply with sense lines

In addition to fixed voltages supplies, a variable voltage supply is also valuable. An ideal supply would cover 0 to 30 V at a current rating of 2 A. This would be adequate for almost every application. Independent monitoring of voltage and current is useful, and it is very desirable to be able to turn off the output without turning off the power supply. This allows the output voltage to be set prior to connection.

Most power supplies (both fixed and variable) have some form of overcurrent protection. This can be a simple current limit or a foldover circuit where the voltage falls to zero once the overcurrent limit is reached. Overcurrent protection by means of fuses should be avoided.

Power supplies are relatively cheap (particularly fixed voltage units), but in the author's experience most workshops are poorly equipped. Ideally there should be one fixed 5 V/± 15 V and one variable supply per person.

Digital instruments 14.5

Logic circuits can be monitored with meters or scopes, but this is rather an 'overkill' as analogue devices are being used to measure digital circuits which can only be in two states.

Logic probes are devices designed to monitor digital circuits. In the simplest form the circuit of *Figure 14.15* will show a red LED for a '1' and a green LED for a '0'. This circuit would, however, load the circuit, and commercial logic probes have buffers that usually present the same load as one gate input.

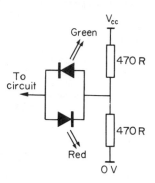

Fig. 14.15 LED logic probe

A typical probe will consist of a unit about the size of a pen, with two LEDs representing a '0' and a '1'. Flying leads connect to the logic supply. The probe tip is applied to the point to be tested, and the state read off the LEDs.

In TTL, in particular, a floating input looks like a '1' and well-designed probes show a distinct reading for a float. Often the '1' and '0' LEDs are designed to light together or a third 'float' LED will light, or no LEDs will light. In cheap probes a float will show as a '1'.

A useful facility in some probes is a pulse stretcher. The LEDs can be connected via a monostable to stretch microsecond pulses up to approximately 0·5 s, allowing sequences to be followed.

A very useful device is the i.c. clip. This device clips on to a digital IC and shows the state of all 14/16 pins on LEDs simultaneously. Usually the circuit is very simple, showing a red LED for a '1' or a float and no LED for a '0'. Most do not include a pulse stretcher. Its use should thus be tempered with some care, although the author personally considers this device more useful than a probe. The clip takes its power from the IC under test through an ingenious arrangement of diodes. This does mean, however, that it interferes with the charging of capacitors on monostables and cannot, in general, be used with timer ICs.

The logic probe and logic clip can only be used in circuits that the eye can follow. This limits their use to low speed and static logic, but they can be used to bench-test high speed boards if the board inputs can be slowed down. For high speed logic circuits a scope is, of course, a necessity, but the logic probe or logic clip should be a part of every engineer's tool kit.

The ultimate fault-finding tool for digital systems is, however, the logic analyser. In its simplest form this operates as a simple oscilloscope to display simultaneous logic states from many parts of a circuit (as idealised logic levels). A typical device can display up to 32 inputs simultaneously. The input circuits of a logic analyser are arranged to have similar characteristics to that of the logic family under test (TTL, CMOS or ECL) so it will respond to transients or glitches in the same way as the circuit itself.

More complex logic analysers have facilities to allow channel inputs to be displayed as bytes in binary, hex, octal or decimal (for fault-finding on microprocessor-based systems) and comparison tests to be made with a pre-stored sequence (called signature analysis). Display triggering from a pre-stored pattern (word triggering) is also commonly provided.

Logic analysers provide an ideal fault-finding tool for digital systems, but they are not cheap instruments. As a result they can only be financially justified for companies dealing with a large number of digital systems.

Transistor testers 14.6

Instruments for testing transistors cause a good deal of disagreement between engineers. There are those who think they are invaluable, and would never be without one, whereas there are those who think that by the time you have unsoldered the device you want to test you might as well try a new transistor anyway. Finally there are those who think that you can do all useful tests on a transistor with a multimeter.

Basically, a transistor tester should be able to

(1) Identify whether the device is pnp or npn.
(2) Identify whether the device junctions are intact.
(3) Measure leakage current.
(4) Measure the d.c. current gain h_{FE}.
(5) Measure the a.c. current gain h_{fe}.

Transistor testers fall into two main types – static testers and dynamic testers. Static testers use d.c. and can perform tests (1)–(4) above. The basic circuit of a static tester is shown in *Figure 14.16*. The supply is reversed by SW_1 for pnp or npn. I_{ceo} is measured directly with SW_2 open. To measure h_{FE}, SW_3 is set to calibrate, and the base current set by VR_1. With SW_3 in read, the collector current is read allowing h_{FE} to be calculated.

Dynamic testers perform the static tests (1)–(4) in a similar manner, but drive the transistor with a.c. to measure h_{fe}. This is done by utilising the transistor in a normal amplifier circuit, injecting a signal from an internal oscillator and reading the output a.c. voltage; or by utilising the transistor as part of an oscillator circuit.

The majority of transistor testers require the transistor to be removed from the circuit because the impedance elsewhere in the circuit will distort the readings. In-circuit transistor testers do exist, and operate by utilising very short current pulses. These will, in general, correctly identify a faulty transistor, but sometimes show a working transistor as being faulty.

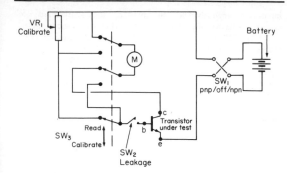

Fig. 14.16 Static transistor tester

Passing mention should be made of dynamic curve tracers. These are specialist devices and utilise the X, Y inputs on an oscilloscope to display the complete transistor characteristics. They are specialist devices and very expensive.

The simple wet finger and diode test using a multimeter is described in Chapter 17 for people who can do without a transistor tester. Alternatively, a simple tester can be built, using one of the designs appearing in the monthly magazines.

14.7 Signal generators

Signal generators are used for signal injection fault-finding (see Chapter 16). They fall into two classes: RF generators and AF generators.

14.7.1 RF generators
An RF generator works over the range from around 100 kHz to over 30 MHz. Specialist communications RF generators work at frequencies in excess of 1 GHz. A typical RF generator will have a frequency range switch, and a fine adjusting dial to allow any frequency in the range to be selected. The internal oscillator is usually some variation of an LC oscillator, with the coarse range switch selecting L, and the fine tune dial adjusting C.

RF generators are used to fault-find in radio receivers, so a modulated signal is needed. In cheaper models AM only is provided, whereas in more expensive models AM and FM are provided.

The output level from the RF generator can be adjusted by an attenuator switch for sensitivity measurements. In expensive models a level meter is provided. The normal output level is only a few hundred millivolts into a 75 Ω load.

The major difference between a cheap RF generator and its more expensive counterpart lies in the frequency stability. A cheap RF generator frequency will drift considerably with time and temperature. This does not matter for the repair of a car radio, but would be intolerable for a UHF transceiver with a bandwidth of 10 kHz.

14.7.2 AF generators

AF signal generators are used for testing audio circuits, and cover the range from a few hertz to around 100 kHz. A simple AF generator usually consists of a phase shift oscillator and can be used to identify a fault in a totally defunct amplifier circuit.

AF generators are also used, however, to trace distortion in an otherwise correctly functioning amplifier. For these tests the output from the generator needs to be a very pure sine wave with negligible harmonies. Such instruments are considerably more expensive than the simple fault-finding AF generator.

A common test with audio amplifiers is the measurement of the bandwidth. As explained in Chapter 4, an audio amplifier should have a flat response from around 30 Hz to a frequency in excess of 12 kHz.

A square wave has many harmonics, and a general indication of the frequency response of an amplifier can be obtained from the test shown in *Figure 6.10*. A square wave is applied to the amplifier input, and the output observed with a scope. If the response is level, all frequencies will be amplified equally and the square wave will not be distorted.

It is very easy to obtain a square wave from a sine wave by the use of a Schmitt trigger, and sine/square outputs are provided on even the cheapest AF generator.

Wobbulator 14.8

An RF amplifier has a well-defined bandwidth, and for some applications (notably television receivers) the bandwidth has to have a specific shape. The response of an RF amplifier can be observed directly by the use of a wobbulator and an oscilloscope.

The basis of a wobbulator is shown in *Figure 14.17*. The heart of the circuit is a voltage-controlled RF oscillator. The frequency is swept up and down by a sawtooth voltage from the timebase. The output frequency thus sweeps across the frequency range of interest, and is applied to the amplifier input. Careful design ensures that the amplitude of the oscillator output is constant, despite the frequency variation.

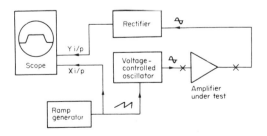

Fig. 14.17 Wobbulator

The amplifier output is rectified and the resulting d.c. voltage is a measure of the amplifier gain, and will be varying as the input frequency varies.

The ramp voltage is now applied to the X input of a conventional scope, and the rectified amplifier output to the Y input. The resulting trace will be a direct visual representation of the amplifier response.

14.9 Crosshatch and pattern generators

A colour TV picture can be considered as comprising three pictures superimposed: one red, one green and one blue. If peculiar colour fringes are not to be apparent to the viewer, these three pictures must match in size and linearity. The setting of a colour TV to avoid fringing is known as 'convergence adjustment' and is done using an instrument called a crosshatch generator.

This instrument generates a TV pattern to make any misalignment obvious. The most useful pattern is shown in *Figure 14.18(a)*, and any colour fringing will show up as in *Figure 14.18(b)*. The output is modulated on to an RF carrier to allow it to be plugged into the aerial socket of a domestic TV. Convergence adjustments can then be carried out on a standard signal.

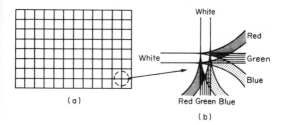

(a)

White

White

Red

Green

Blue

Red Green Blue

(b)

Fig. 14.18 Crosshatch generator

A simple crosshatch generator is a fairly cheap instrument, but more complex (and expensive) pattern generators are available for laboratory use. A typical instrument would provide:

(1) Crosshatch and dots for convergence as above.
(2) Grey scale steps from black through grey to white for setting contrast and RGB amplifiers.
(3) White, red, green, blue rasters for colour-purity tests.
(4) Colour bars to check decoding (often incorporated with grey scale).
(5) Fine black/white gratings for observations of video amplifier response and ringing.

General observations 14.10

Most engineers suffer from a lack of instruments, and it is surprising what work is done with an ancient meter having a matchstick jammed in the current trip. Instruments are often the first victim of an economy drive, which is a serious mistake.

If finance is not available to purchase instruments, a good alternative is to construct them. With the possible exception of a good two-beam oscilloscope, designs for all the instruments described in this chapter have appeared in monthly electronics magazines.

15
Power supplies

15.1 Introduction

All electronic circuits require some external power source. Usually
this is provided either from the domestic mains or from batteries. The
voltages required can be as small as 1·5 V in a hearing aid, to 25 kV
for the final anode of a colour TV, and at currents from a few
microamps to several tens of amps. This chapter describes the various
types of power supply used in electronic equipment.

15.2 Transformer rectifier circuits

The majority of electronic circuits run off the 240 V, 50 Hz supply.
Figure 15.1 shows a block diagram of the simplest form of power
supply. The transformer produces a.c. at a low voltage. This low
voltage a.c. is rectified by a rectifier circuit to give d.c. The output
from a rectifier circuit alone has a high ripple content, and is of little
use in electronic applications. Some form of smoothing is normally
added to provide a stable supply with minimal ripple.

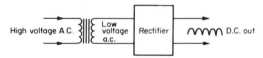

Fig. 15.1 Simple power supply

15.2.1 Transformers
The transformer is often the bulkiest and most expensive item in an
electronic system. Transformers are specified by their output
voltage(s) and their rating in VA. The VA rating is the product of the
secondary a.c. voltage and the secondary a.c. current. The secondary
voltage is usually specified at full load, and will rise with decreasing
load. The variations of output voltage with load is specified by the
regulation, which is defined as

$$\text{Regulation} = \frac{\text{Offload voltage} - \text{Full load voltage}}{\text{Offload voltage}} \times 100\%$$

Typical values for the regulation are between 10% and 20%.

Transformers sometimes suffer from insulation breakdown,
allowing 240 V mains to pass on to the secondary winding. This will
certainly cause component damage and may present an electrical
shock hazard. Transformers with primary and secondary windings on
the same former usually have an interwinding screen between
primary and secondary. The screen is connected to earth, and will
protect against primary to secondary shorts.

Transformers are electromagnetic devices, and emit a 50 Hz electromagnetic field. In circuits employing high gain a.c. amplifiers, the field can be troublesome and the power supply is often contained in a Mu-metal screened box. An alternative solution is to use specially wound toroidal transformers. These are wound around a circular core and have virtually no external field.

A very cheap form of transformer construction is the autotransformer. The construction consists of a single winding with the output taken from a tap (*Figure 15.2*). Autotransformers are potentially dangerous since the secondary is not isolated from the mains. In particular, if the common line is connected to 240 V, the entire secondary circuit will be live. The Variac style of variable transformer is an autotransformer, and great care should be taken with the wiring.

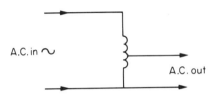

A.C. in ∿

A.C. out

Fig. 15.2 Autotransformer

Transformers are heat-producing devices, the heat being generated from eddy current and I^2R losses. Adequate ventilation should therefore be provided for power supplies. Eddy current losses are quite small, but I^2R losses can be considerable. A rough estimation of the dissipation can be obtained from the regulation.

15.2.2 Rectifier circuits

Rectifier circuits are based on the differing forward and reverse characteristics of semiconductor diodes. These allow current flow from anode to cathode, but block current in the reverse direction.

Rectifier circuits can be constructed in several ways, and these are best summarised by means of *Table 15.1*. This relates output voltage to secondary a.c. voltages and lists other constraints on the rectifiers.

Table 15.1 *Rectifier circuits*

		Without capacitor	With capacitor
Half-wave	$V_{\text{d.c.}}$	$0{\cdot}45V_{\text{a.c.}}$	$1{\cdot}4V_{\text{a.c.}}$
	$I_{\text{a.c.}}$	$1{\cdot}7I_{\text{d.c.}}$	$3I_{\text{d.c.}}$
Full wave	$V_{\text{d.c.}}$	$0{\cdot}45V_{\text{a.c.}}$	$0{\cdot}7V_{\text{a.c.}}$
	$I_{\text{a.c.}}$	$0{\cdot}8I_{\text{d.c.}}$	$I_{\text{d.c.}}$
Bridge	$V_{\text{d.c.}}$	$0{\cdot}9V_{\text{a.c.}}$	$1{\cdot}4V_{\text{a.c.}}$
	$I_{\text{a.c.}}$	$1{\cdot}1I_{\text{d.c.}}$	$1{\cdot}7I_{\text{d.c.}}$

Rectifier diodes are normally specified by peak inverse voltage (PIV, sometimes denoted V_{RRM}) and forward current (I_F). A 1N4003 is, for example, a 200 V, 1 A diode. The peak inverse voltage is the maximum voltage the diode will block. The peak of an a.c. waveform is 1·4 times the r.m.s. voltage. Mains-borne spikes may be superimposed on the a.c. waveforms, so it is advisable to use diodes with a PIV of at least twice the r.m.s. voltage of the a.c. being rectified. The cost of diodes does not increase greatly for higher PIV ratings and it is best to err on the side of safety. Diodes failing because of excessive inverse volts tend to go short circuit.

The forward current is the forward current averaged over one mains cycle. The load current is a reasonable approximation.

There are in addition three constraints which will be found on the diode data sheets. The first is the absolute maximum forward current, denoted by I_{FSM}. This is the instantaneous peak current. When the smoothing circuits are described it will be seen that the diode current is not a sine wave, but consists of a high current pulse. Normally I_{FSM} is several orders of magnitude higher than I_F. For example, the 1N4000 series has an I_F of 1 A and an I_{FSM} of 30 A.

The second characteristic is the leakage current. This is the current flowing through the diode in the back-biased direction. The leakage current can range from a few microamps for a small diode to several milliamps for a large-power diode.

Finally, we have the voltage drop across the diode while it is conducting. In a small rectifier the voltage drop will be about 0·7 V, whereas in a power rectifier it can rise to 3 V. The voltage drops need to be taken into account in calculating output voltages, particularly for the bridge rectifier where there are two voltage drops in series.

Rectifier diodes come in a variety of cases, with current ratings up to 100 A and PIV of over 1 kV. Power rectifiers need cooling (a 10 A diode with a 2 V forward drop will be dissipating 20 W), and stud-mounting encapsulations are used to allow the diode to be screwed into a heat sink.

Bridge rectifiers can be obtained in encapsulated form, with two a.c. input connections and two output connections. These, like simple diodes, are specified by PIV and current. High current bridge rectifiers are provided with a mounting lug for attaching to a heat sink.

15.2.3 Smoothing circuits

The output from any rectifier circuits will be a pulsating d.c. waveform. Before it can be used with any electronic circuit, the ripple must be reduced to a low level.

The simplest way to do this is to add an electrolytic capacitor across the supply. *Figure 15.3* is a conventional bridge rectifier capacitor smoothing power supply.

Voltage and current waveforms for the circuit are drawn in *Figure 15.4*. The capacitor is charged up to the peak volts of the a.c. waveform, then slowly discharges through the load. The capacitor discharges at a rate determined by the load current – the more current is drawn, the larger is the ripple.

The ripple voltage is given, to a reasonable approximation, by

$$V_r = \frac{It}{C}$$

where I is the load current, C the smoothing capacitor (farads), and t the ripple period (0·01 s for full-wave rectification, 0·02 s for half-wave rectification).

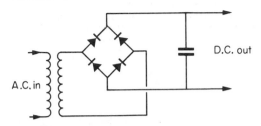

Fig. 15.3 Simple smoothed supply

The above equation assumes that the ripple is linear, whereas it is in reality exponential. Where the ripple is only a few percent of the supply voltage this is almost true.

From *Figure 15.4* it can be seen that the current through the rectifier diodes consists of a narrow pulse. The larger the value of the smoothing capacitor, the narrower the current pulse, but the greater its magnitude. The actual peak current is determined by several indeterminate factors such as the resistance of the transformer secondary windings and the forward characteristics of the rectifier diodes.

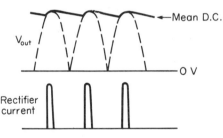

Fig. 15.4 Voltage and current waveforms

The ripple voltage can be reduced further by the use of an LC filter or RC filter, as shown in *Figure 15.5(a)* and *15.5(b)*. Filtering reduces the ripple considerably and causes the current pulse in *Figure 15.4* to be smaller and wider.

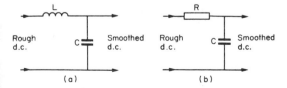

Fig. 15.5 Filter circuits: (a) LC filter; (b) RC filter

The LC and RC filters were very popular in valve circuits. Unfortunately, valve supplies were high voltage and low current, whereas semiconductor circuits need low voltage high current supplies. LC filters suffer from saturation of the inductor core, and to avoid this the choke has to be physically large with attendant problems from cost and weight. Similarly the resistance in an RC filter needs to be of low value if the d.c. voltage drop and heat dissipation are to be reasonable. A low value of resistance reduces the effectiveness of the filter.

The once common filter stages are thus rather a rarity in semiconductor equipment. Where low ripple is required, it is usual to use a regulator circuit, as described below.

15.3 Regulator circuits

As electronic equipment has become more complex, the specifications of the power supplies have become more stringent. The mains supply can vary by some 10%, and in simple transformer/rectifier supply this change will be reflected in the output voltage. The regulation of transformer outputs is also of the order of 10%, so the possible variation in supply voltage from a simple power supply can be around 20%. This would be totally unacceptable for many electronic systems.

Figure 15.6 shows a block diagram of a regulated power supply. It consists of a conventional transformer/rectifier/smoothing supply and a circuit to maintain the output voltage constant despite variations in load current and the transformer secondary voltage.

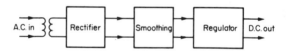

Fig. 15.6 Regulated power supply

15.3.1 Zener diode regulator

The simplest regulator is the zener diode circuit shown in *Figure 15.7(a)*. This circuit can be considered as consisting of the ideal components in *Figure 15.7(b)*. The battery V_z represents an ideal zener, and the resistor R_z the zener slope resistance (typically between 1 and 10 Ω).

The bleed current, I_1, has to be greater than the sum of the maximum load current plus the minimum zener diode current. The value of R$_1$ is given by

$$R_1 = \frac{V_{in} - V_z}{I_1}$$

The minimum value of V_{in} should be used in the above equation, taking into account mains variation and transformer regulation.

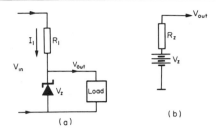

Fig. 15.7 Zener diode regulator: (a) diode circuit; (b) equivalent circuit

In the unloaded state, I_1 will flow through the zener. Under these conditions the zener dissipation is given by

$$P = I_1 V_z$$

The zener dissipation will rise with decreasing load current.

There are two important parameters to be defined for a regulated power supply. The first is the stabilisation factor, which is defined as

$$S = \frac{\text{Change in output volts}}{\text{Change in input volts}}$$

This stabilisation factor is a measure of how well the regulator responds to supply ripple and supply variations.

For the circuit shown in *Figure 15.7*,

$$S = \cfrac{1}{\left(1 + \cfrac{R_1}{R_L} + \cfrac{R_1}{R_z}\right)}$$

The second parameter is the output resistance, defined as

$$R_{\text{out}} = \frac{\text{Change in output volts}}{\text{Change in load current}}$$

The output resistance determines how the regulator responds to changes in load current.

For a zener diode regulator, if $R_1 \gg R_z$, the output resistance is simply R_z. In reality, the zener diode is not itself a particularly good regulator, but is the basis for more complex regulators described below.

15.3.2 Principles of regulated supplies

A block diagram showing the basic elements of a regulated power supply is given in *Figure 15.8*.

The output voltage is compared with a stable reference voltage (usually a zener diode). An error signal is produced, which is used by a controlling device to raise or lower the output voltage accordingly.

The regulated supply is thus an example of a closed-loop system incorporating negative feedback.

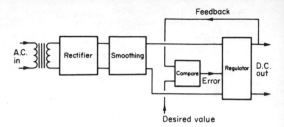

Fig. 15.8 Regulated supply with feedback

There are two basic types of regulator circuit. The first is the series regulator, where the controller is in series with one power supply line. The second is the shunt regulator, where the controlling element is across the load and shunts part of the supply current.

15.3.3 Series regulators
The simplest series regulator is the emitter follower circuit shown in *Figure 15.9*. Normal transistor action reduces variations in the zener current by h_{fe}, and the output resistance is given by

$$R_{out} = \frac{r_z + h_{ie}}{h_{FE}}$$

The stabilisation factor is given by

$$S = \frac{1}{1 + K}$$

where

$$K = \frac{h_{fe}}{h_{oe}} h_{ie}$$

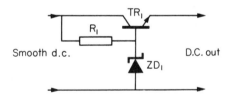

Fig. 15.9 Simple series regulator

For a typical transistor, with $h_{fe} = 100$, $h_{ie} = 1$ kΩ and, $h_{oe} = 50 \times 10^{-6}$ mhos, the output resistance approximates to 10 Ω and the stabilisation factor to 0·05%. The stabilisation factor will, of course, be worse than this because of the variation in V_z caused by variations in current through R_1. The value of R_1 can, however, be considerably larger than R_1 in *Figure 15.7*, and the stabilisation factor will be correspondingly improved.

It should be noted that all the parameters in the two equations above are subject to wide tolerances, and the equations should be treated purely as guides to the expected results.

The classic series regulator circuit is shown in *Figure 15.10*. This gives adequate performance for most applications. Resistor R_1 provides base current for the series regulator TR_1. Transistor TR_2 is an error amplifier, comparing the voltage on the slider of RV_1 with the zener voltage ZD_1.

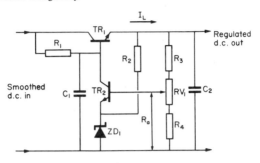

Fig. 15.10 Practical series regulator

If the output voltage rises, the voltage on TR_2 base starts to rise, causing TR_2 to draw more current. This reduces the base voltage on TR_1, and brings the output voltage back to the correct level. If the output voltage falls, TR_2 draws less current and TR_1 base voltage rises to compensate. The circuit is a closed loop and corrects itself for changes in load.

The output voltage is given by

$$V_{out} = \frac{R_3 + RV_1 + R_4}{R_a} \times (V_z + 0.5)$$

The 0.5 V in the above equation is the base emitter voltage of TR_2.

Capacitor C_1 is sometimes included to prevent high frequency oscillation (which can occur in closed-loop circuits under some circumstances), and C_2 to improve the transient response.

The basic constraint on the series regulators is the dissipation in TR_1. This is given by

$$P = (V_{in} - V_{out})I_L$$

and should be calculated for maximum V_{in} and I_L. Obviously the dissipation increases with load current.

15.3.4 Shunt regulator
Figure 15.11 shows a common form of shunt regulator. Transistor TR_1 is the regulating transistor connected across the output. Resistor R_1 passes current given by

$$I_1 = \frac{V_{in} - V_{out}}{R_1}$$

This current splits into I_L and I_s, the latter being controlled by TR_1.

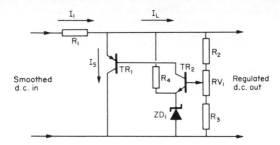

Fig. 15.11 Shunt regulator

Transistor TR_2 is an error amplifier similar to that in *Figure 15.10*. If the output voltage rises, TR_2 turns TR_1 on harder increasing I_S and reducing the output voltage.

Unlike the series regulator, the dissipation in TR_1 increases with decreasing load current, and maximum dissipation occurs with no load when all of I_1 passes through TR_1.

Under these conditions, the dissipation of TR_1 is given by

$$P = V_{out} \cdot I_1$$

The dissipation in R_1 is constant under normal operation, and is given by

$$P_r = (V_{in} - V_{out})I_1$$

Obviously the maximum load current must be less than I_1, because TR_1 must pass current in order to regulate the output voltage. Should the load attempt to draw more, the voltage will fall, and the short circuit current is simply given by

$$I_{sc} = \frac{V_{in}}{R_1}$$

If short circuits are foreseen, the dissipation for R_1 should be calculated, using

$$P_r = \frac{V_{in}^2}{R_1}$$

15.3.5 Integrated circuit regulators

It is becoming increasingly less economic to design and build a regulator circuit. Integrated circuit regulators are available at little more expense than the power transistors necessary in *Figures 15.10* and *15.11*. These are very simple to use, since they have just three terminals, labelled In, Out and Common.

Regulator i.c.p.s are normally sold in fixed voltages, the commonest being 5 V, 12 V, 15 V, 24 V. They can, however, be made adjustable by the use of the circuit in *Figure 15.12*. The output voltage is given by

$$V_{out} = \frac{R_1 + R_2}{R_2} V_{icp}$$

R_1 and R_2 can, of course, be replaced by a variable resistor.

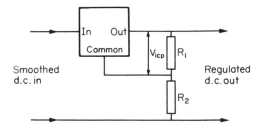

Fig. 15.12 Integrated circuit regulator

Protection circuits 15.4

Ideally, two forms of protection are needed – the first to protect the
regulator from short circuits in the load, the second to protect the
load from failures in the regulator which could cause the output
voltage to rise. The latter is particularly important with integrated
circuits. A 5 V supply rising to 8 V could destroy several hundred
pounds' worth of TTL.

15.4.1 Overcurrent protection

There are several forms of overcurrent protection. The first type is
current limiting protection. The output voltage remains constant up
to a certain current level; thereafter any further decrease in load
resistance causes the voltage to fall, and the supply simply provides
constant current. The series regulator in *Figure 15.13* has this form of
protection provided by R_5 and TR_3. Above a certain current
determined by R_5, transistor TR_3 will turn on, reducing the output
voltage until the voltage across R_5 is 0·7 V. The limiting current is
thus

$$I_{sc} = \frac{0·7}{R_5}$$

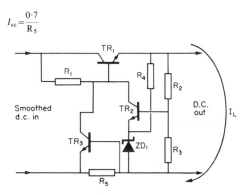

Fig. 15.13 Series regulator with overcurrent protection

The second form of current protection is the current trip. In its crudest form this is a fuse or electromagnetic cut-out, but electronic versions use an overload circuit to trigger a memory flip-flop which reduces the output voltage to zero. The supply is restored either with a reset button or by turning off and on again.

Finally we have the foldback current limit. This is similar to current limit protection, but the voltage and current are reduced which has the advantage of reducing the dissipation in the regulating device.

Integrated circuit regulators usually have foldback current limit built into them.

Current limits can cause problems with loads having an initial current surge (e.g. indicator lamps). Foldback protection and cut-out protection can actually lock out a circuit which they should, in theory, drive with ease.

15.4.2 Overvoltage protection

If a regulator circuit fails, the output voltage can rise to the voltage provided by the bridge rectifier. If RV_1 in *Figure 15.10* had a break in the track on the positive side of the slider, for example, TR_2 would turn off, and TR_1 would cause V_{out} to rise until it was just a few volts below V_{in}.

Most forms of overvoltage protection are last-ditch methods and give catastrophic indications such as blown fuses. They are based on the so-called 'crowbar' technique which shorts the voltage from the rectifier.

A typical crowbar circuit is shown in *Figure 15.14*. If the voltage rises above the zener voltage ZD_1, thyristor Th_1 turns hard on, causing the fuse to blow.

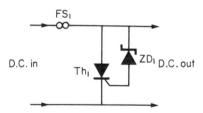

Fig. 15.14 Crowbar protection

15.5 Switching regulators

In both the series and shunt regulators the circuit dissipates a large amount of heat. In a large electronic system, power supply heat causes problems with cubicle cooling, often necessitating fan cooling with attendant troubles from noise and poor reliability, plus the possibility of damage if the fans fail unnoticed.

The switching regulator provides a very neat way of providing a regulated supply with little dissipation. The circuit uses a series regulator transistor, but unlike a conventional regulator it is either turned hard on or fully off. The transistor feeds the load through a choke filter which smooths out the current pulses (*Figure 15.15*).

The control circuit consists of a fixed frequency oscillator with variable mark/space controlled by the error amplifier. Because TR_1 is either (a) full on with high current but low V_{ce}, giving low dissipation, or (b) full off with zero current and high V_{ce}, giving low dissipation, a very cool compact power supply can be built.

Many commercial high current supplies are now designed around the switching regulator. They can be identified by the oscillator whistle and their low case temperature.

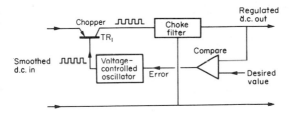

Fig. 15.15 Switching regulator

EHT power supplies 15.6

The design of power supplies to provide voltages above 1 kV presents several difficulties to the electronics engineer. It would be possible, in theory, to use a conventional transformer rectifier circuit, but in practice diodes have insufficient PIV and the insulation problems on the transformer secondary would be almost insurmountable.

EHT power supply design is based almost exclusively on the Cockcroft-Walton voltage multiplier shown in *Figure 15.16*.

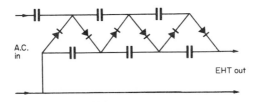

Fig. 15.16 Voltage multiplier

Where a stabilised EHT is required, it is usual to use a conventional regulator supply to feed an oscillator which is stepped up to the required voltage by a transformer and voltage multiplier (*Figure 15.17*). A much attenuated EHT is fed back to the oscillator power supply to control the oscillator voltage supply and hence its output amplitude.

Needless to say, EHT supplies should be treated with due respect and caution.

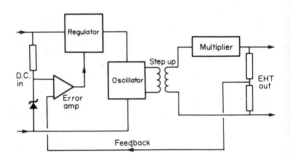

Fig. 15.17 EHT power supply

15.7 **D.C. to d.c. inverters**

The electronics engineer is often presented with the problem of providing several voltages from a single source such as a battery. D.C. to d.c. inverters take a d.c. voltage in and give a larger d.c. voltage out.

In their simplest form, d.c. to d.c. inverters consist of an oscillator, step-up transformer and rectifier. Usually, for simplicity and cost-saving, the oscillator and transformer are combined by using a blocking oscillator. *Figure 15.18* shows a typical d.c. to d.c. inverter. Transistors TR_1 and TR_2 conduct alternately, the frequency of oscillation being determined by the primary inductance and the saturation flux of the core.

The oscillation frequency is usually made quite high (approximately 1–10 kHz) to reduce the size of the transformer and smoothing components.

If rectifiers are not used on the output, the circuit becomes a d.c. to a.c. inverter. The circuit can be made to operate at 50 Hz to provide standby power for mains equipment. The output is, however, a square wave which limits its use to applications such as lighting.

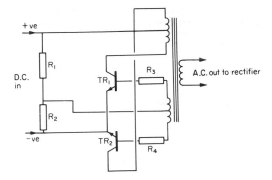

Fig. 15.18 D.C. to d.c. inverter

Batteries 15.8

The designer of portable equipment has little choice but to rely on
batteries. The use of electrical power from batteries is one of the most
expensive power sources known to man, and battery-powered circuits
should be designed to reduce the load current to a minimum.

Battery life is defined in ampere-hours (Ah), and to a first
approximation the life can be determined by dividing the ampere-
hours by the load current. Usually the capacity, in ampere-hours, is
defined at a particular current. At higher currents the capacity is
lower.

For some reason, capacities for dry cell (non-rechargeable)
batteries are not given. Possibly this is because there seems to be a
wide variation in supposedly identical batteries. *Table 15.2* gives
rough figures (based on experience) for common battery sizes.

Table 15.2 *Approximate hours of useful life versus load current (based
on 4 hours' use per day)*

| Battery | Load (mA) | | | | | | | |
	1	5	10	20	50	100	250	500
HP2	—	—	500	250	100	50	15	—
HP7	—	300	150	50	10	—	—	—
HP11	—	600	300	120	50	20	5	—
PP3	—	70	20	10	—	—	—	—
PP7	—	600	200	100	10	—	—	—
PP9	—	—	500	200	50	10	—	—

Rechargeable cells are usually nickel-cadmium cells (nicads) with
capacities up to 1 Ah, and various forms of lead acid with capacities
up to 40 Ah. Battery data sheets usually specify the maximum
charging current.

Nicad batteries can easily be damaged by overcharging, and it is recommended that before charging they are discharged fully, then charged at constant current for a known time. Constant current chargers are available for this purpose.

15.9 Lossless dropper

If it is required to run voltage equipment direct off the mains, the cost of a transformer can be saved by using a dropper. Resistors can be used for this purpose, but the I^2R heat is usually a problem. Capacitor droppers can, however, be used and *Figure 15.19* shows a typical circuit.

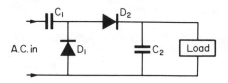

Fig. 15.19 Lossless (reactive) dropper

The output voltage is determined by the relative impedances of C_1 and C_2 at the supply frequencies. The circuit is not recommended for domestic use.

16

Maintenance, fault-finding and safety

Introduction 16.1

Electronic equipment is exceptionally reliable, and it is by no means unusual for an item as complex as a computer to run continuously for several years without failure. It is generally agreed that when failures do occur in electronic equipment they follow the classic bathtub curve of *Figure 16.1*.

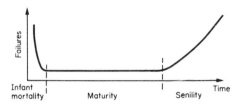

Fig. 16.1 Bathtub curve

The first portion is known as 'infant mortality'. The failure rate is high, as faulty components and bad solder joints are found. This period is usually measured in weeks, and can be overcome by a 'soak test' before use if time permits. Often the infant mortality can be accelerated by taking the equipment through several temperature cycles.

The second period is known as 'maturity'. The failure rate is very low, and this period lasts for several years. During this period, failures are random. It is rather important for maintenance purposes to follow the implication of 'random failures'. Electronic equipment behaves in a somewhat different manner from other engineering systems. If you want an IC that has to last 10 000 h, your best bet would be to use one that had already run 10 000 h. Electronic equipment does not, in general, deteriorate with age, and routine replacement of parts would take you back into the infant mortality period. A good rule for electronic equipment is therefore 'leave well alone'.

The third period is known as 'senility'. Failure rates start to rise and continue rising until the equipment is replaced. The failures are not usually electronic, but are related to the structure of the equipment. Plugs and sockets lose their spring and become intermittent, solder joints start to oxidise, vibration causes leads to break.

Reliability is a vague term, but is generally taken to mean the percentage of time that equipment is working. If we call the time the equipment is working 'Up time' and the out-of-service time 'Down time' we can quantify reliability in the term 'Availability', defined as:

$$\text{Availability} = \frac{\text{Up time}}{\text{Up time} + \text{Down time}}$$

There are two factors that affect reliability. The first of these is obviously how often an item fails. This is known as the Mean Time Between Failure or MTBF. With modern electronic equipment this should be in terms of thousands of hours. Note that the MTBF for a complete item depends on the MTBF of all the constituent parts: ICs, semiconductors, passive components, connections, soldered joints etc. No equipment can be more reliable than its least reliable item.

The second factor is how long it takes to repair equipment once it has failed. This is quantified as Mean Time To Repair or MTTR. This is affected by availability of spares, ease of maintenance, availability of test equipment, clarity of manuals and the competence of the maintenance personnel.

A third factor can be included for items that require regular servicing. Large computer systems, for example, usually have a six-monthly service where disc drive alignments are checked and similar preventative maintenance is performed. This service time must be included in the availability calculation.

Availability can now be redefined in its more useful form:

$$\text{Availability} = \frac{\text{MTBF}}{\text{MTBF} + \text{MTTR} + \text{Service}}$$

A piece of equipment that fails once a week (168 hours) and takes 15 minutes to repair each time has an availability of 99·85%. Availability is not the whole story however; most people would call the above equipment unreliable, but its availability is quite good. In general, users instinctively call equipment unreliable if its MTBF falls below about 6 months or its availability below 99%. MTBFs of several years should be possible on even complex items of electronic equipment.

16.2 **Maintenance**

·In engineering in general, there are three types of maintenance: preventative, planned (sometimes called performance maintenance) and corrective (maintenance by breakdown).

Preventative maintenance covers replacement of parts on a service time basis, and is based on the premise that equipment fails after X hours. This is obviously very necessary for replacement of mechanical parts, but as explained previously it can do more harm than good in electronic equipment. The only items that should be considered in this category are items such as air filters, batteries and possibly relay contacts. A case can be made for cleaning dust out of equipment at regular intervals, but there are those who consider that this transfers dust from places where it is doing no harm to places where it most definitely will.

Planned maintenance is a scheduled check of equipment performance. In many types of equipment a single failure might not lead to a complete failure, and as such might go undetected. In addition, adjustments such as the zero on d.c. amplifiers and the alignment on RF receivers tend to drift with age. A performance check will test if the equipment is still performing within its design specification, allowing suitable repairs or adjustments to be made before total failure occurs. Safety equipment (interlocks, etc.) should also be checked at regular intervals.

The final category is corrective maintenance. This is a formal way of saying 'mend it when it breaks'. A large percentage of electronic equipment will either work or not work, and any failure or degradation of performance will be immediately apparent. For this type of equipment it is usually best to adopt a 'maintenance by repair' philosophy and not touch it until it fails.

The repair of electronic equipment is a topic that is discussed further in the following section.

Fault-finding and repair 16.3

Good fault-finding starts at the design stage, with accessible components, good circuit diagrams and well thought out documentation. Unfortunately, all too often circuit diagrams are drawn along the lines of a car wiring diagram rather than a drawing that can be understood at first sight. Every engineer involved in maintenance can tell stories about TV cameras that have to be completely disassembled to change components on the PCB, or circuit diagrams in which a signal weaves from page to page without cross-referencing. With a little thought at the design stage the maintenance engineer's job can be made much easier.

Fault-finding can be classified into two stages. First-line maintenance is concerned with getting the equipment working again. At this level repairs are done by board changing or sometimes by replacing an entire unit. The personnel doing first-line maintenance need not be highly qualified in electronics.

Second-line maintenance is done by qualified personnel at the bench, and faults are found and repaired down to component level.

The importance placed on these two levels of maintenance will depend on the particular location. A factory using thyristor drives may expect its electricians to do first-line maintenance, but have no second-line maintenance on site. Faulty boards would then be returned direct to the manufacturer for repair. A domestic equipment service department, however, will do some first-line maintenance by board-changing, but will also often go directly to the second level.

16.3.1 First-line maintenance
Equipment designers should always remember that most first-line maintenance is done by non-technical personnel. Documentation should be as simple as possible, and preferably of the block diagram type. All inputs and outputs should have monitoring points, and tests should not require specialised equipment.

In the late 1960s the Royal Navy undertook a study of first-line maintenance, and a team at HMS Collingwood came up with a proposal called FIMS (Functionally Identifiable Maintenance Systems). This is an organised system of block diagrams to lead non-technical personnel to either a replaceable unit (which can be as large as a computer, or as small as a PCB) or to a simple circuit on which an electrician can fault-find.

FIMS arranges equipment into a hierarchy of functions, as shown in *Figures 16.2–16.4*. Each block corresponds to one page of the circuit diagram, and on the diagram every input and output will have test procedures specified allowing the fault to be located to one block. F1 could be a computer system supplying a reference to a thyristor drive F2. Tests show that F2 is faulty. At the next level down we have *Figure 16.3*, with F2 split into five blocks. Again tests are specified, and we find F2.2 has failed. The small marker on F2.2 shows that this is a replaceable unit. Had the tests shown that F2.3 was faulty we would go to another level where F2.3 was split further. Eventually all blocks end up as replaceable blocks or a simple circuit diagram, like F2.5 shown in *Figure 16.4*. A complex computer-controlled thyristor drive has thus been broken down into easily understandable tests.

FIMS is not cheap, but for complex equipment in critical applications it works very well. Its very nature means that the original equipment design has to be done with maintenance in mind.

An alternative approach to FIMS is the use of fault-finding trees or flow charts. These lead the first-line maintenance technicians through the tree to the fault. A typical example is shown in *Figure 16.5*. Like FIMS, the use of fault-finding trees imposes the need to consider maintenance at the design stage.

16.3.2 Second-line maintenance

Second-line maintenance takes place in a (hopefully) well-equipped workshop by (hopefully) well-trained personnel. According to circumstances the workshop can belong to the user, or be a manufacturer's service department.

There are two basic methods of fault-finding, called signal injection and signal tracing. These are summarised in *Figure 16.6(a)* and *16.6(b)*. Both techniques assume a linear signal flow, and both aim to limit the fault to increasingly small areas. Signal tracing assumes the input signal to be correct, and the signal is traced with instruments until it vanishes. Signal injection works by injecting a signal at points from the output backwards, until a point is reached where the output is no longer obtained. Both techniques are equally valuable and the choice really depends on the instruments available.

When there is a considerable throughput of identical units for repair and test, it is worth considering automated test techniques. Computer-controlled test rigs can be obtained which will carry out a preset test procedure on a piece of equipment and identify a fault to a single component.

The bane of every engineer's life is the intermittent fault. These are rarely caused by faulty components, the more common causes being dry joints, loose plugs and cracks in PCB tracks. There is no easy solution, although faults can often be traced by utilising heat from a hair-dryer or cold from a freezer spray. Even when an intermittent fault has been repaired, the user never has the same confidence again. In these circumstances the reader might like to consider, as a last resort, the author's solution of replacing any boards having intermittent faults with new boards.

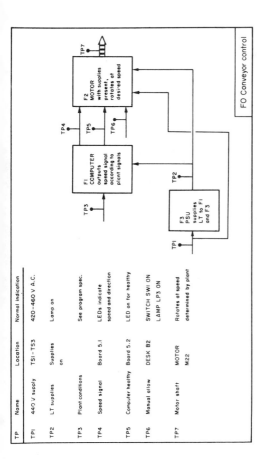

TP	Name	Location	Normal indication
TP1	440 V supply	TS1-TS3	420-460 V A.C.
TP2	LT supplies	Supplies on	Lamp on
TP3	Plant conditions		See program spec.
TP4	Speed signal	Board 5.1	LEDs indicate speed and direction
TP5	Computer healthy	Board 5.2	LED on for healthy
TP6	Manual allow	DESK B2	SWITCH SW1 ON LAMP LP3 ON
TP7	Motor shaft	MOTOR M22	Rotates at speed determined by plant

Fig.16.2 First-level FIMS chart

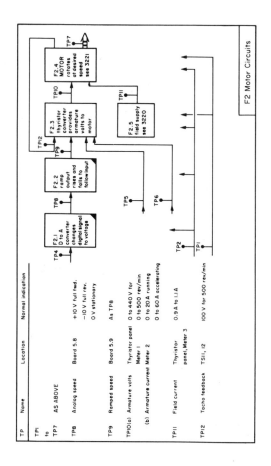

TP	Name	Location	Normal indication
TPI to TP7	AS ABOVE		
TP8	Analog speed	Board 5,8	+IO V full fwd. −IO V full rev. O V stationary
TP9	Ramped speed	Board 5,9	As TP8
TPIO(a)	Armature volts	Thyristor panel Meter I	0 to 440 V for 0 to 500 rev/min
(b)	Armature current	Meter 2	0 to 20A running 0 to 60A accelerating
TPII	Field current	Thyristor panel, Meter 3	0.9 A to 1,1A
TPI2	Tacho feedback	TSII, I2	IOO V for 500 rev/min

Fig. 16.3 Second-level FIMS chart

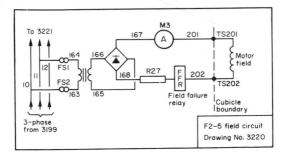

Fig. 16.4 Bottom-level FIMS drawing

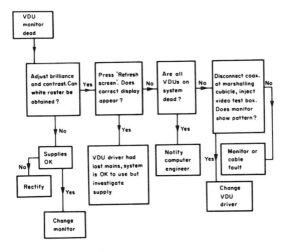

Fig. 16.5 Flow chart fault-finding

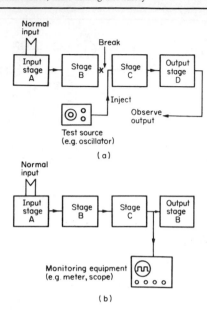

Fig. 16.6 Fault-finding techniques: (a) signal injection; (b) signal tracing

16.4 Safety

The Health and Safety at Work Act puts very strong responsibility for safety at work on both employer and employee. The ramifications of this Act are beyond the scope of this book, but everyone in industry should ensure that they are fully aware of its implications.

The installation of all electronic equipment should comply with the current IEE Regulations for Electrical Equipment (or such regulations as apply in other countries, where applicable). In addition, protection should be given against ingress of oil, water, dust, etc. Special Regulations for hazardous locations (e.g. mines) should be observed.

Where heat is produced, ventilation ducts should be kept clear and free air flow allowed to avoid fire hazards. Fire extinguishers provided for electronic equipment should be of the type recommended for use with electrical fires (i.e. dry powder, CO_2 or BCF). In large installations, automatic BCF systems should be installed, with manual lock-off when people are in the area.

All units operating in excess of 250 V should be clearly labelled 'DANGER HIGH VOLTAGE', and have interlocks to ensure that the unit is turned off before doors can be opened or panels removed. Test switches may be fitted to allow operation by engineers for test and repair purposes, but they must only be used by competent persons, not working alone and taking full responsibility for their own safety.

All persons working on electrical equipment should receive training in first aid. In particular, emphasis should be given on mouth-to-mouth resuscitation and treatment for electrical shock.

Engineers working in laboratory conditions are generally at less risk, even though exposed live terminals on power supplies seem to be very common. Particular care should be taken with several domestic items having a neutral connected chassis. If the plug is wired incorrectly the entire chassis can be live. The ideal solution is to have the bench 240 V supply fed from an isolating transformer. The old alternative is to sit on a stool and keep one hand in your pocket!

When the lethality of electricity is considered, the safety record of the electronics industry is very good. The average engineer is at far more risk from routine industrial accidents (falls, cuts, etc.) than from electric shock. Field service engineers are more likely to be involved in road accidents. Industrial safety is a wide-ranging subject, and since the Health and Safety at Work Act was passed, safety has become the responsibility of each and every worker.

17
Reference data

17.1 Resistors (see also Section 2.1)

17.1.1 General
Resistors in series:

$$R = R_1 + R_2 + R_3 + \ldots$$

Resistors in parallel:

$$\frac{1}{R} = \frac{1}{R_1} + \frac{1}{R_2} + \frac{1}{R_3} + \ldots$$

or for two resistors:

$$R = \frac{R_1 R_2}{R_1 + R_2}$$

$$\text{Dissipation} = W = E \times I = I^2 R = \frac{E^2}{R}$$

where E is the potential in volts, R is in ohms, I is in amps, and W is in watts.

17.1.2 Colour code
Resistors are identified by the following colour code:

Coding is done by colour bands:

Black	0	Green	5
Brown	1	Blue	6
Red	2	Violet	7
Orange	3	Grey	8
Yellow	4	White	9

17.1.3 Preferred values
Resistors are commonly sold in 12 values plus decades. This is known as the E12 series. This can be expanded to 24 values with the E24 series:

E12
1·0 1·2 1·5 1·8 2·2 2·7 3·3 3·9 4·7 5·6 6·8 8·2

E24 as E12 plus
1·1 1·3 1·6 2·0 2·4 3·0 3·6 4·3 5·1 6·2 7·5 9·1

Resistors are often sold by the BS 1852 method of marking. The multiplier is represented by a single letter. Thus:

R = × 1	K = × 1000	M = × 1 000 000
4R 7	4K 7	4M 7
330R	680K	12M

To this is added a letter signifying the tolerance:

$$F = 1\%; G = 2\%; J = 5\%; K = 10\%; M = 20\%$$

Thus:

6K8G is $6800\,\Omega \pm 2\%$

Capacitors (see also Section 2.2) 17.2

17.2.1 General
Capacitors in series:

$$\frac{1}{C} = \frac{1}{C_1} + \frac{1}{C_2} + \frac{1}{C_3} + \ldots$$

or for two capacitors:

$$C = \frac{C_1 \cdot C_2}{C_1 + C_2}$$

Capacitors in parallel:

$$C = C_1 + C_2 + C_3$$

Current through a capacitor:

$$I = C\frac{\mathrm{d}V}{\mathrm{d}t}$$

Voltage across a capacitor:

$$V = \frac{1}{C}\int I\,\mathrm{d}t$$

where V is the potential in volts, C is in farads, I is in amps, and t is in seconds.

17.2.2 Capacitor colour codes
Identification of colour codes on capacitors is not as straightforward as for resistors. The colour coding follows the values given in Subsection 17.1.2, but several marking methods are used. In general, the value is expressed in picofarads.

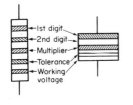

Tolerance	> 10 pF	< 10 pF
Black	20%	
Brown	1%	0·1 pF
Red	2%	0·25 pF
Green	5%	
White	10%	1 pF

The working voltage colour is multiplied by 100 (e.g. yellow = 400 V).
Tantalum electrolytics use a slightly different code:

	Digits	Multiplier	Working voltage
Black	0	× 1 μF	10
Brown	1	× 10 μF	—
Red	2	× 100 μF	—
Orange	3	—	—
Yellow	4	—	63
Green	5	—	16
Blue	6	—	20
Violet	7	—	—
Grey	8	× 0·01 μF	25
White	9	× 0·1 μF	3
Pink	—	—	35

The right-hand lead is positive when viewed from the spot side.

17.2.3 Preferred values
Capacitors generally follow the E12 values given in Subsection 17.1.3.
Values are given in farads with the multipliers:
pico = 10^{-12}, nano = 10^{-9}, micro (μ) = 10^{-6}. Thus:

$$1\ \mu\text{F} = 1000\ \text{nF};\ 1\ \text{nF} = 1000\ \text{pF}$$

17.3 Inductors (see also Section 2.3)

17.3.1 General
Inductors in series:

$$L = L_1 + L_2 + L_3 + \ldots$$

Inductors in parallel:

$$\frac{1}{L} = \frac{1}{L_1} + \frac{1}{L_2} + \frac{1}{L_3} + \ldots$$

Note that the magnetic fields of close-mounted inductors will interact.

Voltage across an inductor:

$$V = L\frac{dI}{dt}$$

where V is in volts, I is in amps, L is in henrys, and t is in seconds.

Current through an inductor:

$$I = \frac{1}{L}\int V\,dt$$

17.3.2 Identification
There is no common scheme for inductor values.

A.C. circuits 17.4

17.4.1 General
The instantaneous values of voltage (e) and current (i) are given by

$$e = E_{peak} \sin 2\pi ft; \; i = I_{peak} \sin 2\pi ft$$

where f is the frequency. $2\pi f$ is usually represented by ω.

A.C. is usually referred to by its root mean square (r.m.s.) value, given by

$$E_{r.m.s.} = 0.707 E_{peak} \qquad \left(\text{correctly } \frac{\sqrt{2}}{2} E_{peak} \right)$$

Less commonly used is the average value over one half-cycle, given by

$$E_{av} = 0.637 E_{peak}$$

17.4.2 Reactances
Reactance of inductor:

$$X_L = 2\pi f L$$

Reactance of capacitor:

$$X_C = \frac{1}{2\pi f C}$$

where L is in henrys, C is in farads, f is the frequency in hertz, and X is in ohms.

Current through a single capacitor or inductor is given by

$$I = \frac{V}{X}$$

where I is in amps, V is r.m.s. volts, and X is the reactance as above.

The current in an inductor lags the voltage by 90°.

The current in a capacitor leads the voltage by 90°.

17.4.3 Impedance of circuits containing L, C and R
Impedance:

$$Z = \sqrt{[R^2 + (X_L - X_C)^2]} \text{ ohms}$$

where X_L and X_C are calculated as in Subsection 17.4.2.

Current:

$$I = \frac{V}{Z}$$

The angle of lead or lag is given by

$$\tan \phi = \frac{X_L - X_C}{R}$$

where V is r.m.s. volts, R is in ohms, L is in henrys, and C is in farads.
Cos ϕ is referred to as the power factor.
The current lags if $X_L > X_C$ and leads if $X_C > X_L$.

17.4.4 Resonance (see also Subsection 4.6.4 and Section 6.2)
Resonance occurs in an a.c. circuit when the reactances of the inductance and capacitance are equal, i.e.

$$2\pi f L = \frac{1}{2\pi f C}$$

It follows that the resonant frequency is given by

$$f = \frac{1}{2\pi \sqrt{(LC)}}$$

The series resonant circuit of Subsection 17.4.3 exhibits minimum impedance at resonance given by R.

The parallel resonant circuit exhibits maximum impedance at resonance. This is determined by the resistor of the inductor, and is given by

$$R = \frac{\omega^2 L^2}{r} = \frac{L}{Cr} = \frac{Q}{\omega C}$$

In the equation above, Q is the magnification factor defined as

$$Q = \frac{\omega L}{r} \text{ at resonance}$$

17.5 Multipliers

Standard multipliers used in electronics are

pico	10^{-12}	kilo	10^{3}
nano	10^{-9}	mega	10^{6}
micro	10^{-6}	giga	10^{9}
milli	10^{-3}		

Semiconductors 17.6

17.6.1 Transistor lead identification

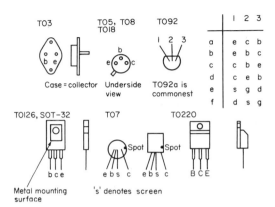

	1	2	3
a	e	c	b
b	e	b	c
c	c	b	e
d	c	e	b
e	s	g	d
f	d	s	g

17.6.2 Transistor coding

Pro-electron code (e.g. BC107):

First letter	A	Germanium
	B	Silicon
Second letter	A	Diode
	C	Audio transistor
	D	Power transistor
	E	Tunnel diode
	F	High frequency transistor
	L	High frequency power transistor
	S	Switching transistor
	U	Power switching transistor

Third letter and subsequent digits identify the device.

Devices beginning with O (e.g. OC36, OA81) are coded under the European Valve Code.

JEDEC code (e.g. 2N3055): The 1N and 2N prefix is a military approved code, with 1N denoting a diode and 2N a three-terminal device. The subsequent digits define the device.

Manufacturers' codes: Many semiconductor manufacturers utilise their own coding prefixes. Examples are: Ferranti ZT; Motorola MJE; Newmarket NKT. Components in equipment are often marked with the equipment manufacturers' part number.

17.6.3 Integrated circuit identification

	Linear circuit prefixes	Digital circuit prefixes
Ferranti	ZL, ZLA, ZN, ZLD	ZN
General Electric	PA, GEL	
Intersil	ICL	
Motorola	MC, MFC	MC
National	LF, LH, LM	DM, DS
Mullard	TAA, TAB, TBA, TAD	FJH, FJY, FJJ, FJL, N
Plessey	SL	
RCA	CA	
Texas	SN72, SN76	SN74
SGS	U, TAA, TAB, TBA, TAD	U
Signetics	SE, NE	
Siemens	TAA, TAB, TBA, TAD	FLH, FLL, FLY, FLJ

Digital ICs are usually TTL or CMOS.

TTL is identified by a code of the form 74nnn, where nn defines the device. In addition, the following letters define the device construction:

L   Low power
H   High speed
S   Schottky
LS   Low power Schottky

CMOS is identified by a code of the form 74nnn, where nnn defines the device.

Both CMOS and TTL device codes will incorporate manufacturers' prefixes and suffixes denoting packaging, temperature range, etc.

17.6.4 Testing semiconductors

Simple go/fail tests for semiconductors can be performed with very simple equipment. Diodes and transistors can be tested with a multimeter on ohms range (but note that on most multimeters the positive terminal is negative when on ohms).

Diodes can be tested for conduction in one direction, and no conduction in the other.

Transistors can be tested in several stages:

(1)   Test for the existence of the base/emitter and base/collector diodes.

(2)   Test for leakage from collector to emitter (should be negligible for signal transistors, but possibly quite large on power transistors).

(3)   Test for current gain. Connect meter on ohms from collector to emitter (observe correct polarity). This will show leakage current as above. Touch damp finger from base to collector. This will cause base current to flow, and in a working transistor will cause an increase in collector current which will show on the meter.

It is advisable to practise the above test on a known good transistor.

Thyristors can be tested with the simple circuit below:

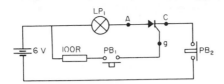

The lamp will light, and stay lit, when PB$_1$ is pressed. The lamp will extinguish and stay out when PB$_2$ is pressed.

Thyristors usually fail short circuit from anode to cathode, and this condition can easily be found with a multimeter.

Connectors   17.7

The DIN standard devised by the German Industrial Standards Board is widely used for the connection of audio equipment. This utilises the connectors shown below. The 3-way and the 180° 5-way are the commonest.

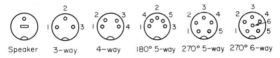

Pin allocations are defined as below for 3-way and 180° 5-way connectors:

	Mono	*Stereo*
Microphone	Input 1 0 V 2 Pin 3 available for polarising voltage	Input LH 1 Input RH 4 0 V 2 Pins 3 and 5 available for polarising voltage
Tape recorder inputs and monitor outputs	Input 1 0 V 2 Output 3	Input LH 1 Input R4 4 0 V 2 Output LH 3 Output RH 5
Tape recorder replay output	Output, low Z 1 0 V 2 Output, high Z 3	Output LH, low Z 1 Output RH, low Z 4 0 V 2 Output LH, high Z 3 Output RH, high Z 5
Amplifiers	Output to tape 1 0 V 2 Input from tape 3	Output LH 1 Output RH 1 0 V 2 Input LH 3 Input RH 5

Variations on the above exist between different manufacturers.

17.8 **Power ratios**

It is usual to express the relationship between power levels as a logarithmic ratio. The basic unit is the bel, defined as

$$\text{Ratio (bel)} = \log_{10} \frac{P_2}{P_2}$$

The bel is too large a unit for everyday use, and the practical unit is the decibel:

$$\text{Ratio (dB)} = 10 \log_{10} \frac{P_2}{P_1}$$

If impedances are equal, since $P \propto V^2$ we can relate voltages similarly:

$$\text{Voltage ratio (dB)} = 20 \log_{10} \frac{P_2}{P_1}$$

17.9 **Time constants**

Many timing circuits follow an exponential curve, defined as

$$X = X_m(1 - e^{-t/T})$$

This is an exponential rise to a final value X_m with a time constant T. The time constant is the time taken to reach 63% of the final value.

The voltage on a capacitor charging through a resistor from E_m is given by

$$E = E_m(1 - e^{-t/T}), \text{ where } T = RC$$

It is useful to remember that for 1 kΩ and 1 μF, $T = 1$ ms.

Index

Oscilloscopes How to use them
How they work   Second Edition
Ian Hickman

Ian Hickman, experienced in both
professional and hobbyist electronics, has
written this book to help all oscilloscope
users – and potential users. After
introducing basic principles for readers new
to the subject, he explains in detail the
features of typical simple and advanced
real-time oscilloscopes, plus accessories
such as probes and cameras. He advises on
how to choose and operate scopes, and how
to avoid common pitfalls; he also describes
special-purpose instruments, from small
portable scopes to storage scopes and
spectrum and logic analysers. Finally, to
give readers a better understanding of how
oscilloscopes work, he explains the
principles of the cathode-ray tube and basic
scope circuitry.

Softcover. 128 pages.
216 × 138 mm. 0 600 33373 6

Beginner's Guide to Amateur Radio
Second Edition
F G Rayer, Revised by Gordon J King

Whether you are new to radio, or have
become interested by way of CB, this book
will further whet your appetite and put you in
good stead for passing the Radio Amateurs'
Examination and becoming a licensed radio
amateur.

Softcover. 192 pages.
186 × 123 mm. 0 600 33368 X

Heinemann Newnes

**Op-Amps Their principles and
applications**   Second Edition
J Brian Dance

The book is intended both for the technician
and the home constructor who require
enough information about op-amps to use
them in conventional circuits without having
to expend much time and effort in making a
thorough study of the subject. The text is
written in a simple non-mathematical style
and is specifically directed to the non-
academic reader. A practical approach has
been adopted from the very first chapter and
numerous circuits are included with all
component values.

Softcover. 112 pages.
216 × 138 mm. 0 600 33372 8

Newnes Electrical Pocket Book
Nineteenth Edition
E A Reeves

Since the 18th edition many new advances
have been recorded in electrical
engineering, so this new version has been
extensively re-written and re-arranged. One
of the major changes is the expansion of the
chapter on computers and programmable
controllers. The present text also takes into
account the latest amendments to the 15th
Edition of the IEE Wiring Regulations.

Electrical and mechanical engineers,
services installation contractors and
technicians will continue to find the Newnes
Electrical Pocket Book an invaluable ready-
reference source.

Softcover. 520 pages.
165 × 100 mm. 0 408 01575 6

Beginner's Guide to Radio
Ninth Edition
Gordon J King

"Written in a non-technical, highly readable
style, with a minimum of mathematics, this
guide provides the newcomer to radio with
an enjoyable introduction to the subject. It
will open the door to further reading and to
greater skill in handling radio equipment,
whether for work or leisure." *Radio &
Electronics World*

Softcover. 272 pages.
186 × 123 mm. 0 408 01456 3

**Newnes Mathematics Pocket Book for
Engineers**
J O Bird

This book presents, in concise form, all the
relevant mathematical formulae and data
required by student and practising
engineering technicians. Because no
previous mathematical knowledge is
assumed, the pocket book will be of interest
to students following courses at all levels,
from CSE to BTEC level 5. It will also be a
valuable ready-reference for practising
engineers, because the clear logical
structure of the text enables the reader to
identify swiftly the section relevant to his
needs.

Softcover. 308 pages.
165 × 108 mm. 0 408 01330 3

Heinemann Newnes